About Pearson

Pearson is the world's learning company, with presence across 70 countries worldwide. Our unique insights and world-class expertise comes from a long history of working closely with renowned teachers, authors and thought leaders, as a result of which, we have emerged as the preferred choice for millions of teachers and learners across the world.

We believe learning opens up opportunities, creates fulfilling careers and hence better lives. We hence collaborate with the best of minds to deliver you class-leading products, spread across the Higher Education and Test Preparation spectrum.

Superior learning experience and improved outcomes are at the heart of everything we do. This product is the result of one such effort.

Your feedback plays a critical role in the evolution of our products and you can contact us - reachus@pearson.com. *We look forward to it.*

CLASS

8

Trishna's

PEARSON IIT FOUNDATION

Chemistry

Thirteenth Edition

2025

Pearson

Photo Credits

Chapter 1 Opener: ShutterStockStudio/Shutterstock
Chapter 2 Opener: ggw/Shutterstock
Chapter 3 Opener: Garsya/Shutterstock
Chapter 4 Opener: Inna Bigun/Shutterstock
Chapter 5 Opener: amenic181/Shutterstock
Chapter 6 Opener: 1481615/Shutterstock
Chapter 7 Opener: mewaji/Shutterstock

ISBN 978-93-6159-312-3

First Impression

Published by Pearson India Education Services Pvt. Ltd, CIN: U72200TN2005PTC057128.

Head Office: 1st Floor, Berger Tower, Plot No. C-001A/2, Sector 16B, Noida - 201 301, Uttar Pradesh, India.

Registered Office: Featherlite, 'The Address' 5th Floor, Survey No 203/10B, 200 Ft MMRD Road, Zamin Pallavaram, Chennai - 600044

Phone: 044-66540100

Website: in.pearson.com, Email: companysecretary.india@pearson.com

Compositor: Saksham Printographics, Delhi
Printed in India at MP Printers (A Unit of D B Corp Ltd), Noida 201305

Brief Contents

Contents

Preface

"If you have a great ambition, take as big a step as possible in the direction of fulfilling it. The step may only be a tiny one, but trust that it may be the largest one possible for now."

Mildred McAfee

The *Pearson IIT Foundation* Series has been created keeping in mind the learner's ambition to excel in a competitive examination like IIT-JEE. The series can be used in addition to the books being studied in school to attain that extra edge required to strengthen the concepts and prepare well for future endeavours.

Why Start Early with Pearson IIT Foundation

Classes VI to X are the base years of a learner's academic life. In these years learner explore their interests and determine the goals they wish to attain. *Pearson IIT Foundation* series is filled with interactive learning that not only nurtures a learner's interest in science and mathematics but also strengthens their concepts.

The series uses real-life examples and application-based problems to teach theoretical concepts. The objective of this series is to help learners cultivate an analytical mind.

Most of the lessons to be learnt are introduced to the learners in the books for class VI. As they get promoted to higher classes, new topics are added to these lessons. This additive method helps the learners' span their learning over four standards, from VI-X. Thus, learners are not overwhelmed by the introduction of completely new lessons every time they are promoted to a new class.

While their learning is being spanned across five years, so is their ability to resolve doubts for further conceptual clarity. For instance, they can use concepts learnt in class VI to solve questions in class VII. If, in case, they get stuck while answering a question, the learners can infer for themselves that they might be lacking in conceptual clarity. They can then approach their teachers, requesting them to explain the concept once again. This helps the learner to clarify their concepts while revising the lessons previously learnt.

Since classes VI-X are deemed to be a student's formative years, we, at Pearson, aim to provide a foundation level course which serves more than just a standard curriculum.

Here is how it makes a difference to a learner's overall learning...

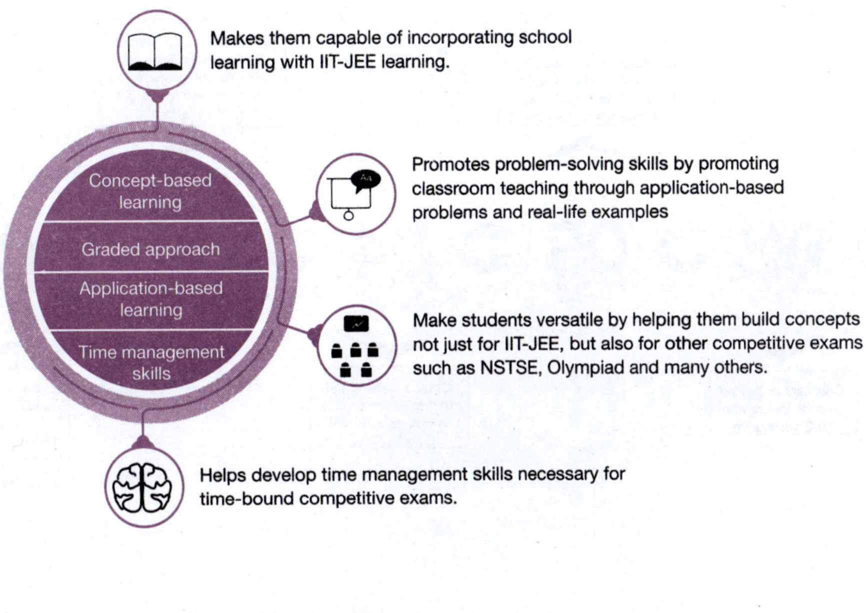

Other Uses of the Series

Instead of limiting themselves to IIT-JEE, a learner can also use this series to prepare for several other competitive examinations such as NSTSE, National and International Olympiads, NEET, BITSAT, etc. This series offers a level of concept learning that empowers learners to handle the challenging nature of questions posed in these examinations. Moreover, this will also allow the learners to have an early insight into their key strengths as well as improvement areas and help them work on themselves.

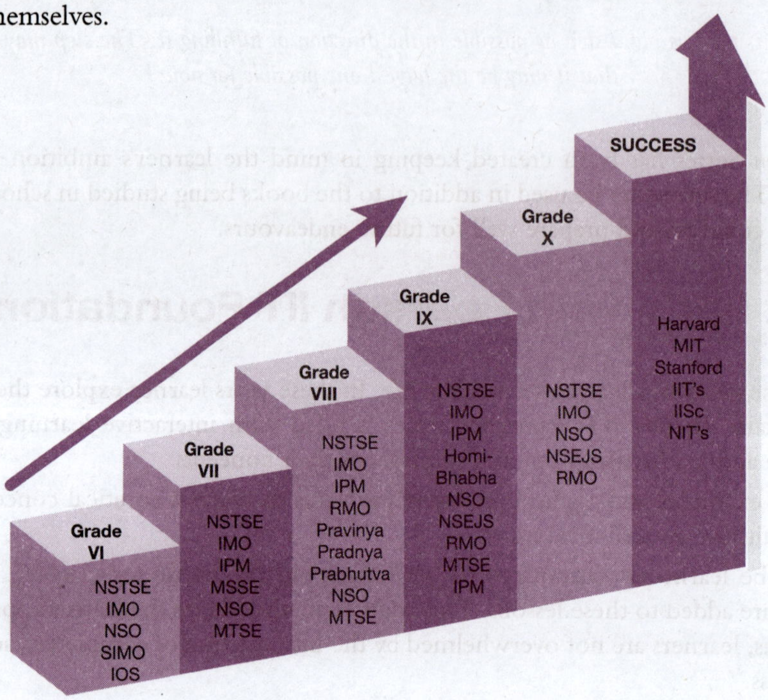

[IMO: International Mathematics Olympiad; NSO: National Science Olympiad, IOS: International Olympiad of Science, NSTSE: National Level Science Talent Search Examination, MTSE: Maharashtra Talent Search Examination, RMO: Regional Mathematical Olympiad, PPP: Pravinya Pradnya Prabhutva, NSEJS: National Standard Examination in Junior Science, IIT: Indian Institute of Technology, IISc: Indian Institute of Science, NIT: National Institute of Technology.]

Highlights of the Series

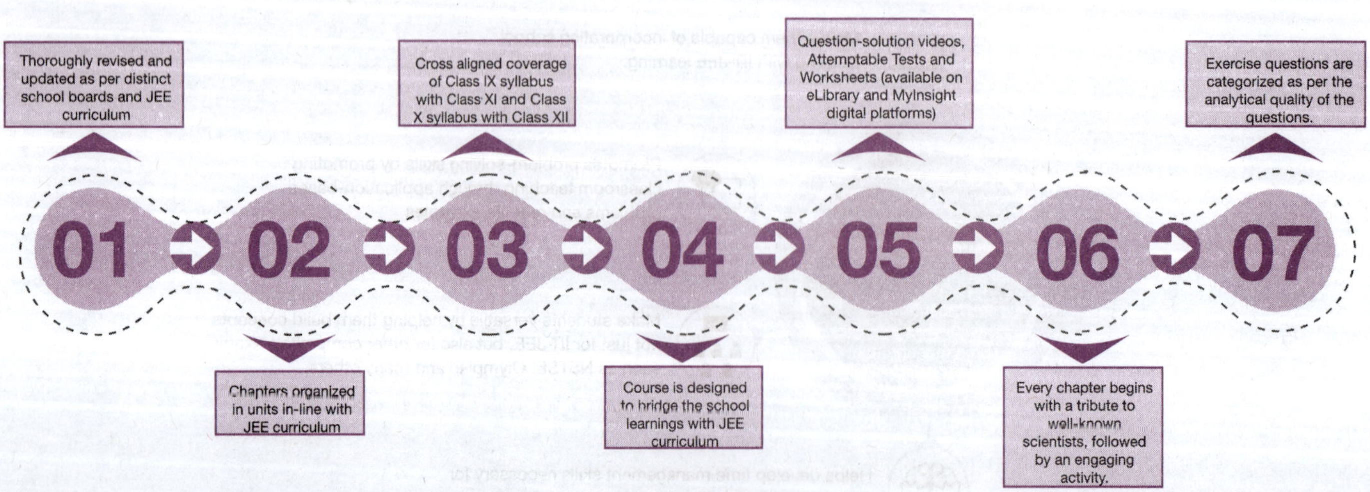

Pearson IIT Foundation series provides a perfect blend of learning through theory and practice questions with a fusion of school and JEE curriculum. It is imperative to note that this series would be as profound as you want it to be. Therefore, to get maximum benefit from this book, we recommend following the given study plan.

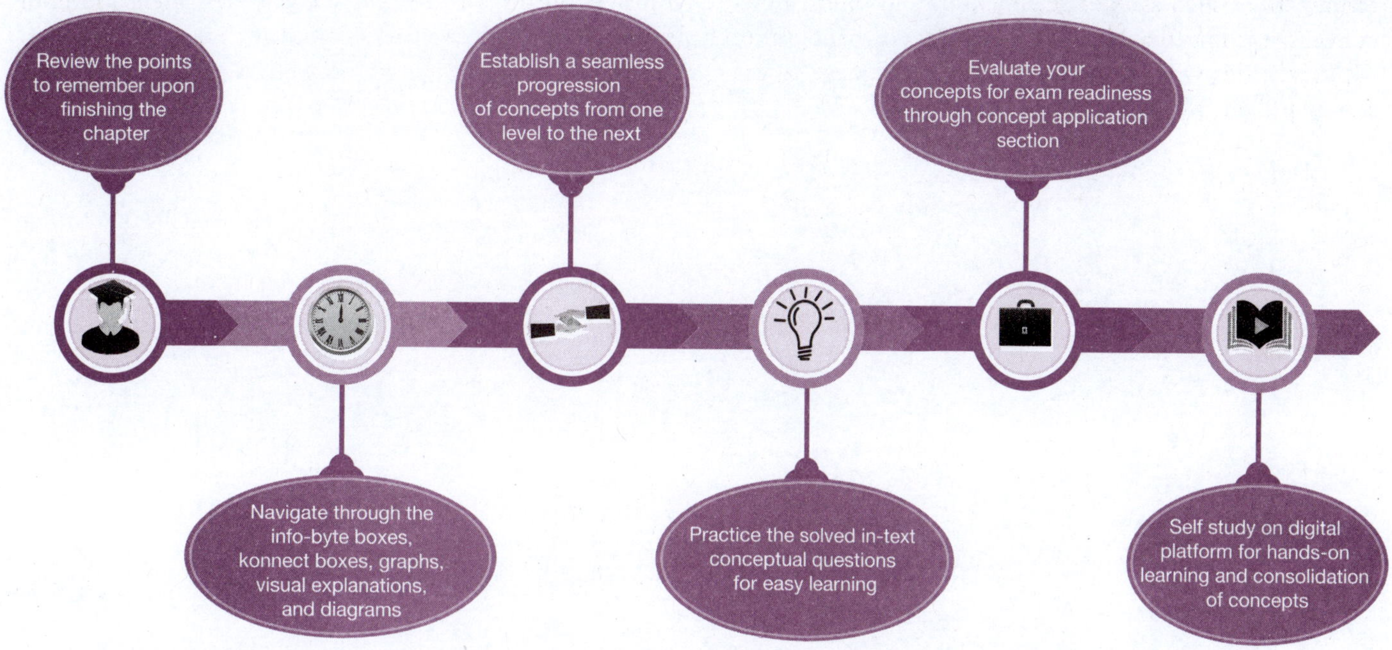

To provide a graded learning approach, the exercise part of each chapter is categorized by using four icons for question tagging. The question categorization helps the learners assess their own problem-solving and analytical skills and motivates them to improve to reach their objectives.

The following icons are used to categorize the questions with specific meanings:

Real-life Situations Questions: 

Analytical Questions: 

Conceptual Questions: 

Value-based Questions: 

With this refined and well-tuned course from Pearson, students will become more confident when they enter the competitive world for actual IIT-JEE preparation. The effort put in today will transform into a valuable asset, contributing to success in future competitive examinations.

Chapter Insights

Remember

Before beginning this chapter, you should be able to:

- understand the concept of matter and atoms.
- review the classification of matter and their

Remember section will help them to memorize and review the previous learning on a particular topic

Key points will help the students to identify the essential points in a chapter

Key Ideas

After completing this chapter, you should be able to:

- understand the kinetic molecular theory and inter-relationship among various measurable properties of gases.
- understand mole as the chemical counting

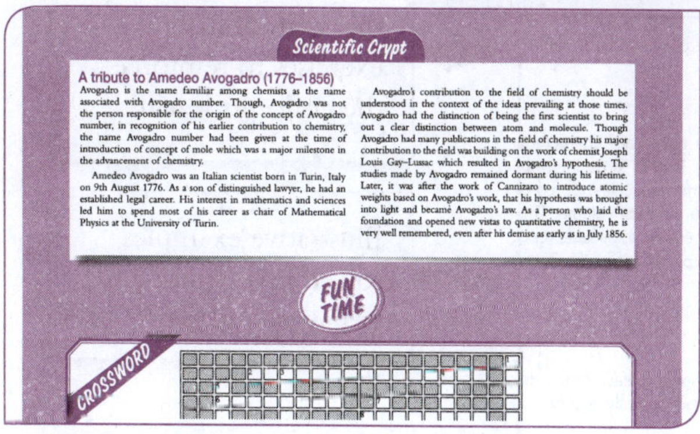

Scientific Crypt

A tribute to Amedeo Avogadro (1776–1856)

Avogadro is the name familiar among chemists as the name associated with Avogadro number. Though, Avogadro was not the person responsible for the origin of the concept of Avogadro number, in recognition of his earlier contribution to chemistry, the name Avogadro number had been given at the time of introduction of concept of mole which was a major milestone in the advancement of chemistry.

Amedeo Avogadro was an Italian scientist born in Turin, Italy on 9th August 1776. As a son of distinguished lawyer, he had an established legal career. His interest in mathematics and sciences led him to spend most of his career as chair of Mathematical Physics at the University of Turin.

Avogadro's contribution to the field of chemistry should be understood in the context of the ideas prevailing at those times. Avogadro had the distinction of being the first scientist to bring out a clear distinction between atom and molecule. Though Avogadro had many publications in the field of chemistry his major contribution to the field was building on the work of chemist Joseph Louis Gay–Lussac which resulted in Avogadro's hypothesis. The studies made by Avogadro remained dormant during his lifetime. Later, it was after the work of Cannizaro to introduce atomic weights based on Avogadro's work, that his hypothesis was brought into light and became Avogadro's law. As a person who laid the foundation and opened new vistas to quantitative chemistry, he is very well remembered, even after his demise as early as in July 1856.

Scientific Crypt provides information about well-known scientists related to the chapter. The engaging activity is also given in the form of a crossword to keep the learners interested.

INTRODUCTION

The study of matter in different perceptions is dealt by a branch of science named Chemistry. Matter can be classified on the basis of molecular composition as elements, compounds, and mixtures. Various elements are given names and symbols, and the names and formulae of various compounds have been derived based on certain rules. The study of naming these compounds and derivation of formulae for these are the prerequisites for representing chemical reactions in the form of chemical equations. Therefore, the language of chemistry,

Introduction section helps to lay the foundation of the following chapter and leads the way for further learning

Concepts are explained in a well-structured and lucid manner

Symbols and Formulae

All elements are represented by means of their symbols. A symbol represents the atom of an element, which may consist of a single letter or a combination of letters derived either from its English name or its Latin name.

A **symbol** is the shorthand notation that represents a single atom of an element.

Examples:

Element	Symbol
Hydrogen	H
Mercury (formerly known as hydrargyrum)	Hg

Konnect boxes are some add-on information of related topic

Konnect

A common example of neutralization is our body's response to heartburn. Antacids are bases that neutralize the excess stomach acid.

Info Bytes!

The kinetic theory of gases is based on the assumption that gases are composed of a large number of tiny particles (atoms or molecules) that are in constant, random motion. This movement is what gives rise to pressure and temperature.

Info bytes are interesting trivia and facts that engage young minds and keep the grey cells ticking!

EXAMPLE 1.5 Gas laws are universally applicable for all gases whereas such universal laws could established for solids and liquids. Comment on this statement.

SOLUTION

Gases differ from solids and liquids in the extent of intermolecular forces of attraction. Since gases are characteriz negligible forces of attraction, the molecules behave independent of the neighboring molecules. Due to large intermo spaces, the coefficient of volume expansion is same for all gases. Moreover, in case of gases, the molecules are cons as point masses and hence, the volume occupied by the molecules is negligible in comparison to the total volume. The the physical behavior of all gases being similar, certain laws could be established which are universally applicable. In c liquids and solids, the molecules are considered as rigid spheres and the coefficient of volume expansion is not uniform substances, such universal laws cannot be established.

EXAMPLE 1.6 Boyle's law says that pressure and volume are inversely proportional to each other. Ho when a balloon is blown, both volume and pressure increase continuously. Justify.

SOLUTION

When a balloon is blown continuously, more and more air is forced into the balloon that increases the volume as wel

Examples are given in the form of in-text exercises to reinforce the concepts learnt

Illustrative examples solved in a logical and step-wise manner

POINTS TO REMEMBER

- ✔ A symbol is the shorthand notation that represents a single atom of an element.
- ✔ A formula is the shorthand notation which represents a single molecule of an element or compound.
- ✔ The properties of solids and liquids differ widely from substance to substance, but the gases generally obey some common rules known as the gas laws.
- ✔ Boyle's Law states that the volume of a given mass of a gas is inversely proportional to
- ✔ Vapor density (VD) of a gas or vapor is the ratio of the mass of a certain volume of gas or vapor to the mass of the same volume of hydrogen gas when their volumes are measured under similar conditions of temperature and pressure.
- ✔ A mole is defined as the quantity of substance that contains the same number of elementary particles or chemical units as the number of atoms present in 12 g of C-12 isotope.
- ✔ Dalton's law states that 'the total pressure exerted by a mixture of non-reacting gases

Points to remember summarises the concepts and topics presented in each chapter

PRACTICE QUESTIONS CLASSROOM WING

Very Short Answer Type Questions

Directions for questions from 1 to 5:
Fill in the blanks.

1. The percentage of sulphur in SO_2 is __________ and __________ in SO_3.
2. The vapor density of SO_2 gas is __________ the vapor density of O_2 gas.
3. The molecular formula of a gas with vapor density 15

(A) Reaction between an acid and a base from salt and water
(B) Reaction between zinc and dil. H_2SO_4
(C) Preparation of oxygen from potassium nitrate
(D) Preparation of CO_2 from its constituents

9. What is the molarity of HCl solution containing 0.4 moles in 200 mL of the solution?
10. Calculate the volume occupied by 11 g of CO_2 gas at

Short Answer Type Questions

26. A spherical balloon of volume 253 mL is to be with helium gas at STP from a cylinder containi at 20 atm and 127°C. If the cylinder can hold water, then calculate the number of balloons th be filled up.
27. The composition of a gaseous mixture is N_2 =

Essay Answer Type Questions

41. The density of a mixture of He and O_2 at STP is 1.25 g/L. What is the partial pressure of O_2?
42. A bottle is heated from 27°C to 127°C at constant pressure. What fraction of air gets expelled?
43. An oxide of Cr contains 68.5% of Cr by weight. Find

Different typologies of questions have been included in the *Classroom Wing* which help students to develop the problem-solving skill

Competition Wing has been integrated chapter-wise in the exercise part to prepare students for various competitive examinations.

Graded as per complexity: Level 1; Level 2; and Level 3

PRACTICE QUESTIONS COMPETITION WING

Level 1: Apply your Concepts

Direction for questions from 1 to 8:
State whether the following statements are true or false.

1. Doubling the pressure of a gas at constant temperature, doubles the volume occupied by the gas.
2.

16. 'ous' acid of a non-metal 'X' has 2 'O' atoms. Per acid of the same non-metal has the formula _______.
17. The ratio of the gram atomic weight of nitrogen and oxygen is __________.
18. Pressure exerted by water vapor in moist gas is called

Level 2: Review Your Concepts

51. Out of oxygen, carbon dioxide, sulphur dioxide an nitrogen, which among these gases possesses maximu density at a given temperature and pressure?
52. If the Avogadro number is 9×10^{23}, calculate th weight of 1 mole of CO_2 gas.
53. A gas cylinder is filled with helium at 2000 mm. Du

Level 3: Assess Your Concepts

74. At constant temperature and at 4 atm pressure, the given amount of gas occupies 6 L. If the pressure is increased by 6 atm, calculate the percentage change in the volume of the gas.
75. A gaseous mixture contains 48 g of SO_2 and 33 g of CO_2 at constant temperature and pressure. Calculate the average molecular mass of the gaseous mixture.
76. Calculate the ratio of rates of diffusion of three isotopes of hydrogen protium, deuterium and tritium, respectively, at the same temperature and pressure.

Level 2: Review Your Concepts

41. (a) A neutral atom of an element has a nucleus with nuclear charge 12 times and mass 24 times that of hydrogen. Calculate the number of electrons, protons and neutrons in its stable positively charged ion.
    (b) A dipositive ion and a dinegative ion are isoelectronic. What is the difference between their mass numbers if the number of neutrons in both the atoms is equal to their atomic numbers?
42. An atom 'X' has a mass of protons 36,740 times that of electrons. Find out the correct representation of the atom. The number of neutrons is 1 unit less than the protons.
43. If 'a' is the number of electrons in a dipositive ion and it has three neutrons more than the number of protons, write the atomic number and mass number.
44. Assuming that x is the mass of the electron and y is the total mass of protons in $_8O^{18}$, write the value of y in terms of x.

53. Rutherford's α-ray scattering experiment was conducted in order to test the validity of Thomson's model. What results were expected from this experiment?
54. If the average atomic mass of chlorine is 35.5, then find the percentage abundance of the two isotopes of chlorine wh
55. The electr $a + 2b$, a a
    (a) Write
    (b) Calcu
    (c) If the is 22.5
56. Compare in α-rays aluminiu results.

32. Give the differences between isotopes and isobars.
33. In J. J. Thomson's experiment, what observations were found when:
    (a) a small obstruction was placed in the path of cathode rays.
    (b) a paddle wheel is placed between cathode and anode.

37. An at shell Find
38. Mass 1653 atom

Essay Answer Type Questions

39. Write down the
    (a) electronic configuration,
    (b) number of valence electrons,

41. (a) St
    (b) If

The icons are used for categorisation of the questions in Classroom Wing and Competition Wing

PRACTICE QUESTIONS JEE-NEET SPECIAL WING

Multiple-Answer Type Questions

Directions for questions from 1 to 5:
Select one or more correct alternative(s) from the given choices.

1. The trivalent negative ion of an element 'X' is 2,8,8. Identify the configurations which correspond to elements that form ions which are isoelectronic with the stable ion of X.
   (a) 2,8,18,7 (b) 2,8,6

4. The mass of an electron is considered as 'x' units. The atoms of elements having equal number of neutrons are known as isotones. Identify the correctly matched sets among the following.

	Mass of protons	Mass number	Representation of isotone of the element
(a)	12859x	2Z+1	$_{7}N^{15}$
(b)	29392x	2Z+2	$_{18}Ar^{36}$
	25718x	2Z+1	$_{14}Si^{29}$
	36740x	2Z	$_{19}K^{39}$

Comprehension-Based Questions

Directions for questions from 6 to 10:
Read the content given in the following passa answer the questions given below.
The following diagram represents a discharg experiment representing the discovery of funda particles. A gas is taken in the discharge tube at high

Match The Column

18. The substances in the respective physical states are given in column I and the thermal characteristics are given in column II.

	Column I		Column II
(a)	Solid A	(i)	Cools down at the

JEE-NEET Special Wing is curated specifically for targeted preparation of JEE and NEET examinations.

Hints and Explanations

Classroom Wing

Very Short Answer Type Questions

1. 50%, 40%
2. higher than
3. Relation between vapor density and molecular weight. C_2H_6
4. 16/N
5. 40.043%
6. Since the molecular weight of hydrogen is less than

11. $\frac{P_1V_1}{T_1} = \frac{P_2V_2}{T_2}$
    = 5/9
12. Mole fraction = $\frac{\text{No. of moles of a Substance}}{\text{Total number of moles of all substances in the mixture}}$
    Sum of mole fraction in a mixture = 1
    = 0.7
13. $\frac{r_1}{r_2} = \sqrt{\frac{M_2}{M_1}}$

Hints and Explanation for key questions of classroom wing, competition wing and JEE-NEET special wing along with highlights on the common mistakes that students usually make in the examinations

Competition Wing

Level 1: Apply your Concepts

20. Calcium bisulphate → $Ca(HSO_4)_2$
    Ferric sulphate → $Fe_2(SO_4)_3$
    Calcium bisulphite → $Ca(HSO_3)_2$
    Ferrous sulphate → $FeSO_4$
    (i) → (C); (ii) → (D); (iii) → (B); (iv) → (A)
21. 80 g of SO is equal to 1 mole. 1 mole of any gas at STP occupies 22.4 L.
    Hence, the correct option is (a).
22. At low pressure and high temperature, inter-molecular forces of attraction among the gas molecules are negligible. Hence, the gases behave ideally.
    Hence, the correct option is (a).
23. (4) HCl + NaOH → NaCl + H_2O → Double displacement
    (3) $Cl_2 + H_2 \rightarrow HCl$ → Combination
    (2) $Mg + H_2SO_4 \rightarrow MgSO_4 + H_2$ → Displacement
    (1) NaCl Na + Cl → Decomposition

(C) potassium bicarbonate → $KHCO_3$

% of potassium = $\frac{39}{100} \times 100 = 39\%$

(D) potassium sulphide → K_2S

% of potassium = $\frac{39 \times 2}{110} \times 100 = 70.90\%$

∴ increasing order is (D) > (A) > (B) > (C)

Hence, the correct answer is (d).

38. Let the vapor density of compound be x
    Empirical formula weight = $x/2$
    Molecular formula weight = $2x$
    $n = \frac{\text{Molecular formula weight}}{\text{Empirical formula weight}} \times \frac{2x}{\left(\frac{x}{2}\right)} = 4$
    Molecular formula = $4 \times A_2B_4 = A_8B_{16}$
    Hence, the correct answer is (b).
39. Let the bivalent metal ion be M^{2+}, then the formula of the compound formed will be $M(ClO_4)_2$.
    1 mole of compound contains 8 N oxygen atoms.

JEE-NEET Special Wing

Multiple-Answer Type Questions

Solutions for questions 1 to 5:

	No. of electrons	No. of neutrons	Mass number	Representation	Ratio A/Z
(a)	94	150	244	$_{94}E^{244}$	$\frac{244}{94}=2.6$
(b)	57	81	138	$_{57}E^{138}$	$\frac{138}{57}=2.4$
(c)	71	105	176	$_{71}E^{176}$	$\frac{176}{71}=2.5$
(d)	79	117	196	$_{79}E^{196}$	$\frac{196}{79}=2.5$

1. The configuration of the atom 'X' corresponding to the given trivalent negative ion could be 2,8,5. The element with configuration 2,8,6 can form stable divalent nega- configuration 2,8,8,2 can form stable divalent positive ion with 2,8,8 configuration.

   Hence, choice (b) and choice (c) follow.

2. The configuration of the element 'M' would be 2, 8, 10, 2. The atomic number of the element would be 22. The mass of protons = 22 × 1837 = 40414. The configuration of the preceding element is 2,8,9,2. It can form both divalent and trivalent ions. Addition of 8 electrons makes the 'M' shell completely filled.

   Hence, choice (a), choice (b) and choice (c) follow.

3.

	No. of electrons	No. of neutrons	Mass number	Representation	Ratio A/Z
(c)	71	105	176	$_{71}E^{176}$	$\frac{176}{71}=2.5$
(d)	79	117	196	$_{79}E^{196}$	$\frac{196}{79}=2.5$

WORKSHEET

CHAPTER 1: MOLE CONCEPT, STOICHIOMETRY AND BEHAVIOR OF GASES

DW

DW: Downloadable worksheets supplementing textual exercises for hand-on learning

Direction for questions from 1 to 5:
Select the correct alternative from the following option.

1. A rubber balloon which is permeable to all the isotopes of hydrogen is filled with pure tritium. It is placed in a closed box containing pure hydrogen under similar conditions of temperature and pressure. Identify the correct observation regarding the balloon.
   (a) The balloon first expands and then contracts.
   (b) The balloon first contracts first and then expand.
   (c) The balloon expands.

Directions of questions from 6 to 10:
State whether the following statements are true or false.

6. 80 g of SO_3 corresponds to 1 mole.
7. Real gases behave ideally at high pressure and low temperature.
8. Reaction between an acid and a base form salt and water.
9. Equal volumes of all gases possess unequal number of moles at constant temperature and pressure.

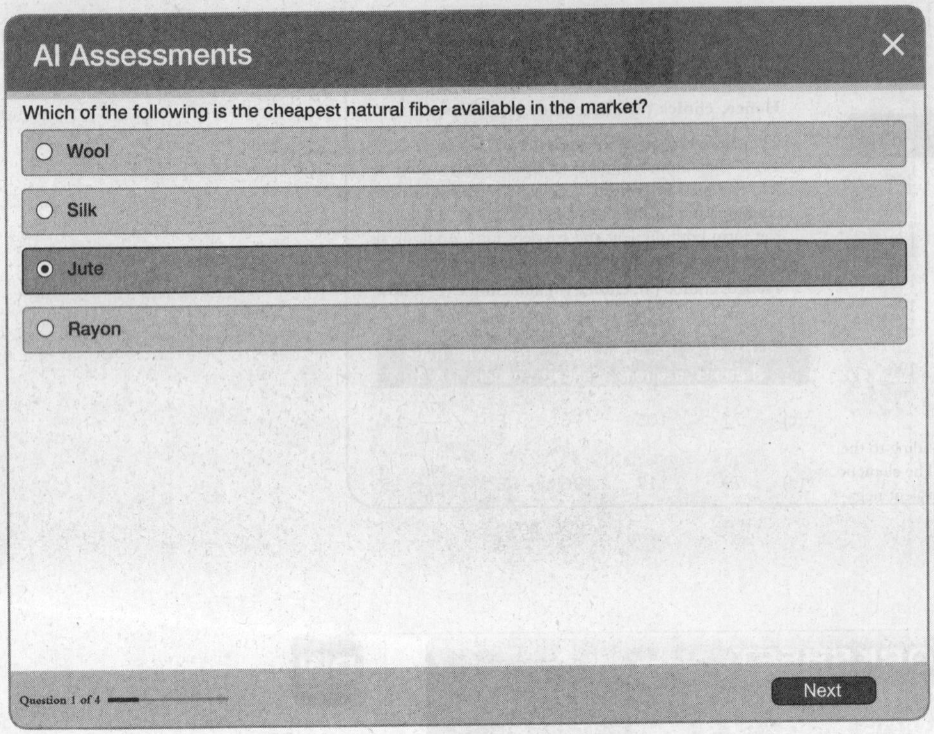

AT

AT: Attemptable Tests for assessing understanding of concepts and getting a clear picture of your exam readiness

51. Na_2CO_3 is dissolved in water at 25°C. Which of the following is/are correct regarding the given statement?
    (a) In this solution anionic hydrolysis take place.
    (b) The concentration of H^+ ion in the given solution is less than 10^{-7} mole/L

Video icon: Audio and visual learning to difficult questions for effective learning and retention

CHAPTER

1

Atomic Structure

Remember

Before beginning this chapter, you should be able to:

- define matter and properties of matter.
- describe atoms and molecules.

Key Ideas

After completing this chapter, you should be able to:

- understand the concept of atom as an indivisible particle.
- explain the models of an atom based on the concept of subatomic particles and the concept of nucleus.
- study concept of atomic number, mass number, isotopes and isobars.
- know about arrangement of electrons around the nucleus and form a structure of atom.

Scientific Crypt

A Tribute to Joseph John Thomson (1856 – 1940)

Sir Joseph John Thomson was born in Cheetham Hill, a suburb of Manchester in England on December 18, 1856. In 1870, he enrolled at Owens College, Manchester and entered Trinity College, Cambridge in 1876. He took up the prestigious post of Cavendish professor of Experimental Physics at Cambridge. He was also Honorary Professor of Physics in Cambridge in Royal Institution.

His keen interest in atomic structure was reflected in his Treatise on the motion of Vortex Rings for which he won the Adams prize in 1884. The most significant achievement of Thomson was the study of Cathode rays which culminates in the discovery of electron. Many scientists were inspired by his Cathode ray tube experiment.

In 1897, 30th april, he announced that cathode rays were negatively charged particles and named them as 'corpuscles'. He also announced that the mass of these particles are 1000 times smaller than a hydrogen atom and proclaimed that atoms are constituted of these particles. He is the pioneer to envisage the existence of subatomic particles. He invented a method for separating different kinds of atoms and molecules by the use of positive rays which led to the discovery of isotopes.

In addition to these, he was the author of many books. Few of those books are 'The Structure of Light', 'The Corpuscular Theory of Matter', 'Ray of Positive Electricity', 'The Electron Chemistry and his autobiography, 'Recollection and Reflection'. Thomson became Master of Trinity College, Cambridge in the year 1918. He worked there till his last breath. Sir J.J. Thomson passed away on August 30, 1940 and was buried in Westminister Abbey.

FUN TIME

CROSSWORD

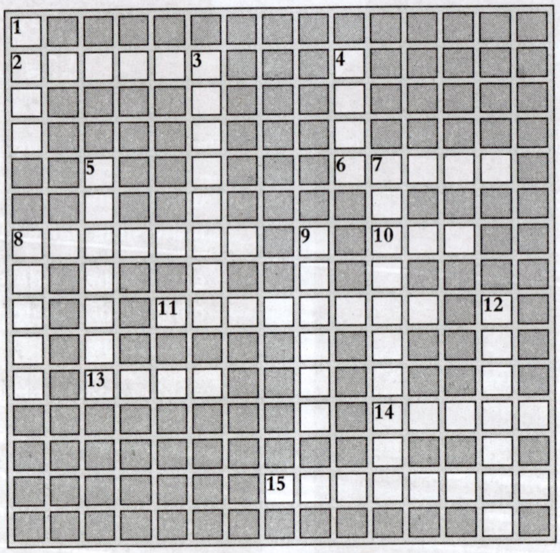

Across

2. Element with atomic number eight
6. Circular path round the nucleus along where electrons revolve
8. Watermelon model of an atom was given by ______
10. The number of valence electrons in calcium.
11. Atoms of an element with different number of neutrons.
13. Total number of protons and neutrons present in an atom is called ______ number.
14. The electronic configuration in which the valence shell is filled with eight electrons.
15. Neutron was discovered by ______.

Down

1. Concept of stationary orbits was proposed by ______.
3. Protons and neutrons present in the nucleus are collectively called ______.
4. Relative charge of neutron is ______.
5. Isotope of hydrogen with zero neutrons.
7. Planetary model of an atom was given by ______.
8. The ______ shell is the valence shell of sodium.
9. The number of protons in the nucleus is known as ______ number.
12. Outermost shell in an atom is known as ______ shell.

INTRODUCTION

The constituents of the universe, by convention, can be many celestial bodies but in reality there is matter and space. The study of matter dates back to as early as 600 BCE where both ancient Indians and Greeks were important pioneers in the study of matter. In ancient India, Maharishi Kannada propounded that matter is made up of small indestructible particles called ***Paramanu***. Ancient Greek philosophers, such as, Democritus, Epicurus and Leucippus theorized that matter is made up of small particles called atoms. The word 'atom' was coined because these small particles of matter were assumed to be indestructible. In Greek language, ***atom*** means the '***incapability of being cut***.' These achievements about atom were merely speculations. Later, based on the experimentation, John Dalton postulated the theory of atoms. In due course, the discovery of electrons, protons and neutrons proved atom to be divisible. The idea of the subatomic particles paved the way for further researches on the arrangement of these particles in the atom, which led to the development of various atomic models depicting the structure of the atom.

Historical Aspects of the Atom

In 1808, John Dalton proposed the atomic theory based on the various laws of chemical combination known at that time. The theory has been well accepted during the 19th century as it could help in explaining the laws of chemical combination. However, the basic conception of Dalton that an atom is indivisible has been proved to be wrong after the discovery of subatomic particles.

Dalton's Atomic Theory

Dalton's atomic theory is mainly based on the law of conservation of mass, the law of definite proportions and the law of multiple proportions which were formulated by Lavoisier.

The main postulates of Dalton's atomic theory are the following:

1. Matter is composed of tiny indivisible particles called atoms. They can neither be created nor be destroyed nor be transformed into atoms of another element.
2. Atoms of a given element are identical in all respects.
3. Atoms of different elements are different from each other.
4. Atoms of different elements take part in the chemical reaction and combine in a simple integral ratio to form compounds.
5. When elements react, the atoms may combine in more than one simple whole number ratio.

Konnect

John Dalton, despite his ground-breaking work on atomic theory, was colourblind. In fact, the condition is sometimes referred to as 'Daltonism'.

Dalton's atomic theory has been contradicted with the advancement of science, and hence, modified on the basis of further research and discoveries as listed hereunder.

1. With the discovery of subatomic particles, i.e., the electron, proton and neutron, it was concluded that atoms can be further divided.
2. Discovery of isotopes proved that atoms of the same element may possess different atomic weights, i.e., atoms of same elements may not be identical in all respects.
3. In some cases, atoms of different elements are found to have same mass number. For example, calcium and argon are found to have same mass number.

Though Dalton's atomic theory could not give convincing explanation to any of the above facts, it laid the foundation for the development of modern atomic theory.

The basic postulate of Dalton's atomic theory which says that 'atoms are the tiniest particles of matter which take part in the chemical reaction' is, however, accepted in modern atomic theory with experimental evidence.

The discovery of radioactivity led to the discovery of the fundamental particles in the atom.

Discovery of Fundamental Particles

Dalton's postulate which suggested that atoms are the tiny indivisible particles were proved wrong by the discovery of the subatomic particles also known as the **fundamental particles.** In this section we will study about the discovery of those particles but first let us know about the instrument which was majorly used for these discoveries.

Cathode Ray Tube (CRT)

An experiment to investigate the phenomenon that takes place when a high voltage is applied through a tube containing gas at low pressure laid the foundation to the discovery of fundamental particles.

In 1878, Sir William Crooke, while conducting an experiment using a special glass tube called **discharge tube**, found certain visible rays travelling between two metal electrodes. These rays are known as **Crooke's rays** or **cathode rays.** The discharge tube used in the experiment is now referred to as **Crooke's tube** or more popularly as **cathode ray tube (CRT).**

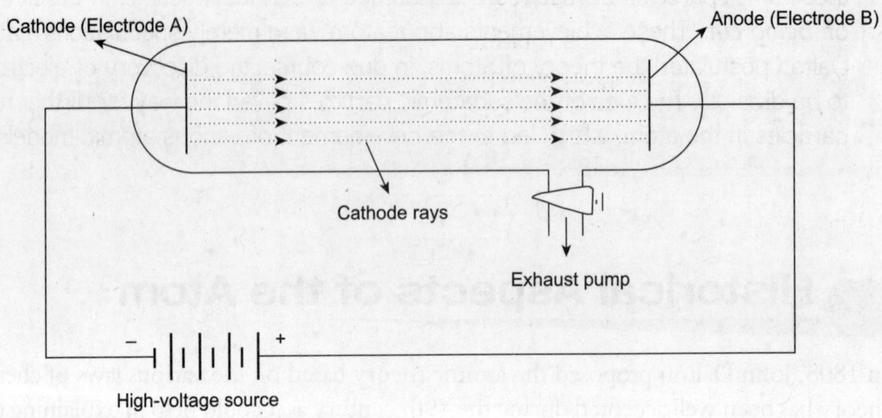

Figure 1.1 Cathode ray tube

Construction

1. A discharge tube is a long glass tube sealed at the two ends. It consists of two metal plates—A and B connected to high voltage.
2. The two plates A and B act as electrodes. The electrode A which is connected to the negative terminal of the battery is called **cathode** (negative electrode).
3. The electrode B which is connected to the positive terminal is called an **anode** (positive electrode).
4. There is a side tube which is connected to an exhaust pump. The exhaust pump is used for lowering the pressure inside the discharge tube.

Discovery of Electron

J. J. Thomson also found that when a high voltage of 10,000 V was applied between the electrodes present in a partially evacuated CRT, a bright spot of light was formed on the screen coated with a fluorescent material, placed at the other end of the tube.

The fluorescent material coated on the screen started to glow because it was struck by the rays which originated from the cathode. Since these rays were emitted by the cathode, he named these rays as **cathode rays.**

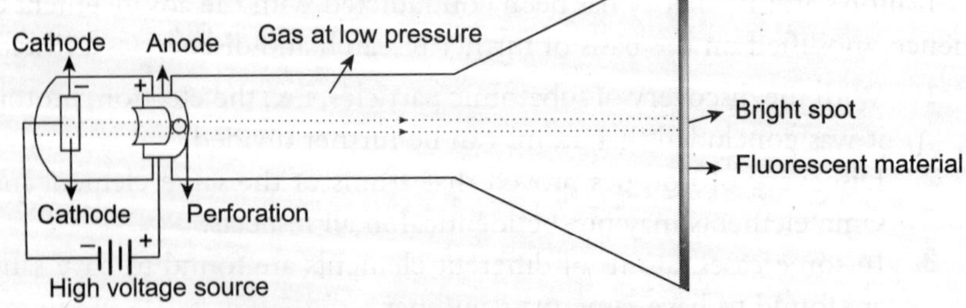

Figure 1.2 J. J. Thomson's cathode ray tube

J. J. Thomson and others studied the properties of these cathode rays by conducting the following experiments:

Experiment I

A small metal object is placed between cathode and anode.

Observation: A shadow which is of the same shape as the object is observed on the wall opposite to the cathode.

Conclusion: The cathode rays travel in straight lines.

> **Info Bytes!**
> Sir J.J. Thomson, who discovered the electron, was also the mentor to Rutherford who discovered the proton.

Experiment II

A light paddle wheel is placed between cathode and anode.

Observation: The wheel starts rotating.

Conclusion: Cathode rays are made up of small particles having mass and kinetic energy.

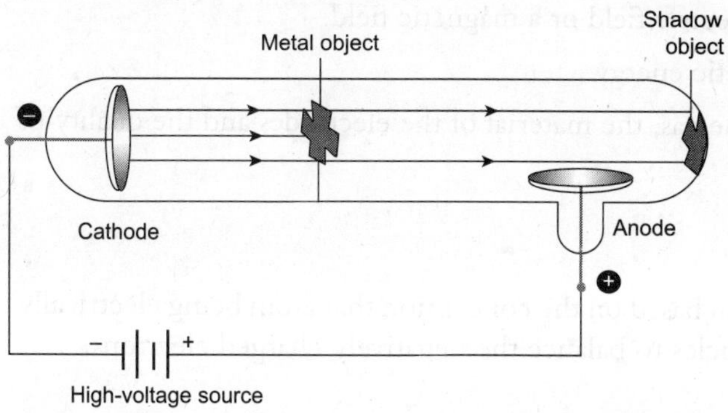

Figure 1.3 Experiment for rectilinear movement of cathode rays

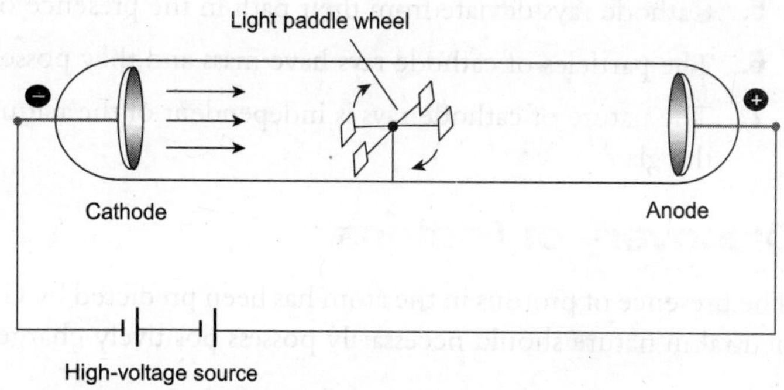

Figure 1.4 Experiment for proving that cathode rays possess mass

Experiment III

Cathode rays are passed through an electric field.

Observation: The rays move on a curved path towards the positive plate of the electric field.

Conclusion: The cathode rays are negatively charged particles.

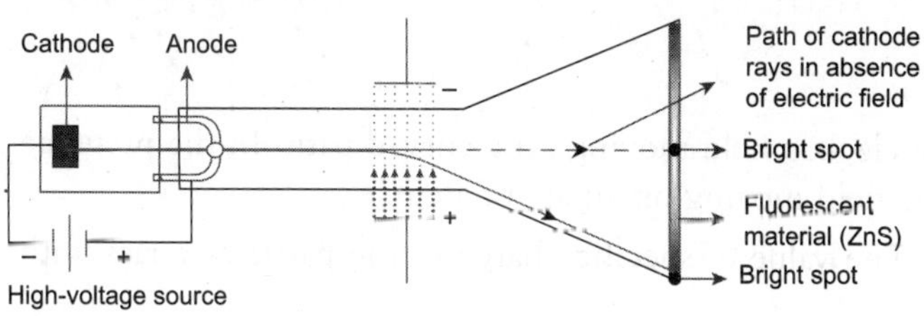

Figure 1.5 Schematic diagram of deflection of cathode rays in the presence of electrical field

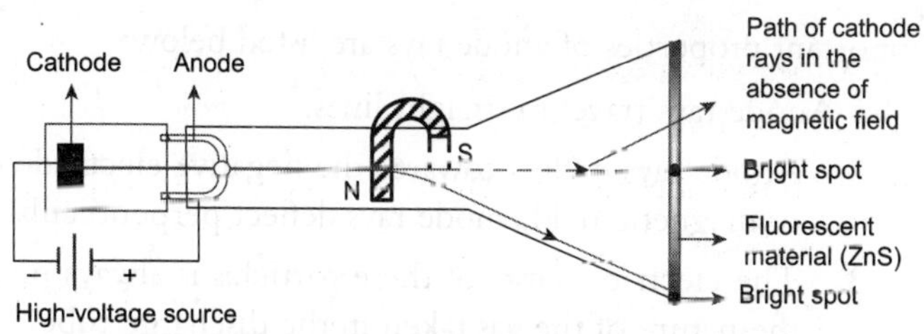

Figure 1.6 Schematic diagram of deflection of cathode rays in the presence of magnetic field

Experiment IV

Cathode rays are passed through a magnetic field.

Observation: The deflection of the rays is perpendicular to the applied magnetic field.

Conclusion: The cathode rays constitute negatively charged particles.

Experiment V

These experiments were repeated by taking different gases in the discharge tube.

Observation: The deflections produced were the same for cathode rays for all gases.

Conclusion: The nature of the cathode rays depends neither on the nature of the gas inside the tube nor on the cathode used.

During his experiments in the presence of applied electric and magnetic fields, he found out the concept called charge to mass ratio or specific charge or e/m ratio of the cathode rays.

Cathode Rays

Cathode rays are a stream of negatively charged particles.

Properties of the Cathode Rays

Important properties of cathode rays are listed below:

1. Cathode rays originate from cathode and travel towards anode.
2. Cathode rays travel in straight lines.
3. Cathode rays consist of a stream of particles.
4. The particles of the cathode rays are negatively charged. These negatively charged particles are called **electrons**.
5. Cathode rays deviate from their path in the presence of an electric field or a magnetic field.
6. The particles of cathode rays have mass and they possess kinetic energy.
7. The nature of cathode rays is independent of the nature of the gas, the material of the electrodes and the quality of the glass.

Discovery of Protons

The presence of protons in the atom has been predicted by Goldstein based on the conception that atom being electrically neutral in nature should necessarily possess positively charged particles to balance the negatively charged electrons.

Goldstein's Experiment

Goldstein repeated the cathode ray experiment by using a perforated cathode.

Observation: In addition to the cathode rays originating from cathode some rays travelled from the anode towards the cathode.

Conclusion: The anode rays are constituted of positively charged particles.

Anode Rays

Properties of Anode Rays

Important properties of anode rays are listed below:

1. Anode rays travel in straight lines.
2. Anode rays deflect towards the negative electrode of the electric field moving on a curved path. In the presence of magnetic field, anode rays deflect perpendicular to the field moving on an arc of a circle.
3. The electric charge of these particles is always positive. The value of specific charge of the particles varies with the nature of the gas taken in the discharge tube.
4. The mass of the particles was same as the atomic mass of the gas in the discharge tube.

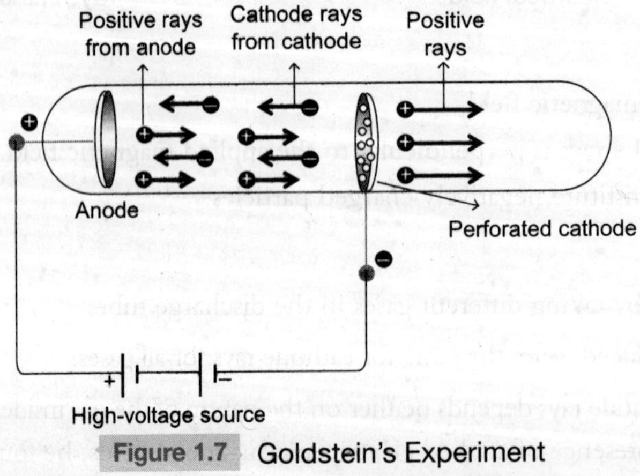

Figure 1.7 Goldstein's Experiment

Goldstein assumed the rays (i.e., positive ions) travelling from anode to cathode as protons. Later discoveries proved that the lightest positively charged particle is that of hydrogen and is named proton.

EXAMPLE 1.1 Calculate the specific charge of an electron.

SOLUTION

Charge of electron = -1.6022×10^{-19} Coulomb (negative because the electron has a negative charge).
Mass of electron = 9.1094×10^{-31} kg.

$$\text{Specific charge of electron} = \frac{charge}{mass} = \frac{-1.6022 \times 10^{-19}\ \text{Coulomb}}{9.1094 \times 10^{-31}\ \text{kg}}$$

$$= -1.76 \times 10^{11}\ \text{C/kg.}$$

EXAMPLE 1.2 Calculate the value of the specific charge of a beta particle. Find the ratio of specific charges of an electron to the beta particle.

SOLUTION

A beta particle is essentially an electron (or positron), hence their masses and charges are the same.
Mass of a beta particle = 9.1094×10^{-31} kg (same as an electron)
Charge of beta particle = -1.6022×10^{-19} C (negative because beta particle, being an electron, has a negative charge)
Specific charge of beta particle = charge/mass

$$\text{Specific charge of electron} = \frac{charge}{mass} = \frac{-1.6022 \times 10^{-19}\ \text{Coulomb}}{9.1094 \times 10^{-31}\ \text{kg}}$$

$$= -1.6022 \times 10^{-19}\ \text{C}/9.1094 \times 10^{-31}\ \text{kg}$$

$$= -1.76 \times 10^{11}\ \text{C/kg}$$

$$\text{Ratio of the specific charge of electron and beta particle} = \frac{-1.76 \times 10^{11}\ \text{C/kg}}{-1.76 \times 10^{11}\ \text{C/kg}} = 1:1$$

Discovery of Neutrons

The mass of an atom is concentrated in its nucleus and the mass of the electrons is negligible. Hence, the mass of an atom was expected to be equal to the mass of the protons in it.

Except in the case of hydrogen, the mass of an atom was found to be always greater than the total mass of the protons present inside the atom. Further, the unaccounted mass of atom, i.e., (mass of atom – mass of protons) was either equal to or a multiple of the mass of proton.

Based on the above observation, it was assumed that an atom contains one more kind of particle which has the same mass as that of the proton but without any charge. These particles were named as neutrons and were found to be electrically neutral. In 1932 James Chadwick proved the existence of neutrons by bombarding beryllium nucleus with alpha particles.

Table 1.1 Characteristics of Fundamental Particles

Fundamental particles	Charge	Mass	Relative charge
Electron (e)	-1.6×10^{-19} C -4.8×10^{-10} e.s.u.	9.1×10^{-31} kg (or) 0.00055 amu	−1
Proton (p)	$+ 1.6 \times 10^{-19}$ C $+ 4.8 \times 10^{-10}$ e.s.u.	1.67×10^{-27} kg (or) 1.0078 amu	+1
Neutron (n)	0	1.72×10^{-27} kg (or) 1.0083 amu	0

The study of the properties of the fundamental particles, such as, electrons and protons led to the conception of various atomic models.

Atomic Models

Atomic model is the description of depicting the arrangement of various fundamental particles inside the atom. Different atomic models have been proposed by John Dalton, J. J. Thomson, Rutherford and Bohr. The systematic study of various basic atomic models gives an insight into the understanding of the primary structure of the atom.

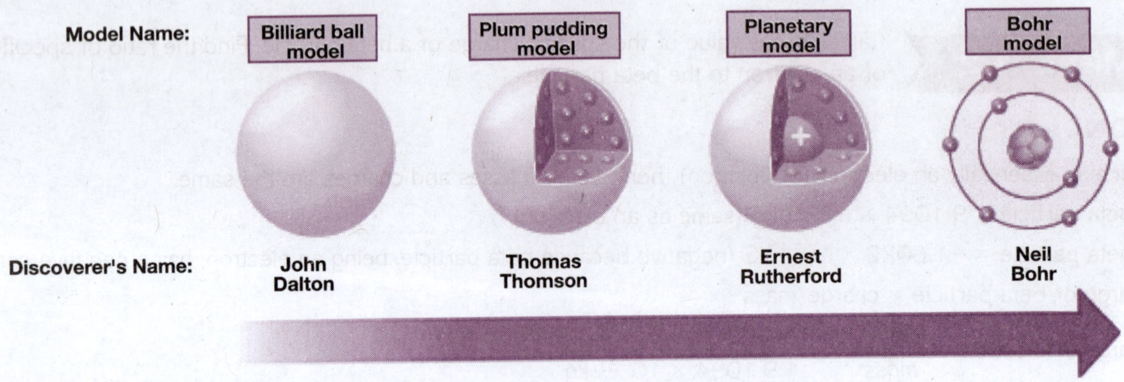

Figure 1.8 Timeline of Atomic Models

Thomson's Atomic Model

J. J. Thomson proposed his atomic model in 1903 prior to the discovery of protons itself.

According to J. J. Thomson, an atom contains negatively charged particles called **electrons** uniformly spread inside a sphere of thinly spread mass of positive charge. This model has been called by different names, such as, **watermelon model, plum pudding model** or **an apple pie model**. The total positive charge of the sphere is equal to the total negative charge of electrons and for this reason atom remains electrically neutral.

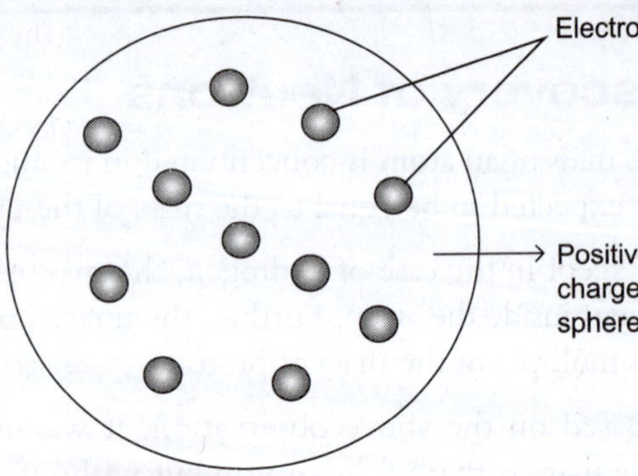

Figure 1.9 Thomson's atomic model

Drawback of Thomson's Model

The model could not explain how the positively charged particles are shielded from the negatively charged particles without getting neutralized.

After J. J. Thomson, Ernest Rutherford carried out a series of experiments from 1905 to 1911 to test the correctness of Thomson's atomic model.

Rutherford's α-particle Scattering Experiment

Ernest Rutherford in 1911 gave the concept of nucleus based on the results of his experiment known as **α-particle scattering experiment.**

Rutherford bombarded a thin gold foil with α-particles. The foil was surrounded by a spherical screen of zinc sulphide. The α-particles were condensed to a narrow beam by passing them through a pair of positively charged parallel plates.

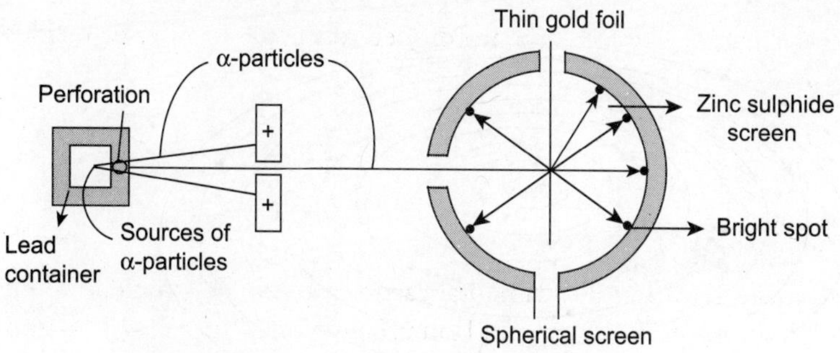

Figure 1.10 α-particle scattering experiment

Konnect

Rutherford estimated the diameter of the nucleus to be of the order of 10^{-13} cm and that of the atom to be 10^{-8} cm. Thus, the diameter of the nucleus is about 10^5 times smaller than the diameter of the atom.

Observations and Conclusion of Rutherford's Atomic Model

1. Most of the α-particles passed straight through the gold foil without any deflection.
2. Few α-particles were deflected through small angles and few were deflected through large angles.
3. Very few (1 in 20,000) α-particles completely rebounded.

On the basis of these observations, Rutherford concluded that Thomson's atomic model could not be correct because of the following reasons:

1. Most of the α-particles passed straight through the gold foil. This proves that atoms must have large empty space.
2. Since very few particles completely rebounded, he concluded that the total positive charge of the atom is concentrated at the centre of the atom. They are not thinly spread in the form of a sphere. The tiny central positively charged core was named as **nucleus**.
3. The large deflection of the α-particles could take place only because of the close encounter of the α-particles with the central positively charged core, i.e., the nucleus.

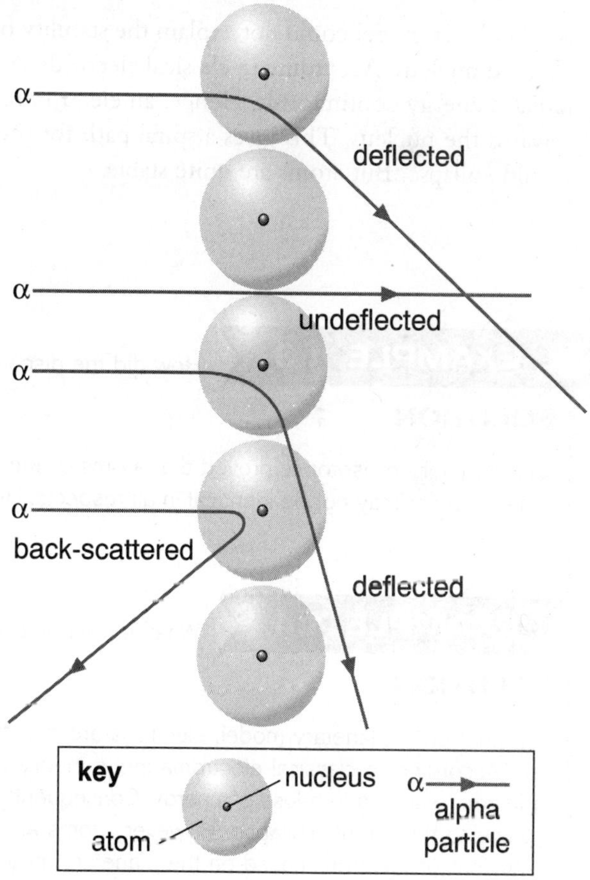

Figure 1.11 Pictorial representation of the observations shown in α-particle scattering experiment

Postulates of Rutherford's Atomic Model

Main postulates of Rutherford's atomic model are mentioned below:

1. Atom consists mostly of empty space.
2. The entire positively charged particles are present in the centre of the atomic sphere. This concentrated positively charged mass within the atom is called **nucleus**.
3. The size of the nucleus is very small compared to the size of the total volume of the atom.
4. The electrons within an atom must revolve around the nucleus at various distances at very high speeds in order to counterbalance the electrostatic force of attraction between protons and electrons.

Rutherford's atomic model can be compared with the solar system. Planets revolve round the sun in the solar system. Similarly electrons revolve round the nucleus in an atom. Hence, Rutherford's atomic model is also called **planetary model.**

Figure 1.12 Rutherford's atomic model (left) and illustration of solar system (right)

Drawbacks of Rutherford's Atomic Model

Rutherford's model could not explain the stability of an atom. Electron is a charged particle moving around the oppositely charged nucleus. According to classical electrodynamics, an electrically charged particle revolving around in a circular path radiates energy continuously. Hence, an electron revolving around the nucleus should radiate energy and gradually move towards the nucleus. This gives a spiral path for the electron which should finally collide with the nucleus and the atom would collapse. But atoms are quite stable.

EXAMPLE 1.3 How did the discovery of isotopes contradict Dalton's atomic theory?

SOLUTION

The discovery of isotopes proved that atoms of the same element may possess different atomic weights, that is atoms of the same element may not be identical in all respects. Hence, discovery of isotopes contradicted Dalton's atomic theory.

EXAMPLE 1.4 What is the primary limitation of Rutherford's planetary model in explaining atomic stability?

SOLUTION

In Rutherford's planetary model, electrons are depicted as revolving around the nucleus much like planets revolve around the sun. According to classical electromagnetic theory, any charged particle in motion, like these revolving electrons, should emit radiation, resulting in a loss of energy. Consequently, the electrons should spiral inward and eventually crash into the nucleus, leading to the atom's collapse. However, atoms are observed to be stable in nature. This discrepancy between the expected behaviour of electrons based on the planetary model and the observed stability of atoms represents the primary limitation of Rutherford's model. Hence, this model couldn't fully explain why atoms remain stable over time.

EXAMPLE 1.5 According to Rutherford, electrons move around the nucleus at very high speed. How did he correlate this with the stability of an atom?

SOLUTION

If the electrons are at rest, they should fall into the nucleus due to electrostatic forces of attraction. In order to balance this force of attraction towards the nucleus, they must be under the action of another force away from the centre of the nucleus. This is possible only if the electrons are in a state of motion along a circular path with very high speed.

Bohr's Atomic Model

In 1913, Niels Bohr proposed his atomic model which explained the stability of an atom.

Postulates of Bohr's Atomic Model

Main postulates of Bohr's atomic model are mentioned below:

1. Electrons revolve around the nucleus only in certain permissible circular paths called **orbits** or **shells.**
2. The electron in each orbit has a definite energy.
3. The energy of an electron remains constant as long as it revolves in a particular orbit. Hence, these are called **stationary orbits.**
4. An electron moves from a lower-energy level to a higher-energy level when it absorbs energy from an external source.
5. An electron gives out energy while jumping from a high-energy level to a low-energy level.

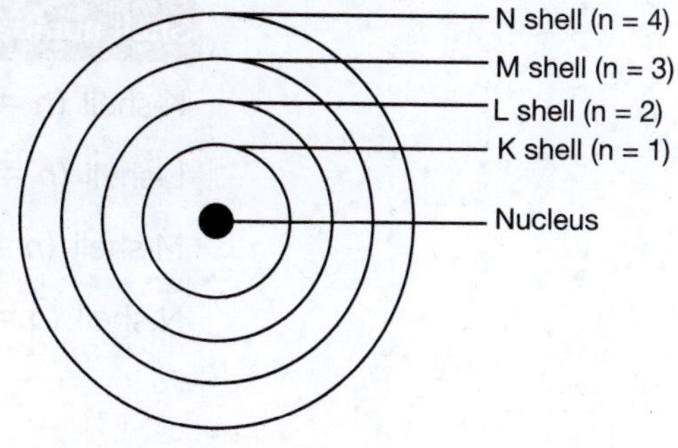

Figure 1.13 Bohr's atomic model

Atomic Number and Mass Number

The number of protons present in the nucleus of an atom is called its **atomic number** and is denoted by the letter Z. The total number of protons and neutrons present in the nucleus of an atom is called **mass number** and is denoted by the letter A.

For example, a chlorine atom has 17 protons and 18 neutrons in its nucleus. Hence, its atomic number (Z) is 17 and its mass number (A) is 35 and is represented as ${}_{17}Cl^{35}$.

Isotopes

Atoms of an element must have the same atomic number, but their mass number can be different due to the presence of different number of neutrons. These atoms of an element having different number of neutrons are called **isotopes**.

For example, hydrogen occurs in nature in three different isotopic forms—protium (${}_1H^1$), deuterium (${}_1H^2$) and tritium (${}_1H^3$).

The atomic number of all the three isotopes is 1, but their mass numbers are 1, 2 and 3, respectively. The percentage of protium is maximum in the natural sample of hydrogen, i.e., 99.98%.

> **Info Bytes!**
>
> Isotopes are responsible for the fractional values of atomic weight in some species.

Isobars

Atoms of different elements having the same mass number but different atomic number are called **isobars**.

For example, calcium and argon are found to have the same mass number. ${}_{20}Ca^{40}$ and ${}_{18}Ar^{40}$.

Isotones

The atoms of elements having the same number of neutrons are called isotones.

Electronic Configuration of the Atoms

Electrons move around the nucleus in different orbits.

The maximum number of electrons which can be presented in a particular orbit was given by Bohr and Bury. This is known as **Bohr–Bury scheme of electronic configuration**.

If n represents the shell number, then the maximum number of electrons which can revolve in that particular shell is given by the formula $2n^2$.

Table 1.2 Maximum number of electrons in shells

Shell numbers	Maximum number of electrons
K-shell ($n = 1$)	$2n^2 = 2 \times 1^2 = 2$
L-shell ($n = 2$)	$2n^2 = 2 \times 2^2 = 8$
M-shell ($n = 3$)	$2n^2 = 2 \times 3^2 = 18$
N-shell ($n = 4$)	$2n^2 = 2 \times 4^2 = 32$

However, the maximum number of electrons which can be present in the outermost orbit, i.e., valence shell is 8. The maximum number of electrons that can be present in the penultimate and the anti-penultimate shells is 18 and 32, respectively. An atom is considered to be stable if its outermost orbit contains 8 electrons.

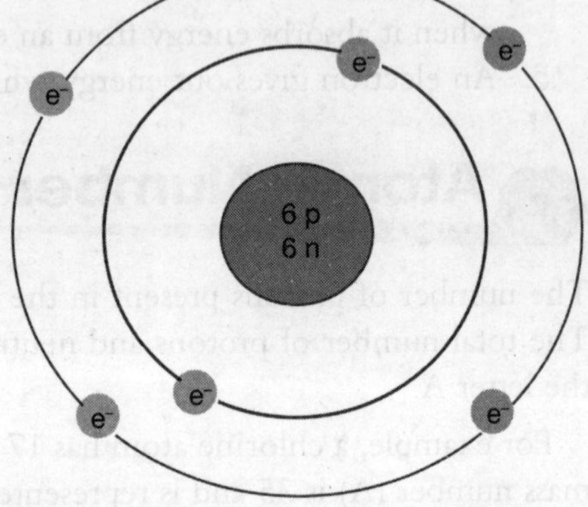

Figure 1.14 Geometrical representation of carbon

Examples:

1. **Sodium:** Atomic number 11
   Electronic configuration: 2,8,1
2. **Chlorine:** Atomic number 17
   Electronic configuration: 2,8,7
3. **Iron:** Atomic number: 26
   Electronic configuration: 2,8,14,2

Geometrical Representation of Structure of an Atom

The diagrammatic representation of electronic configuration of an atom is called **geometrical representation**. For a structure of an atom, it can be described using following examples:

1. The atomic number of carbon is 6 and the mass number of carbon is 12.
   Number of electrons = 6
   Number of neutrons = 6
   Number of protons = 6
2. The atomic number of aluminium is 13 and its mass number is 27.
   Number of electrons = 13
   Number of neutrons = 14
   Number of protons = 13

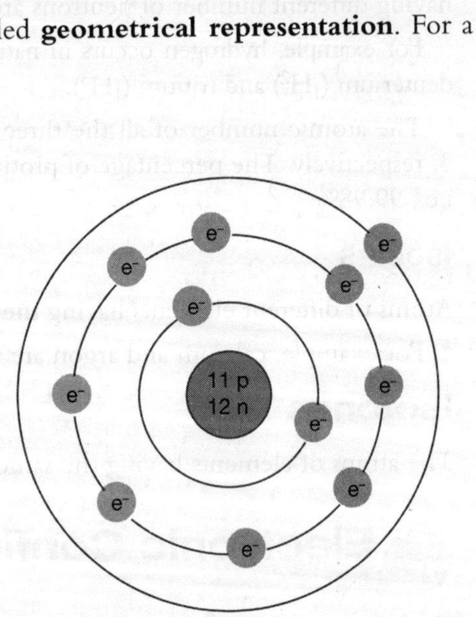

Figure 1.15 Geometrical representation of sodium

Valence Shell and Valence Electrons

Valence shell of an element is the outermost shell in an atom.

For example, $_{11}Na^{23}$ – 2, 8, 1 … Here 1 electron is filled in the last shell, i.e., M-shell. Therefore, M-shell is the valence shell.

The electrons filled in the valence shell are called **valence electrons.** In the above example, there is one valence electron which belongs to the M-shell.

EXAMPLE 1.6

An element X consists of 20 protons and 20 neutrons. Mention the atomic number and mass number, and represent the element with atomic number and mass number.

SOLUTION

As X consists of 20 protons ⇒ atomic number, (Z) is 20.

As number of neutrons = 20, mass number, (A) = atomic number + number of neutrons

∴ A = 20 + 20 = 40

∴ Mass number, (A) = 40

The element is calcium and can be represented as ${}_{20}Ca^{40}$.

EXAMPLE 1.7

How was Bohr able to explain the stability of an atom?

SOLUTION

According to Bohr's atomic model, each orbit or shell is associated with a definite amount of energy, and hence, they are also called **energy levels**. As long as the electron revolves in a particular orbit, the electron does not lose energy. Therefore, these orbits are called **stationary orbits** and the electrons are said to be in stationary energy states. When an electron moves from lower-energy level to higher-energy level, it absorbs energy from an external source and gives out energy while jumping from a higher-energy level to a lower-energy level. Thus, he explained the stability of an atom.

EXAMPLE 1.8

The mass of positively charged particles present in an atom is found to be 11,022 times that of an electron. Identify the element and write its electronic configuration.

SOLUTION

The mass of a proton is 1837 times that of an electron.

$$\text{Number of protons} = \frac{11,022}{1837} = 6$$

Hence, element is carbon and its electronic configuration is 2, 4.

EXAMPLE 1.9

In an atom, the number of neutrons is 58.7% more than that of protons. The number of electrons in the neutral atom is 92. Find out the number of protons, neutrons and mass number, and represent the atom with atomic number and mass number..

SOLUTION

Since the number of electrons in the neutral atom is 92.

∴ Atomic number (Z) is 92 and number of protons is 92.

Number of neutrons = 92 + (58.7/100) × 92 = 146.

Mass number, (A) = atomic number + number of neutrons.

Mass number = 92 + 146 = 238.

Representation ${}_{92}X^{238}$.

EXAMPLE 1.10

The mass number of an atom is 31. If the atom has 5 electrons in M-shell, calculate the number of neutrons.

SOLUTION

The electronic configuration of the element is 2, 8, 5. Therefore, its atomic number is 15 and the number of neutrons = mass number – atomic number

∴ Number of neutrons = 31 – 15 = 16.

POINTS TO REMEMBER

- ✔ In 1808, John Dalton proposed the atomic theory based on the various laws of chemical combination known at that time. The theory has been well accepted during the 19th century as it could help in explaining the laws of chemical combination.
- ✔ Dalton's postulate which suggested that atoms are the tiny indivisible particles were proved wrong by the discovery of the subatomic particles also known as the fundamental particles.
- ✔ In 1878, Sir William Crooke, while conducting an experiment using a special glass tube called discharge tube, found certain visible rays travelling between two metal electrodes. These rays are known as Crooke's rays or cathode rays.
- ✔ Atomic model is the description of depicting the arrangement of various fundamental particles inside the atom.
- ✔ J. J. Thomson proposed his plum pudding atomic model in 1903 prior to the discovery of protons itself.
- ✔ Ernest Rutherford in 1911 gave the concept of nucleus based on the results of his experiment known as α-particle scattering experiment.
- ✔ The tiny central positively-charged core was named as nucleus.
- ✔ Rutherford's model could not explain the stability of an atom.
- ✔ In 1913, Niels Bohr proposed his atomic model which explained the stability of an atom.
- ✔ The number of protons present in the nucleus of an atom is called its atomic number and is denoted by the letter Z.
- ✔ The total number of protons and neutrons present in the nucleus of an atom is called mass number and is denoted by the letter A.
- ✔ Atoms of an element having different number of neutrons are called isotopes.
- ✔ Atoms of different elements having the same mass number, but different atomic number are called isobars.
- ✔ The maximum number of electrons which can be presented in a particular orbit was given by Bohr and Bury. This is known as Bohr–Bury scheme of electronic configuration.
- ✔ The diagrammatic representation of electronic configuration of an atom is called geometrical representation.
- ✔ Valence shell of an element is the outermost shell in an atom.The electrons filled in the valence shell are called valence electrons.

PRACTICE QUESTIONS CLASSROOM WING

Very Short Answer Type Questions

Directions for questions from 1 to 8:
Fill in the blanks

1. Discovery of ______ led to the contradiction of the postulate of Dalton's atomic theory.
2. Isotopes differ in the number of ______.
3. Isobars possess the same number of ______.
4. Most of the α-particles passed straight through the gold foil. This proved the existence of ______ in an atom.
5. According to Rutherford, ______ force of nucleus is balanced by the high velocity of revolving electrons.
6. The atoms of the same element may differ in the number of ______.
7. The valence shell of an element of atomic number 35 is the ______ shell.
8. According to Bohr's atomic model, electrons revolve in ______ orbits.

Directions for questions from 9 to 23:
Answer the following questions

9. An atomic model is represented by the figure given below.

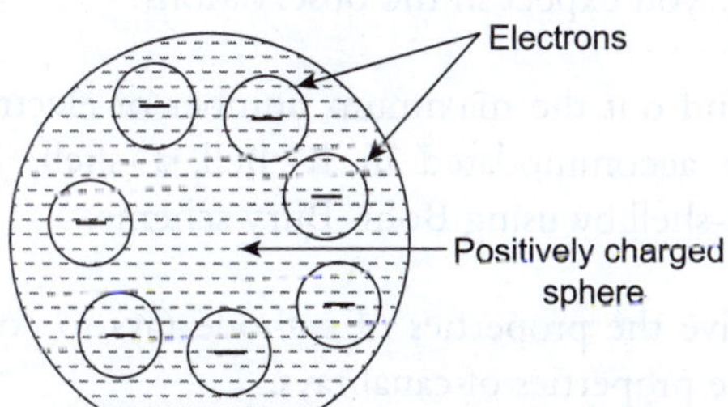

Which fact could be successfully explained by the given atomic model?

10. Which law provided the experimental basis for the postulates of Dalton's atomic theory?
11. Give the geometrical representations of electronic arrangements of the following elements:
(a) fluorine (b) phosphorus
12. What is the maximum number of electrons that can be present in the *n*th shell of an atom?
13. What were the comparative values of diameter of nucleus and atom given by Rutherford?
14. Find the number of valence electrons in the following elements by writing the electronic arrangement in their atoms:
(a) nitrogen (b) sulphur (c) chlorine
15. Why is Rutherford's model called nuclear model?
16. Define atomic number and mass number. How can you represent an atom by using atomic number and mass number? Give two examples.
17. Who discovered neutrons? How was the discovery made?
18. Why is a partially evacuated discharge tube taken for Thomson's experiment?
19. How did Rutherford explain the stability of atom?
20. Name the isotopes of hydrogen and give the number of neutrons present in each of them.
21. What is the relative mass of proton with respect to hydrogen atom?
22. Which experiment led to the discovery of nucleus?
23. Give the mass and charge of an electron, a proton and a neutron in kg and coulombs, respectively.

Short Answer Type Questions

24. Which of the following numbers: 32, 36, 72, 98; does not correspond to the maximum number of electrons in Bohr's orbit?
25. An atom of an element 'X' loses an electron to get a stable octet. 'Y' also loses two electrons to form the corresponding ion. However, the resultant ion of Y does not possess an octet. Check whether 19 and 30 can be the probable atomic numbers of X and Y.
26. (a) Why does chlorine have fractional atomic mass?
(b) ZnS screen used in α - ray scattering experiment was spherical in shape. How would you justify it?
27. The neutral atom corresponding to a positive ion of an element has 2 incomplete shells. The sum of the electrons in the valence shell and the penultimate shell is

twice the number of electrons in the antepenultimate shell. Calculate the atomic number of the element.

28. Give the postulates of Dalton's atomic theory.

29. What are the observations of α-ray scattering experiment? Based on these observations, how did Rutherford disprove Thomson's model?

30. Write the electronic arrangement for the following elements. Also give the geometrical representations.
(a) Oxygen (b) Argon
(c) Calcium (d) Potassium

31. When different gases are taken in a discharge tube, how do the *e/m* values of cathode rays and canal rays vary?

32. Give the differences between isotopes and isobars.

33. In J. J. Thomson's experiment, what observations were found when:
(a) a small obstruction was placed in the path of cathode rays.
(b) a paddle wheel is placed between cathode and anode.

What were the conclusions drawn on the basis of these observations?

34. Calculate the number of neutrons for the following elements:
(a) $_{11}Na^{23}$ (b) $_{18}Ar^{40}$
(c) $_{17}Cl^{35}$ (d) $_{15}P^{31}$

35. What happens to the cathode rays under a strong magnetic field or an electric field? What is the conclusion made from this?

36. An atom of an element has fourth shell as the valence shell. The difference between electrons present in L- and M-, K- and N-shells are 1 and 0, respectively. Find the atomic number of the element.

37. An atom of an element has one electron in the valence shell and the two inner shells have 8 electrons each. Find the atomic number of that element.

38. Mass of total positive charge present in an atom is 16533 times to that of mass of an electron. Find the atomic number of this element.

Essay Answer Type Questions

39. Write down the
(a) electronic configuration,
(b) number of valence electrons,
(c) number of neutrons and
(d) nature of the element
for the following species:
(1) $_{6}X^{12}$
(2) $_{10}Y^{20}$
(3) $_{19}Z^{39}$

40. Explain how the results of α-ray scattering experiment led to Rutherford's model of atom. Give the postulates and drawbacks of Rutherford's atomic model.

41. (a) State the postulates of Bohr's theory.
(b) If protons, deuterium ions and protium ions are separately used in α - ray scattering experiment instead of α - particles, what type of changes would you expect in the observations?

42. Find out the maximum number of electrons that can be accommodated in K-shell, L-shell, M-shell and N-shell by using Bohr–Bury scheme.

43. Give the properties of cathode rays in comparison to the properties of canal rays.

PRACTICE QUESTIONS COMPETITION WING

Level 1: Apply Your Concepts

Directions for questions from 1 to 8:
State whether the following statements are true or false.

1. The geometric representation of a certain species is given below.

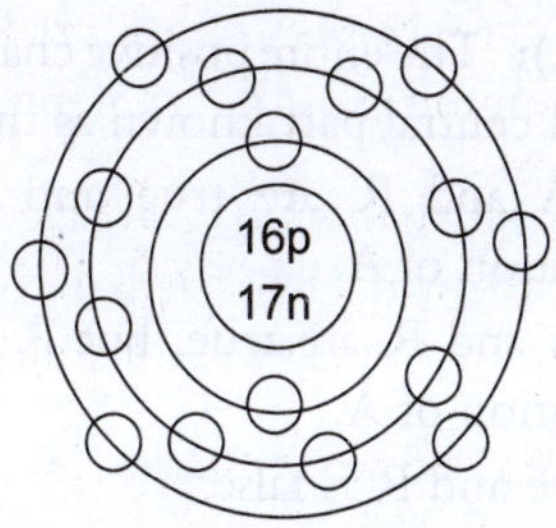

The anion formed from it has the configuration of neon.

2. The geometry given below represent a species that can form a trinegative ion.

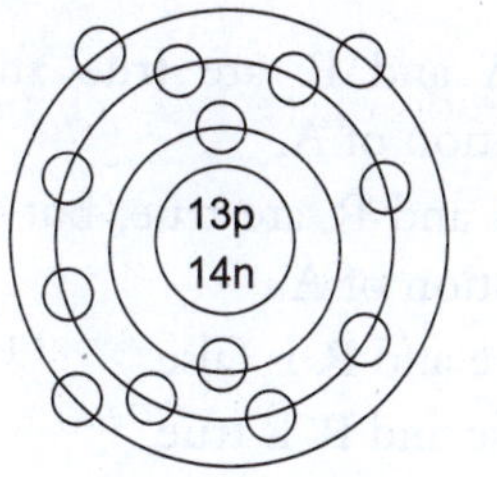

3. Thomson could successfully explain the electrical neutrality of an atom.
4. The e/m ratio of cathode rays is different for different gases.
5. High pressure and low voltage should be maintained in the discharge tube for the production of cathode rays.
6. Mass number is the sum of the number of protons and neutrons in an atom.
7. Cathode rays deflect in the presence of magnetic field.
8. According to Dalton's atomic theory, matter is composed of tiny indivisible particles called atoms.

Directions for questions from 9 to 19:
Fill in the blanks.

9. Protons and neutrons together correspond to ________.
10. Rutherford's theory proposed the concept of ________.
11. The conditions maintained in a discharge tube for the generation of cathode rays are ________ and ________.
12. According to Rutherford, electrons revolve around the nucleus in ________.
13. The discovery of ________ proved that atom is divisible.
14. The maximum number of electrons present in fifth shell is ________.
15. Electron present in ________ orbit cannot lose its energy.
16. The fundamental particle present in anode rays produced by $_1H^1$ is ________.
17. The electrode connected to the negative terminal of a battery in a discharge tube is called ________.
18. The specific charge value of anode rays produced by ________ is the maximum.
19. The sum of protons and neutrons is same in ________.

Directions for question 20:
Match the entries in Column A with the appropriate ones in Column B.

20. Match the values of Column A with those of Column B.

	Column A (Atomic Number)		Column B (Ratio of Electrons in Penultimate Shell to Valence Shell)
(i)	21	(a)	8:1
(ii)	30	(b)	4:1
(iii)	20	(c)	9:2
(iv)	19	(d)	1:1
(v)	18	(e)	9:1

Directions for questions from 21 to 40:
For each of the questions, four choices have been provided. Select the correct alternative.

21. Certain amount of a gas is enclosed in a discharge tube. The bulb in the arrangement given below can be made to glow when:

(a) vacuum is created in the discharge tube.
(b) the gas is replaced by the same amount of an easily ionisable gas.
(c) the other gas of low molecular weight is introduced.
(d) the amount of gas in the discharge tube is decreased.

22. Which of the following corresponds to the incorrect match with respect to their formation?
(a) O^{-2} ion – gain of two electrons
(b) N^{-3} ion – Gain of three electrons
(c) Mg^{+2} ion – Loss of two electrons
(d) K^{+} ion – Gain of one electron

23. ${}_{8}X^{16}$ and ${}_{8}X^{17}$ represent:
(a) isotones (b) isobars
(c) isotopes (d) isosters

24. Arrange the important points of various theories in chronological order.
(1) Presence of electrons in K, L, M and N shells.
(2) Combination of atoms in simple numerical ratio.
(3) Electrical neutrality of atom.
(4) The diameter of the nucleus is 10^{-5} times that of the atom.
(a) 1 2 3 4
(b) 2 3 4 1
(c) 3 4 1 2
(d) 3 2 1 4

25. Two elements X and Y have 6 and 7 electrons in their N- and M-shells, respectively. Find the ratio of atomic numbers of X and Y.
(a) 3 : 4 (b) 1 : 2
(c) 2 : 1 (d) 6 : 7

26. **Assertion (A):** The orbits in which electrons are present are called stationary orbits.
Reason (R): Electrons remain stationary in those orbits.
(a) Both A and R are true and R is the correct explanation of A.
(b) Both A and R are true, but R is not the correct explanation of A.
(c) A is true and R is false.
(d) A is false and R is true.

27. **Assertion (A):** In α-ray scattering experiment, most of the α particles were completely rebounded.
Reason (R): The entire positive charge is concentrated in the small central part known as the nucleus.
(a) Both A and R are true and R is the correct explanation of A.
(b) Both A and R are true, but R is not the correct explanation of A.
(c) A is true and R is false.
(d) A is false and R is true.

28. **Assertion (A):** Energy of orbits increases with distance from the nucleus.
Reason (R): Electrons in the first orbit do not lose energy.
(a) Both A and R are true and R is the correct explanation of A.
(b) Both A and R are true, but R is not the correct explanation of A.
(c) A is true and R is false.
(d) A is false and R is true.

29. According to Thomson, which one of the following statements is correct?
(a) Negative charge of an atom is uniformly distributed throughout the atom.
(b) The volume occupied by positive charge is less than that occupied by the negative charge.
(c) Electrons are embedded in the positive charge which is spread uniformly.
(d) None of the above

30. ${}^{y}_{x}A$, ${}^{y+1}_{x}A$ are two isotopes of element A. Difference between the number of neutrons in the isotopes is:
(a) $1 - 2y$ (b) $1 - x$
(c) 1 (d) $2x - 1$

31. Low pressure is maintained in the discharge tube to:
(a) increase the number of molecules
(b) increase ionisation of gas molecules

(c) decrease the velocity of the rays coming from the cathode

(d) all the above

32. If velocity of α-particles increases, then angle of deviation:

(a) increases
(b) decreases
(c) remains same
(d) cannot be predicted

33. Which of the following unipositive ions possesses all the three subatomic particles?

(a) Helium (b) Deuterium
(c) Tritium (d) Hydrogen

34. The ratio of the number of electrons in the N-shell of A and the M-shell of B with atomic numbers 40 and 32, respectively, is:

(a) 5 : 3 (b) 9 : 5
(c) 5 : 9 (d) 5 : 4

35. Total number of electrons present in the penultimate shell of an element with atomic number 36 is:

(a) 18 (b) 10
(c) 8 (d) 16

36. To draw the geometrical representation for the structure of the oxygen atom the following steps are given. Identify the correct sequence of the steps.

(1) The eight electrons present in the extranuclear part would be distributed in the first two orbits, i.e., K and L. As per the rules, two electrons would occupy the K-orbit and the remaining six electrons occupy the L-orbit.

(2) The atomic number of oxygen is 8.

(3) In the nucleus, 8 protons and 8 neutrons are present and in the extranuclear part, i.e., in the orbits, 8 electrons are present.

(4) Oxygen atom has 8 electrons and 8 protons. The mass number is 16, and hence, the number of neutrons is equal to 8 [$_8O^{16}$].

(a) 2 1 3 4 (b) 3 1 4 2
(c) 2 4 3 1 (d) 3 4 2 1

37. Arrange the following statements in a sequence which involves the calculation of the atomic number and mass number for an atom of an element with 15 electrons and 16 neutrons.

(1) A = Number of protons + Number of neutrons
A = Z + Number of neutrons
A = 15 + 16 = 31

(2) Number of protons and number of electrons are equal in a neutral atom. Hence, the atomic number Z is equal to 15.

(3) Mass number is equal to the total number of protons and neutrons.

(4) Atomic number is 15 and mass number is 31.

(a) 2 4 3 1 (b) 2 3 1 4
(c) 3 2 1 4 (d) 3 2 4 1

38. Many theories and experiments carried out for the study of atom eventually led to the development of its structure. Arrange the given theories or models of atom proposed by different scientists in chronological order.

(1) Planetary model
(2) Watermelon model
(3) Bohr's atomic model
(4) Dalton's atomic theory

(a) 3 2 1 4 (b) 4 1 2 3
(c) 2 1 4 3 (d) 4 2 1 3

39. Rutherford's α-ray scattering experiment led to the discovery of the nucleus and to the conclusion that an atom consists of large empty space. Arrange the following steps in a sequence which explains the experiment and also the above mentioned conclusions.

(1) To make out the observations a spherical ZnS screen was placed surrounding the gold foil.

(2) The substance which acts as a source of α-particles is taken in a lead container and made to pass through a slit between like charged positive plates.

(3) It was observed that most of the particles passed straight through the gold foil, few were deflected through small angles and very few through large angles. However, very few completely rebounded.

(4) A narrow, condensed beam consisting of α-particles is made to bombard on a thin gold foil.

(a) 1 3 2 4 (b) 2 3 1 4
(c) 4 2 1 3 (d) 2 4 1 3

40. If an electron jumps from orbit A to orbit B, it loses energy and if it jumps from C to B, it gains energy. Arrange the orbits in the increasing order of distance from the nucleus.

(a) A < B < C (b) C < A < B
(c) C < B < A (d) A < C < B

Level 2: Review Your Concepts

41. (a) A neutral atom of an element has a nucleus with nuclear charge 12 times and mass 24 times that of hydrogen. Calculate the number of electrons, protons and neutrons in its stable positively charged ion.

(b) A dipositive ion and a dinegative ion are isoelectronic. What is the difference between their mass numbers if the number of neutrons in both the atoms is equal to their atomic numbers?

42. An atom 'X' has a mass of protons 36,740 times that of electrons. Find out the correct representation of the atom. The number of neutrons is 1 unit less than the protons.

43. If 'a' is the number of electrons in a dipositive ion and it has three neutrons more than the number of protons, write the atomic number and mass number.

44. Assuming that x is the mass of the electron and y is the total mass of protons in ${}_8O^{18}$, write the value of y in terms of x.

45. A dipositive ion has an electronic arrangement of 2, 8, 8. Find out the number of electrons, protons and neutrons in that element if its mass number is 40.

46. Atoms of two elements P and Q have 5 electrons in the second and third shells, respectively. What could be the geometrical representations of P and Q? What will the atomic numbers of these elements be?

47. Anode rays are also produced along with cathode rays in the discharge tube under low pressure. Justify.

48. Cathode rays are deflected in electric and magnetic fields. But they are made to pass straight in Thomson's experiment. How do you account for this?

49. If the maximum permissible orbits of elements in nature are limited to $n = 4$, what are the number of possible elements?

50. A metallic element forms an ion with unit charge. The ion has 10 electrons and 12 neutrons. What is the number of electrons, protons and neutrons in its neutral atom? Represent the atom with atomic number and mass number.

51. Nuclear charge of an element B is twice that of A. If A has two completely filled orbits and L-shell is its outermost orbit, find out the atomic numbers of A and B.

52. The number of electrons in a dipositive ion of an element X is 18. If the mass number of X is 4 units more than twice the number of electrons of its ion, calculate the number of protons, electron and neutrons in X.

53. Rutherford's α-ray scattering experiment was conducted in order to test the validity of Thomson's model. What results were expected from this experiment?

54. If the average atomic mass of chlorine is 35.5, then find the percentage abundance of the two isotopes of chlorine which have the mass number 35 and 37.

55. The electronic configuration of an atom A is a, $a + b$, $a + 2b$, a and that of B is a, $a + b$, $3a + 2b$, b.

(a) Write the electronic configurations of A and B.

(b) Calculate their atomic numbers,

(c) If the number of neutrons in A is $5b$ and that in B is $22.5a$, calculate their mass numbers.

56. Compare and contrast the angle of deflection of α-rays in α-rays scattering experiment carried out by taking aluminium foil and gold foil, respectively. Justify your results.

57. Why did Thomson assume that electrons are embedded in a positive mass but not the other way round?

58. (a) The ratio of the number of neutrons present in the two elements X and Y is 5 : 7 and the ratio of mass numbers is 10 : 13. The element X attains a stable octet configuration by losing two electrons from the fourth shell. Calculate the number of protons, electrons and neutrons present in X and Y.

(b) The number of protons in A and B are x and $x - 2$ respectively while that of neutrons in A and B are y and $y + 2$ respectively. What conclusion can you draw regarding A and B from the given information?

59. The dipositive and dinegative ions of different elements possesses an octet configuration in their third shell. Find out the atomic number and number of valence electrons in their neutral atoms.

60. From the following table, identify isotopes and isobars.

Atoms	Number of protons	Number of neutrons
A	X	Z + 2
B	X + 1	Z
C	X − 2	Z + 4
D	X + 1	Z + 1
E	X	Z + 1

61. Based on the information given in the below three statements, answer the following questions.
   (i) Element X has two valence electrons in the M-shell.
   (ii) In element Y, the electrons are distributed in the first three shells. It has eight electrons in the M-shell.
   (iii) Element Z has eight electrons in the penultimate shell, i.e., M.
   (a) Give the electronic configuration of X.
   (b) Which element is stable among X, Y and Z and why?
   (c) In which atom of an element is the number of electrons distributed in all the four shells?
   (d) What is the atomic number of Z in which the number of electrons in the first and the last shell are not the same?
   (e) What are the number of electrons and protons present in Y?

62. In an α-ray scattering experiment, what would happen if protons are used instead of α-particles?

63. An atom of an element has one electron in the valence shell and the two consecutive inner shells have 8 electrons each. Find the atomic number of that element. Write the electronic configuration of preceding and succeeding elements.

Level 3: Assess Your Concepts

64. Discharge doesn't take place at normal atmospheric pressure inside the cathode ray tube. Justify.

65. The *e*/*m* ratio of cathode rays does not change by changing the gas in cathode ray discharge tube. But the *e*/*m* ratio of anode rays changes by changing the gas in the discharge tube. Justify this statement.

66. When the canal ray experiment was conducted by taking helium gas in the discharge tube, *e*/*m* value of the particles was found to be less under low voltage and it was found to be more under high voltage. How do you explain this?

67. Different gases can produce different colours in a discharge tube. Explain with reason.

68. Anode rays produced by isotopes and isobars possess same charge when taken in different discharge tubes. Which among the two sets of anode rays show different deflections in the presence of an electric field?

69. If ${}_{x}^{y}A^{+1}$ or ${}_{x-1}^{y-2}B^{+1}$ were to be used instead of a particles in Rutherford's experiment, which would be better and why?

70. (a) According to Bohr's theory, the electrons revolve round the nucleus in definite paths called orbits. Do the electrons revolve round with same speed in all orbits? Justify.
   (b) A natural sample of an element contains two isotopes A and B. The difference in their atomic mass is 2 units. If the percentage abundance of the lighter isotope A is 25% and its atomic mass is *y*, calculate the average atomic weight.

71. M-shells of two elements A and B have 18 electrons each. The difference in the number of electrons present in the N-shells of A and B is 8. The M-shell is the penultimate shell in B. Predict the range of probable atomic numbers of A and B.

72. Which postulate of Rutherford's theory is not derived from the results of α-ray scattering experiment? On what basis Rutherford could assume that?

73. Predict the possible atomic number(s) of an atom in which the third shell is incompletely filled and maximum 4 more electrons can be added to that shell of the atom.

AT

PRACTICE QUESTIONS JEE-NEET SPECIAL WING

Multiple-Answer Type Questions

Directions for questions from 1 to 5:

Select one or more correct alternative(s) from the given choices.

1. The trivalent negative ion of an element 'X' is 2,8,8. Identify the configurations which correspond to elements that form ions which are isoelectronic with the stable ion of X.

(a) 2,8,18,7 (b) 2,8,6

(c) 2,8,8,2 (d) 2,8,18,2

2. An element 'M' has the electronic configuration in which the ratio of electrons in K and N shells is 1:1 while that of M and L shells is 5:4. Identify the statements which comply with this element.

(a) The mass of protons is 40414 times that of electron.

(b) The preceding element of M forms both divalent and trivalent ions

(c) The 'M' shell can add 8 electrons more to become completely filled

(D) The element can be represented as ${}_{20}M^{40}$

3. An element is represented as $x^{E^{2.5x}}$. Identify the sets of data which comply with the given representation of the element.

	No. of electrons	No. of neutrons
(a)	94	150
(b)	57	81
(c)	71	105
(d)	79	117

4. The mass of an electron is considered as 'x' units. The atoms of elements having equal number of neutrons are known as isotones. Identify the correctly matched sets among the following.

	Mass of protons	Mass number	Representation of isotone of the element
(a)	12859x	2Z+1	${}_{7}N^{15}$
(b)	29392x	2Z+2	${}_{18}Ar^{36}$
(c)	25718x	2Z+1	${}_{14}Si^{29}$
(d)	36740x	2Z	${}_{19}K^{39}$

5. The ratio of neutrons to protons indicates the stability of the various elements. The n/p ratio ranging from 1 to 1.5 is called zone of stability. All the of elements falling in this zone are considered to be stable. The elements which fall out side the zone of stability are unstable and hence are said to be radioactive.

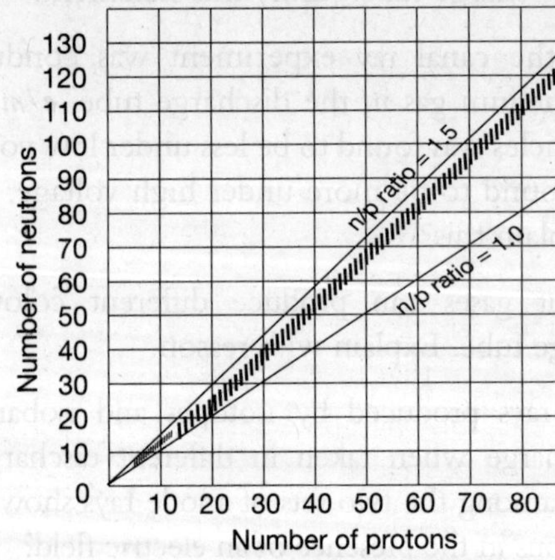

Among the following representations, identify the ones which fall outside the zone of stability.

(a) ${}_{86}A^{222}$ (b) ${}_{84}B^{209}$

(c) ${}_{90}C^{232}$ (c) ${}_{94}D^{244}$

Comprehension-Based Questions

Directions for questions from 6 to 10:

Read the content given in the following passage and answer the questions given below.

The following diagram represents a discharge tube experiment representing the discovery of fundamental particles. A gas is taken in the discharge tube at high voltage and low pressure. Due to the phenomenon of discharge taking place in the discharge tube, a red glow is observed at the end of the discharge tube.

Observe the picture keenly and answer the questions given below. The experiment is conducted by taking various gases in the discharge tube.

Experiments are numbered as I, II and III when hydrogen, deuterium and helium are taken respectively.

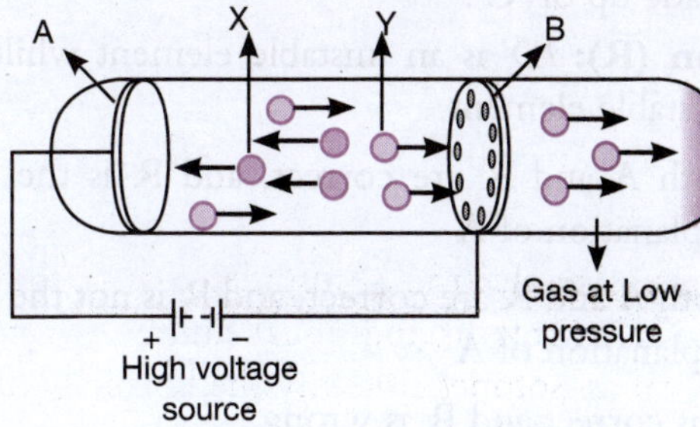

6. Consider the experiment I. If the specific charge of the particle X is 'a'units, identify the specific charge of the particles indicated by 'Y' in terms of 'a'. (Can take the values to the nearest approximation)
   (a) 9×10^7a C/kg (b) 1.7×10^{11} a C/kg
   (c) 2×10^{-4} a C/kg (d) 5×10^{-4} a C/kg
7. From the predicted observations of the experiments I, II and III in the presence of an external electric field of same strength, which of the following conclusions is likely to be wrong?
   (a) The angle of deflection of the particles 'X' keeps on decreasing from experiments I to III
   (b) The angle of deflection of the particles 'X' remains same in all experiments
   (c) The angle of deflection of the particles 'Y' keeps on decreasing from experiments I to III
   (d) Both (a) and (c)
8. Among the following, identify the correct feature of difference between experiment I and experiment III.
   (a) The specific charge of particles 'Y' in experiment III is half of that in experiment I
   (b) The specific charge of particles 'X' in experiment III is half of that in experiment I
   (c) The specific charge of both particles 'X' and 'Y' in experiment III is half of that in experiment I
   (d) The direction of motion of 'X' and 'Y' would be reversed in experiments I and III.
9. What would be the specific charge of the particles 'Y' in experiment II? Consider the values of specific charge of 'X' and 'Y' of experiment I from question number 6.
   (a) 1×10^{-3}a C/kg (b) 5×10^{-4}a C/kg
   (c) 2.5×10^{-4}a C/kg (d) 2.5×10^{7}a C/kg
10. Which among the following statements complies with the experiment III?
   (a) The nature of particles 'Y' depends on the voltage applied
   (b) The nature of particles 'Y' depends on the pressure of gas in the discharge tube.
   (c) The nature of particles 'Y' depends both on voltage applied and pressure of gas in the discharge tube.
   (d) The nature of particles 'Y' for a particular gas does not change with voltage or pressure of the gas in the discharge tube.

Directions for question 11

Read the content given in the following passage and answer the question given below.

The maximum number of electrons in a shell can be given by $2n^2$ where '*n*' takes the value of the shell number or energy level. However, the valence shell can have a maximum of 8 electrons even if the maximum capacity of the shell exceeds 8. This situation can be seen after the elements with atomic number 18. The electronic configuration for the elements succeeding Z=18 After the valence shell is filled with 8 electrons, the incoming electrons occupy the next shell leaving the previous shell incomplete. After 2 electrons are added to the new outer shell, the addition of electrons continues in the previous or penultimate shell. This addition continues till the shell is filled with 18 electrons which is its maximum capacity. This is followed by the continuation of filling of the valence shell till the number of electrons reaches 8.

11. Consider that the number of electrons in K and L shells in an atom of these elements is *a* and *b*.

	Column I Atomic number		Column II No. of electrons in penultimate shell
(i)	30	(a)	(b-a) + 2a
(ii)	25	(b)	(2b-a)
(iii)	22	(c)	(a+b)+3a
(iv)	28	(d)	(b-a)3
(v)	26	(e)	2(b-a)+1

Directions for questions 12 to 17:

Read the content given in the following passage and answer the questions given below.

The following figure indicates an experiment carried out by a well knownscientist which was instrumental in the study of structure of atom. The particles used in the experiment are produced from some source element which undergoes a nuclear reaction to produce the particles. In a nuclear reaction, the sum of atomic numbers on the reactant side should be equal to that in the product side. Same is the case with mass number.

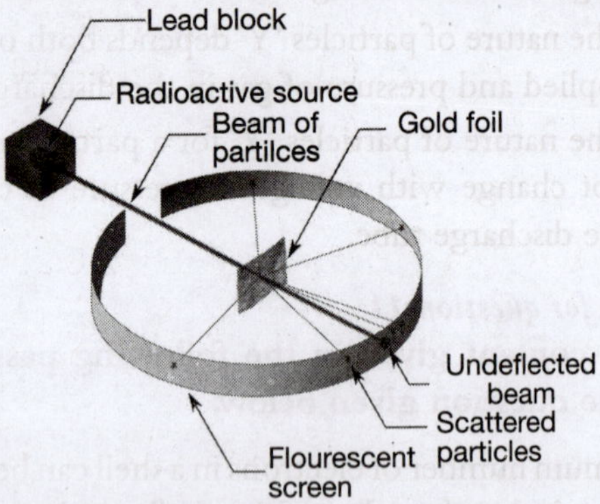

12. The above figure represents the experiment concerned with the discovery of which of the following components of an atom?
(a) Discovery of nucleus
(b) Discovery of neutron
(c) Discovery of electron
(d) Discovery of proton

13. Identify the characteristic which does not comply with the particles used in the above experiment.
(a) The mass of the particle is approximately equal to 1.8×10^{-18} g
(b) The charge of each particle can be approximately equal to 3.2×10^{-19} C
(c) Lead can be a source for the emission of these particles.
(d) Both (a) and (c)

14. Which property of the substance 'B' is exploited in its use for the required purpose in the experiment?
(a) 'B' is highly malleable
(b) 'B' is radioactive substance
(c) 'B' is a fluorescent substance
(d) 'B' has high nuclear charge

15. Among the following, identify the most probable set of substances to be taken for the above experiment to produce the accurate results.

	A	C	D
(a)	Aluminium	Zinc	Plutonium
(b)	Gold	Zinc	Lead
(c)	Platinum	Lead	Uranlum
(d)	Gold	Lead	Platinum

16. **Assertion(A):** The substance 'D' is enclosed in a thick box made up of 'C'.
Reason (R): 'D' is an unstable element while 'C' is highly stable element.
(a) Both A and R are correct, and R is the correct explanation of A
(b) Both A and R are correct, and R is not the correct explanation of A
(c) A is correct and R is wrong
(d) R is correct and A is wrong

17. Which of the following nuclear reactions is associated with the emission of the particles used in the above experiment?
(a) ${}_{12}Mg^{25}\rightarrow$----- + ${}_{13}Al^{25}$
(b) ${}_{84}Po^{212}\rightarrow$------ + ${}_{82}Pb^{208}$
(c) ${}_{90}Th^{232}\rightarrow$-------- + ${}_{91}Pa^{232}$
(d) ${}_{16}S^{35}\rightarrow{}_{17}Cl^{35}$ + -----

Directions for questions 18:

Read the content given in the following passage and answer the question given below.

Most of the elements exist as isotopes. The proportion of various isotopes of an element are constant for a particular element. Isotopes are the atoms of the same element with different mass numbers. That means, isotopes possess same number of electrons and protons but differ in the number of neutrons. The mass number is the sum of protons and neutrons in the nucleus of an atom. It is a whole number. But the atomic masses of some elements are found to have fractional values. The reason for this is the presence of isotopes in the natural sample of the element. The average atomic mass of an element would be calculated based on the proportion of the various isotopes of that element in the natural sample which is called isotopic abundance. Consider an element having two isotopes.

	Element		Mass number of isotope II	Percentage abundances	
				Isotope 1	Isotope 2
(a)	P	(i)	A+2	77.5	22.5
(b)	Q	(ii)	A+1	65.5	34.5
(c)	R	(iii)	A+3	80	20
(d)	S	(iv)	A-1	90	10
(e)	T	(v)	A-2	58	42
(f)	U	(vi)	A-3	85	15

$$\text{Average atomic mass} = \frac{(\%\text{ abundance of isotope 1} \times \text{Mass number}) + (\%\text{ abundance of isotope 2} \times \text{Mass number})}{100}$$

Five elements P, Q, R, S and T having two isotopes each are considered. The atomic mass of isotope 1 is assumed as 'A'. The atomic masses of isotope 2 for each element are given in the following table. The percentage abundances of the two isotopes of these elements are also tabulated in a column.

18. Assume that the average atomic mass calculated for 'R' is taken as 'x'.

	Column I Element		Column II Average atomic mass
(i)	P	(a)	x-1.44
(ii)	Q	(b)	x-0.7
(iii)	S	(c)	x-1.05
(iv)	T	(d)	x-0.25
(v)	U	(e)	x-0.15

ANSWER KEYS

Crossword

Across

2. Oxygen
6. Orbit
8. Thomson
10. Two
11. Isotopes
13. Mass
14. Octet
15. Chadwick

Down

1. Bohr
3. Nucleons
4. Zero
5. Protium
7. Rutherford
8. Third
9. Atomic
12. Valence

Classroom Wing

Very Short Answer Type Questions

1. Isotopes
2. neutrons
3. nucleons
4. empty space
5. electrostatic
6. neutrons
7. fourth shell
8. circular

Competition Wing

Level 1: Apply Your Concepts

1. False
2. False
3. True
4. False
5. False
6. True
7. True
8. True
9. mass number
10. nucleus
11. High voltage and low pressure
12. certain paths
13. Electron
14. 50
15. First
16. Proton
17. Cathode
18. Hydrogen
19. Isobars
20. (i) → (C), (ii) → (E), (iii) → (B), (iv) → (A), (v) → (D)
21. (d)
22. (d)
23. (c)
24. (b)
25. (c)
26. (c)
27. (d)
28. (b)
29. (c)
30. (c)
31. (b)
32. (b)
33. (a)
34. (c)
35. (a)
36. (c)
37. (b)
38. (d)
39. (d)
40. (c)

JEE-NEET Special Wing

Multiple-Answer Type Questions

1. (b, c)
2. (a, b, c)
3. (c, d)
4. (b, d)
5. (a, c, d)

Comprehension-Based Questions

6. (d)
7. (c)
8. (a)
9. (b)
10. (c)
11. (i) → (D), (ii) → (E), (iii) → (A), (iv) → (C), (v) → (B)
12. (a)
13. (b)
14. (c)
15. (c)
16. (b)
17. (b)
18. (i) → (E), (ii) → (D), (iii) → (B), (iv) → (A), (v) → (C)

Hints and Explanations

CLASSROOM WING

Very Short Answer Type Questions

1. Discovery of isotopes led to the contradiction of the postulate of Dalton's atomic theory that atoms of the same element are alike in all aspects.

2. Isotopes differ in the number of <u>neutrons</u>.

3. Isobars possess the same number of <u>nucleons</u>.

4. empty space

5. electrostatic

6. neutrons

7. fourth shell

8. circular

9. The figure represents Thomson's atomic model. From Thomson's experiment, it can be concluded that electrons are the universal constituent of matter.

10. The law of definite proportions provided experimental basis for the postulate of Dalton's atomic theory that atoms of different elements combine in a simple whole number ratio.

11. (a) (b)

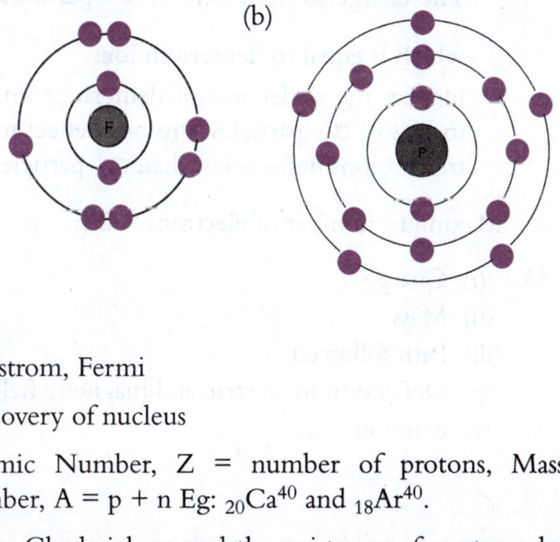

12. $2n^2$

13. Angstrom, Fermi

15. Discovery of nucleus

16. Atomic Number, Z = number of protons, Mass number, A = p + n Eg: $_{20}Ca^{40}$ and $_{18}Ar^{40}$.

17. James Chadwick proved the existence of neutrons by bombarding Be nucleus with α-particles.

18. Negligible intermolecular forces of attraction

19. High velocity of electron counter-balancing the forces of attraction

20. Protium, deuterium and tritium with neutron numbers as 0, 1 and 2, respectively. $_1H^1$, $_1H^2$, $_1H^3$

21. Number of protons in hydrogen

22. Rutherford's α-particle Scattering Experiment

23.

	Mass	Charge
Electron	9.1×10^{-31} kg	1.602×10^{-19} C
Proton	1.6×10^{-27} kg	1.6×10^{-19} C
Neutron	1.6×20^{-27} kg	0

Short Answer Type Questions

24. The electrons number 36 does not correspond to $2n^2$ which gives the maximum number of electrons in Bohr's orbit.

25. *Y* can have an atomic number of 30. The electronic configuration for *Z* = 30 is 2, 8, 18, and 2. On losing two electrons, the resultant dipositive ion gets the configuration of 2, 8, and 18, and does not have an octet. X is *K* (19) and its electronic configuration is 2, 8, 8, and 1. On losing one electron, the resultant mono positive ion gets the configuration of 2, 8, and 8.

26. (a) Existence of isotopes

    (b) Spherical ZnS screen was used in α - ray scattering experiment so that the scintillations can be observed even if there are deflections of any α - particles at larger angles.

27. The electronic configuration of the element is 2, 8, 14, and 2. The atomic number of the element is 26.

28. The main postulates of Dalton's atomic theory are the following:

    (i) Matter is composed of tiny indivisible particles called atoms. They neither be created nor destroyed nor transformed into atoms of another element.

    (ii) Atoms of a given element are identical in all respects.

    (iii) Atoms of different elements are different from each other.

(iv) Atoms of different elements take part in the chemical reaction and combine in a simple integral ratio to form compounds.

(v) When elements react, the atoms may combine in more than one simple whole number ratio.

29. Observations:

(i) Most of the α-particles passing straight
(ii) Large deflections

Conclusions:

(i) Atom to be empty
(ii) Nucleus

30. The electronic configuration is:

Oxygen (O) - 2,6
Argon (Ar) - 2,8,8
Calcium (Ca) - 2,8,8,2
Potassium (K) - 2,8,8,1

31. Atomic mass

32. (i) Atomic number
(ii) Mass number

33. (i) Casting of shadow, path followed by cathode rays.
(ii) Rotation of wheel; have mass and KE.

34. Number of neutrons = A – Z

35. Electric field—move towards positive plate, negatively charged
Magnetic field—deflects perpendicular to the applied magnetic field

36. (i) Number of electrons present in the K- and L shells are 2 and 8.
(ii) Number of electrons in the M- and N shells are 9 and 2.
(iii) Writing electronic configuration i.e., 2, 8, 9, 2. The atomic number is 21 and the element is Scandium.

37. (i) Number of electrons present in the K-, L- and M shells of that atom
(ii) Determination of (n – 1) and (n – 2) based on the number of electrons in the previous shell
(iii) Electronic configuration
(iv) Atomic number

38. (i) Comparison of mass of electron and proton
(ii) Calculation of number of electrons

Essay Answer Type Questions

39. (i) $2n^2$
(ii) Electrons in last orbit
(iii) Mass number – atomic number

40. Model
(i) Nucleus and empty space
(ii) Revolution of electrons

Drawbacks
(i) Instability of atom

41. (a) (i) Definite energy
(ii) Transition of electrons

(b) The deflection of a positively-charged particle by the metal nucleus takes place due to repulsion. The higher the charge and the lesser the mass of the bombarding particle, the greater is the extent of deflection. Hence, the extent of deflection can be compared by comparing the charge to mass ratio of the bombarding particles.

The order of charge to mass ratio of proton, deuterium and tritium ions is as follows:
tritium < deuterium < proton.

The charge to mass ratio of α - particles is $\frac{2}{4} = \frac{1}{2}$ which is equal to deuterium ions.

Hence, the deflection of deuterium ions is equal to that of α - particles. Protons deflect more while tritium ions deflects less than α - particles.

42. Maximum number of electrons = $2n^2$

43. (i) Charge
(ii) Mass
(iii) Path followed
(iv) Deflection in electric and magnetic fields
(v) e/m ratio

Competition Wing

Level 1: Apply Your Concepts

1. False. The anion formed from the given neutral atom is a dinegative ion which has the configuration of argon the electronic configuration of the element is 2, 8 and 6.

2. The given species is a neutral atom with 13 electrons which means 3 electrons in the valence shell. It can lose three electrons to form a tripositive ion with the configuration of neon.

9. The sum of the number of protons and neutrons is called the mass number.

10. Rutherford's theory proposed the concept of the nucleus.

20. (i) → (C) $Z = 21$ corresponds to electronic configuration 2, 8, 9, and 2. The ratio of electrons in a penultimate shell to the valence shell is 9:2.

(ii) → (E) $Z = 30$ corresponds to electronic configuration 2, 8, 18, and 2. The ratio of electrons in a penultimate shell to the valence shell is 9:1.

(iii) → (B) $Z = 20$ corresponds to electronic configuration 2, 8, 8, and 2. The ratio of electrons in a penultimate shell to the valence shell is 4:1.

(iv) → (A) $Z = 19$ corresponds to electronic configuration 2, 8, 8 and 1. The ratio of electrons in a penultimate shell to the valence shell is 8:1.

(v) → (D) $Z = 18$ corresponds to electronic configuration 2, 8 and 8. The ratio of electrons in a penultimate shell to the valence shell is 1:1.

22. K^+ ion is formed by the loss of one electron by a neutral atom.

Hence, D is incorrectly matched.

24. (2) Combination of atoms in a simple numerical ratio.

(3) Electrical neutrality of atom.

(4) The diameter of the nucleus is 10^{-5} times that of an atom.

(1) Presence of electrons in K, L, M, and N shells.

Hence, the correct order is 2 3 4 1

26 The orbits in which electrons revolve around the nucleus are called stationary orbits since the energy of electrons remains constant in those orbits. The electrons are in continuous motion around the nucleus in those orbits and never remain stationary.

Hence, the correct option is (c).

27. A few of the α particles in the experiment were completely rebounded because they hit the nucleus which is a positively small central part and experience repulsion from the positive α particles charged nucleus.

Hence, the correct option is (d).

28. The energy of orbits increases with increase in distance because the nuclear force of attraction decreases with increase in distance. Since the first orbit is associated with the lowest energy, electrons in that orbit do not lose energy at all. Both the statements are correct.

Hence, the correct option is (b).

40.

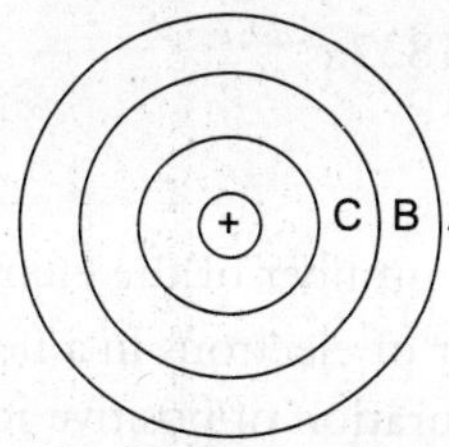

When an electron jumps from a higher orbit to a lower orbit, it loses energy and vice versa.

C is the K-shell near to nucleus.

B is the L-shell followed by C.

A is the M-shell followed by B.

∴ Increasing order of distance from the nucleus is $C < B < A$.

Hence, correct option is (c).

Level 2: Review Your Concepts

41. (a) (A) Number of electrons required to be present in the valence shell of an ion so that the ion becomes stable

(B) Subatomic particles that cause nuclear charge

(C) Number of subatomic particles

(D) Electronic configuration of the stable ion that is formed

(b) Since the dipositive ion and the dinegative ion are isoelectronic, the atomic number of the former element is 4 units more than the later element. Since number of neutrons are equal to that of protons in both the atom, the difference in mass number is 8 units.

42. (a) Mass of electron $= m$

Mass of proton $= 1837 \times m$

No. of protons $= \dfrac{36{,}740}{1837} = 20$

No. of neutrons = 19

Mass number = 39

Atomic number = 20

Representation of the atom or nuclide → $_{20}X^{39}$

43. No. of electrons in a dispositive ion = a

No. of electrons in the neutral atom = $a + 2$

Atomic number = No. of protons = $a + 2 = b$

No. of neutrons = $a + 2 + 3 = a + 5$

Mass number = $(a + 2) + (a + 5) = 2a + 7$

44. Mass of electron = x

Mass of protons = y

No. of protons in $_8O^{18}$ = 8

Mass of one proton = $y/8 = 1837x$

$$\frac{y}{8} = 1837x$$

45. (a) Calculation of the atomic number of the element

(b) Calculation of the number of electrons in a neutral atom based on the configuration of positive ion

(c) The atomic number of a neutral atom

(d) The number of neutrons in a neutral atom based on mass number

(e) 20, 20, 20

46. (a) Number of valence electrons of P and Q and their electronic configuration

(b) Calculation of number of electrons in previous shells of P and Q based on the valence shell and the number of electrons in the valence shell

47. (a) Density of gas molecules inside the discharge tube

(b) The mechanism of production of cathode rays

(c) The origin of anode rays

48. (a) Effect of equal strengths of electric and magnetic fields

(b) The effect of electric and magnetic field on cathode rays

(c) The direction of application of electric and magnetic fields such that there is no resultant deflection

49. (a) Calculation of the maximum number of electrons in each orbit.

(b) The number of elements that depend on electronic configuration.

(c) The maximum number of electrons in the valence shell.

50. (a) Metals form cations

(b) The number of electrons in neutral atom based on the type of ion metals formed

(c) The atomic number of the metal

(d) The calculation of mass number from atomic number and number of neutrons

51. (a) Calculation of number of electrons in first two shells

(b) Calculation of atomic number of A

(c) Calculation of atomic number of B from A

(d) 10 and 20

52. (a) Number of electrons in the corresponding neutral atom

(b) Calculation of mass number

(c) Calculation of number of neutrons from mass number and atomic number

(d) 20, 20, 20

53. (a) Basic concept of atom in Thomson's model

(b) Nature of α-particles

(c) Effect of bombardment of α-particles with atom (according to Thomson)

54. (a) If the percentage abundance of Cl-35 is x, then

$$\frac{x \times 35 + (100 - x)37}{100} = 35.5$$

(b) 75% of Cl-35 and 25% of Cl-37.

55. (a) The electronic configuration of A is 2, 8, 14, 2 and that of B is 2, 8, 18, 6.

(b) Their atomic numbers are 26 and 34, respectively.

(c) The number of neutrons in A is $5b = 30$ and that in B = 22.5 a = 45

∴ Their mass numbers are 26 + 30 = 56 and 34 + 45 = 79, respectively.

56. In the normal α-ray scattering experiment, a gold foil is used. In the place of the gold foil, if aluminium foil is used, the angle of deflection will be less. Charge and mass of aluminium nucleus is less than that of gold nucleus. So, the repulsive forces experienced by α-rays and the impact due to the collision with the aluminium nuclei are less. Hence, the angle of deflections will be less in α-ray scattering experiment using aluminium foil instead of gold foil.

57. Thomson assumed that electrons are embedded in a positive mass as it could explain several observations like only electrons are ejected when a metal is heated and never positively charged particles.

58. (a) Element X attains stability by losing two electrons from the fourth shell, its atomic number is 20, element is calcium.

∴ The mass number of Ca is 40.

Let the mass number of Y is a.

$\therefore \frac{40}{a} = \frac{10}{13} \Rightarrow a = 52$

∴ Mass number of Y is 52.

Number of neutrons in X is 40 – 20 = 20

Let the atomic number of Y be b.

∴ The number of neutrons in Y be 52 – *b*

$\therefore \frac{20}{52-b} = \frac{5}{7} \Rightarrow 52 - b = 28 \Rightarrow b = 24$

∴ Element Y's atomic number is 24 and number of neutrons in Y is 28.

Elements	Number of protons	Number of electrons	Number of neutrons
X	20	20	20
Y	24	24	28

(b) The mass number of A = $x + y$

The mass number of B = $x - 2 + y + 2 = x + y$

∴ A and B are isobars

59. Electronic configurations of dipositive and dinegative ions are 2, 8, 8 if they contain an octet configuration in their third shell. Electronic configurations of neutral atom of dipositive and dinegative ions are 2, 8, 8, 2 and 2, 8, 6. Two and 6 are the valence electrons present in the neutral atoms, respectively and atomic numbers are 20 and 16, respectively.

60. A and E are isotopes because they have same atomic number, i.e., X and mass numbers are different. Similarly, B and D are also isotopes. The mass numbers of A, C and D are X + Z + 2, X + Z + 2 and X + Z + 2, respectively and their atomic numbers are X, X – 2 and X + 1.

Therefore, they are isobars.

Similarly, B and E are also isobars.

61. (a) Electronic configuration of X : 2, 8, 2

(b) Element Y is stable due to the presence of 8 electrons (octet) in the valence shell.

(c) In the element Z, the electrons are distributed in four shells because the N-shell (fourth) is the valence shell.

(d) Since 8 electrons are present in the penultimate shell, i.e., M, 1 electron is present in the N-shell because the number of electrons is not the same in K- and N-shells.

Electronic configuration of Z = 2, 8, 8, 1

Hence, atomic number Z = 19.

(e) Electronic configuration of Y = 2, 8, 8.

Hence, Z = 18 and the number of protons or electrons is 18.

62. If protons are used instead of α-particles, the angles of deflection would be different because the charge of a proton is half of the charge of an α-particle and mass is almost one-fourth of the mass of the α-particle. Angle of deflection depends on both the charge as well as the mass.

63. K-shell → 2 electrons

L-shell → 8 electrons

M-shell → 8 electrons

N-shell → 1

Atomic number = 2 + 8 + 8 + 1 = 19

Preceding element is Ar and electronic configuration is 2, 8, 8, and the succeeding element is Ca and its electronic configuration is 2, 8, 8, 2.

Level 3: Assess Your Concepts

64. (a) Number of gaseous molecules present at high pressure

(b) Effect of pressure on velocity of cathode rays

(c) Relation between velocity and discharge

65. (a) Nature of cathode and anode rays

(b) The composition of anode and cathode rays

(c) Factors influencing *e*/*m* ratio of anode and cathode rays

(d) Change in *e*/*m* with gas for cathode and anode rays

66. (a) The amount of energy required to cause ionisation

(b) Factors affecting *e*/*m* values

(c) Charge on helium gas under low pressure and high pressure

(d) The effect of charge on *e*/*m*

67. (a) Forces of attraction existing between protons and electrons

(b) Energy required for excitation of electrons

(c) Relation between energy emitted by atom and colour of discharge tube

68. (a) Characteristics of isotopes and isobars

(b) Factors affecting e/m of anode rays

(c) Relation between e/m and deflection

69. The results of Rutherford's α-ray scattering experiment are very clear if the deflections are large. As lighter particles show larger deflections, B^{+1} would be preferable.

70. (a) The electrons revolve round the nucleus at high speed in the orbits in order to counterbalance the nuclear forces of attraction. As nuclear force of attraction decreases with increase in distance from the nucleus, the nuclear force of attraction on the electrons decreases. Therefore, electron revolves with lesser velocity to overcome lesser nuclear force of attraction. Thus, the velocity of electron in orbits decreases in the order K > L > M > N.

(b) The average atomic mass of the element

$= (y \times 0.25) + (y + 2) \times 0.75 = y + 1.5$

71. As the penultimate shell of B is the M-shell which possesses 18 electrons, the valence shell should be the N-shell. The possible electronic configuration of B ranges from 2, 8, 18, 1 to 2, 8, 18, 8.

The atomic numbers of B may range from Z = 29 to Z = 36.

The electronic arrangement of A corresponding to the respective arrangement of B ranges from 2, 8, 18, 9, 2 to 2, 8, 18, 16, 2. The atomic number of A may range from Z = 39 to Z = 46.

72. The postulate that the electrons revolve round the nucleus is not derived from the results of α-ray scattering experiment. The results of α-ray scattering gave the idea that entire positive charge is concentrated in a small part which is known as nucleus.

In order to counterbalance the nuclear forces of attraction, the electrons revolve round the nucleus at very high speeds.

73. The electronic configuration of the element could be

2, 8, 14, 2

or

2, 8, 4

Hence, its atomic number could be 26 or 14.

JEE-NEET Special Wing

Multiple-Answer Type Questions

Solutions for questions 1 to 5:

	No. of electrons	No. of neutrons	Mass number	Representation	Ratio A/Z
(a)	94	150	244	$_{94}E^{244}$	$\frac{244}{94}=2.6$
(b)	57	81	138	$_{57}E^{138}$	$\frac{138}{57}=2.4$
(c)	71	105	176	$_{71}E^{176}$	$\frac{176}{71}=2.5$
(d)	79	117	196	$_{79}E^{196}$	$\frac{196}{79}=2.5$

1. The configuration of the atom 'X' corresponding to the given trivalent negative ion could be 2,8,5. The element with configuration 2,8,6 can form stable divalent negative ion with 2,8,8 configuration. The element with configuration 2,8,8,2 can form stable divalent positive ion with 2,8,8 configuration.

2. The configuration of the element 'M' would be 2, 8, 10, 2. The atomic number of the element would be 22. The mass of protons = 22 × 1837 = 40414. The configuration of the preceding element is 2,8,9,2. It can form both divalent and trivalent ions. Addition of 8 electrons makes the 'M' shell completely filled.

3. As given in above table (c) and (d), the ratio A:Z is 2.5.

4.

	Mass of protons	Mass number	Atomic number	Mass number	No. of neutrons	Representation of the element	Isotone
(a)	12859 x	2Z+1	7	15	8	$_7N^{15}$	$_8O^{16}$
(b)	29392x	2Z+2	16	34	18	$_{16}S^{34}$	$_{18}Ar^{36}$
(c)	25718x	2Z+1	14	29	15	$_{14}Si^{29}$	$_{15}P^{30}$
(d)	36740x	2Z	20	40	20	$_{20}Ca^{40}$	$_{19}K^{39}$

5.

	Representation	n/p ratio
(a)	$_{86}A^{222}$	1.58
(b)	$_{84}B^{209}$	1.49
(c)	$_{90}C^{232}$	1.58
(d)	$_{94}D^{244}$	1.6

Comprehension-Based Questions

6. By observing the given figure, 'X' indicates electron while 'Y' indicates proton. Specific charge of electron (X) = a C/kg

   Since, the mass of proton is approximately 2000 times that of an electron and specific charge is the ratio of charge to mass,

   Specific charge of proton (Y) ≈ $\frac{a}{2000}$ C/kg

   Specific charge of proton (Y) in terms of 'a' ≈$5\times 10^{-4}a$

7. The angle of deflection of the particles 'Y' keeps on decreasing from experiments I to III. The particle 'Y' indicates positively charged particles which constitute anode rays. The angle of deflection of these particles keeps on decreasing with the increase in mass of the positively charged particles.

8. The particles 'Y' in experiment I are protons with specific charge e/m. The particles 'Y' in experiment III are alpha particles with specific charge $\frac{2e}{4m}$ which is equal to $\frac{e}{2m}$.

   The specific charge of particles 'Y' in experiment III is half of that in experiment I.

9. Deuterons are the positively charged particles in experiment II. Each deuteron has one unit positive charge like proton but 2 units mass against one unit mass for proton.

   Specific charge of proton (Exp I) =$5\times 10^{-4}\ a$C/kg

   Specific charge of deuteron (Exp II) = $\frac{5\times 10^{-4}a}{2}$

   = 2.5×10^{-4} C/kg.

10. Helium atom consists of two electrons. Under high pressure or low voltage, it is likely to lose one electron to give He^+ ions. They have specific charge equal to $\frac{e}{4m}$ since a helium atom has 2 protons and 2 neutrons in

the nucleus. Under low pressure or high voltage conditions, helium atom is likely to lose both the electrons to give He^{+2} ions. The specific charge of these particles would be $\frac{e}{2m}$. The nature of particles 'Y' depends both on voltage applied and pressure of gas in the discharge tube.

11.

	Column I Atomic number		Column II No. of electrons in penultimate shell
(a)	30	(iv)	$(b-a)3$
(b)	25	(v)	$2(b-a)+1$
(c)	22	(i)	$(b-a)+2a$
(d)	28	(iii)	$(a+b)+3a$
(e)	26	(ii)	$(2b-a)$

12. The given figure represents Rutherford's alpha ray scattering experiment. It is the experiment concerned with the discovery of nucleus.

13. The charge of an alpha particle is equal to double the charge of a proton that is 3.2×10^{-19} C

14. The screen is coated with zinc sulphide which is a fluorescent substance.

15. A : Platinum; C : Lead; D : Uranium

16. The substance 'D' is radioactive material which emits alpha particles. The radioactive material being harmful is kept enclosed in a thick lead block as alpha particles can not penetrate through lead block. Uranium is unstable as its radioactive. Lead is a stable element. This is a true statement, but not the reason for the given assertion.

17. ${}_{84}Po^{212} \rightarrow {}_{2}He^{4} + {}_{82}Pb^{208}$

18. R: Average atomic mass =

$$\frac{(80\times A)+[(20\times(A+3)]}{100} = A + 0.6 = x$$

P: Average atomic mass =

$$\frac{(77.5\times A)+[(22.5\times(A+2)]}{100} = A + 0.45 = x - 0.15$$

Q :Average atomic mass =

$$\frac{(65.5\times A)+[(34.5\times(A+1)]}{100} = A + 0.35 = x - 0.25$$

S : Average atomic mass =

$$\frac{(90\times A)+[(10\times(A-1))]}{100} = A + 0.1 = x - 0.7$$

T :Average atomic mass =

$$\frac{(58\times A)+[(42+(A-2)]}{100} = A + 0.84 = x - 1.44$$

U: Average atomic mass =

$$\frac{(85\times A)[(15\times A-3)]}{100} = A - 0.45 = x - 1.05$$

	Column I Element		Column II Average atomic mass
(a)	P	(v)	x-1.44
(b)	Q	(iv)	x-0.7
(c)	S	(ii)	x-1.05
(d)	T	(i)	x-0.25
(e)	U	(iii)	x-0.15

CHAPTER

2

Classification of Matter

Remember

Before beginning this chapter, you should be able to:

- know about the electron, proton and neutron in an atom.
- define matter and states of matter.

Key Ideas

After completing this chapter, you should be able to:

- study kinetic energy of molecules in different states of matter.
- understand the effect of temperature and pressure on the state of matter and changes taking place in the arrangement of molecules.
- classify matter on the basis of chemical composition.
- discuss the properties of elements, compounds and mixtures, and their applications.
- describe different techniques for the separation of mixtures—based on the properties of the constituents.

Scientific Crypt

A Tribute to Joseph Proust (1754 – 1826)

Every object around us that occupies space and has mass is called matter. Joseph Proust, a French chemist was given credit for his research work on the chemical composition of matter called compounds. Proust performed a series of experiments and stated that different elements react in definite proportions to form a compound.

Joseph Proust was born on 26th September, 1754 at Angers in France. He studied pharmacy and chemistry in Paris and became chief pharmacist at Saltpetriere Hospital in Paris. In 1789 he became director of Royal Laboratory in Madrid. But after the invasion of Spain by Napolean, he returned to France. His greatest contribution to the field of chemistry came in the year 1799 when Proust formulated Law of definite proportions which states that elements always combine in fixed proportions. He demonstrated this by taking copper carbonate and showed that copper carbonate always has fixed proportion of copper, carbon and oxygen. Proust's work gained recognition when Dalton used Proust's law in formulating his atomic theory. Joseph Proust passed away on July 5th, 1826 in Paris. His work and contribution in the field of chemistry is considered as an important milestone in the quantitative chemistry for the future scientific researches.

FUN TIME

CROSSWORD

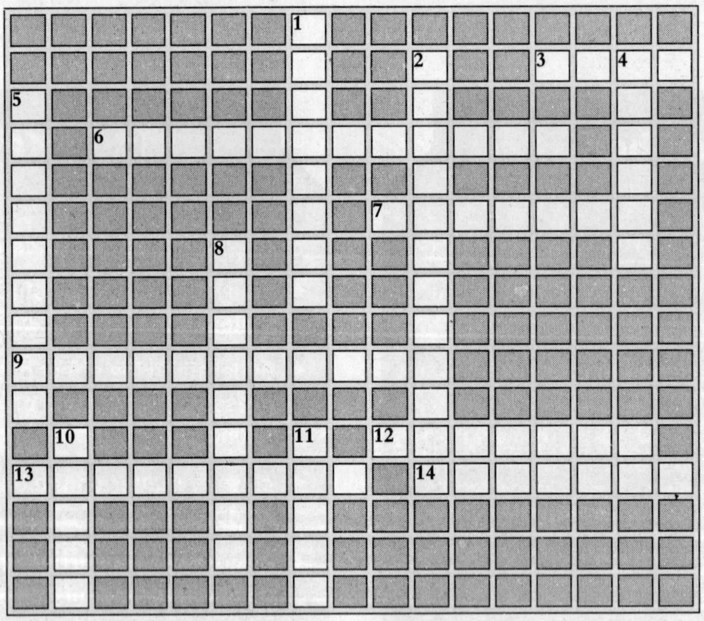

Across

3. The metal with very less tensile strength is _____.
6. Process which involves the change of matter from gas to liquid on cooling
7. Nonmetal which is liquid at room temperature.
9. Boiling is a bulk phenomenon while _____ is a surface phenomenon.
12. _____ acts as a moving phase in chromatography.
13. _____separation method is based on difference in densities of gaseous components.
14. _____ is used in vulcanisation of rubber.

Down

1. _____ separation can be performed to separate nickel from sand.
2. Oil in water is a/an _____ mixture.
4. _____ acts as a catalyst during the hydrogenation of vegetable oils.
5. Every form of matter is composed of small particles called_____.
8. On application of pressure melting point of ice _____.
10. Atomicity of sulphur
11. Molecules in this state possess very low kinetic energy.

INTRODUCTION

There are a variety of objects around us like air, water, stones, trees, etc. that have one thing in common - they all are matter. Anything that has mass and occupies space can be **matter**. Matter is composed of atoms and molecules. The smallest particle of matter that can exist independently and retain all its properties is called **molecule**.

Various Basis of Classification of Matter

On the basis of the forces of attraction existing between the molecules of a substance, matter can be classified as solids, liquids and gases. The characteristics of these three states of matter and the interconversion of a substance from one state to the another represent one aspect of the study of matter.

Matter can also be classified on the basis of chemical composition into three major categories, namely, elements, compounds and mixtures. There are 118 elements discovered till today and these elements are further classified into metals, non-metals and metalloids on the basis of certain characteristic properties. Study of matter also involves study of the properties of various categories of elements. It also includes the study of basic differences between compounds and mixtures, and the study of techniques of separation of different types of mixture.

Classification of Matter on the basis of Forces of Attraction

Molecules are the constituent particles of matter and the characteristics of these molecules and their arrangement in the various states of matter were explained by the kinetic molecular theory of matter.

Info Bytes!

The Kinetic Molecular Theory, which describes the behaviour of matter based on the motion of its particles, has played a key role in explaining phenomena like pressure and temperature. Yet, the thought that everything we see and touch consists of constantly moving tiny particles might sound surreal.

Kinetic Molecular Theory of Matter

Postulates of kinetic molecular theory of matter are listed below:

1. Every form of matter is composed of small particles called **molecules**.
2. The empty space (gaps) that exists in between the molecules is called **intermolecular space**.
3. Molecules exert attractive forces, called **intermolecular forces** of attraction, upon one another. These forces decrease with an increase in the distance between the molecules. The force of attraction between similar molecules is called **cohesive force** and that between dissimilar molecules is called **adhesive force**.
4. The molecules possess kinetic energy due to their motion, and their movement is ceaseless.

Table 2.1 Comparative study of solids, liquids and gases

Parameters	Solids	Liquids	Gases
Packing of molecules	The molecules are closely packed, and therefore, solids have a definite shape, definite volume, high density and negligible compressibility.	The molecules are loosely packed, and hence, liquids do not have definite shape and take the shape of the container. Density of liquids is slightly lesser than solids, and therefore, they are slightly more compressible than solids.	The molecules are very loosely packed, and hence, gases have no definite shape, no definite volume, very low density and very high compressibility.

(Continued.)

Table 2.1 Continued

Parameters	Solids	Liquids	Gases
Intermolecular force of attraction	The molecules have very strong intermolecular force of attraction due to which they are rigid, and expand very less on heating.	The molecules have moderate intermolecular force of attraction which is lesser than solids. These can, thus, flow and expand more than solids when heated.	The molecules have negligible intermolecular force of attraction, and thus, can flow and expand much more than solids and liquids when heated.
Molecular movement	The molecules have only vibratory motion about their mean positions which are fixed. They can, thus, have any number of free surfaces.	The molecules possess translatory and rotatory motions in addition to vibratory motion. The translatory motion is, however, either sideways or downwards. Thus, they have only one free surface and have definite volume.	The molecules possess translatory, rotatory and vibratory motions in all directions randomly. Thus, a gas has no free surfaces and occupy the total volume available for it.
Kinetic energy	The molecules possess very low kinetic energy, and hence, do not diffuse.	The molecules possess higher kinetic energy than in case of solids and can diffuse in certain liquids.	The molecules possess very high kinetic energy and diffuse spontaneously and rapidly.

On the basis of the above parameters, it can be concluded that the arrangement of molecules is the most important factor which determines the state in which the matter exists. This means that the change in molecular arrangement brings about the conversion of matter from one state to another. The molecular arrangement in a particular substance, in turn, depends upon the external conditions of temperature and pressure. Hence, the change in molecular arrangement can be brought about by changing the external conditions of temperature and pressure.

EXAMPLE 2.1 Conduction of heat is not possible through gases. Explain with respect to kinetic molecular theory.

SOLUTION

Conduction of heat in matter takes place by the transmission of agitation of one molecule to the other, and hence, the molecules should be closely packed. But in gaseous state, the molecules are very far from each other. Hence, the heat cannot be transmitted from one molecule to another molecule, and thus, there is no conduction of heat through gases.

EXAMPLE 2.2 A given mass of a gas is present in a cylinder of volume 10 L which can also be filled in a cylinder of volume 1 L. Explain the above statement with suitable reason/s.

SOLUTION

The force of attraction between the gas molecules is negligible. As a result, the intermolecular space between the molecules of the gas is very high. Moreover, the molecules have high kinetic energy. Thus, the molecules are free to move in all directions, and hence, can fill the available space easily, due to which gas can completely occupy a cylinder having volume of 10 L. As intermolecular spaces are large in gas, they can easily be compressed, and hence, the same mass of gas can also be stored in a cylinder with 1L volume.

EXAMPLE 2.3 Gases do not have free surfaces. Explain.

SOLUTION

The molecules of gases possess rotatory, vibratory and translatory motions in all directions at random. Hence, they need to be stored in a closed vessel and have no free surfaces.

Interconversion of States of Matter

The change of matter from one state to another that occurs as a result of a change in external conditions, like, temperature or pressure is called **interconversion of states of matter** or **phase transition**.

The process of phase transition does not produce any change in the mass or composition of the matter. The different processes involving phase transition are given different names on the basis of initial and final states of matter.

Melting

The process which involves the change in state of matter from solid to liquid by heating is called **melting** or **fusion**. The temperature at which a solid changes into a liquid on heating at normal atmospheric pressure is called the **melting point** of that solid.

The heat energy supplied to the solid is absorbed by its molecules. This helps the molecules to overcome the intermolecular force of attraction as a result of which the molecules move apart from each other. The molecules acquire translatory motion in addition to vibratory motion, so, they become free to move, and thus, attain the molecular arrangement of a liquid.

The melting point of solids which expand on melting increases with an increase in pressure while the melting point of solids which contract on melting decreases with an increase in pressure.

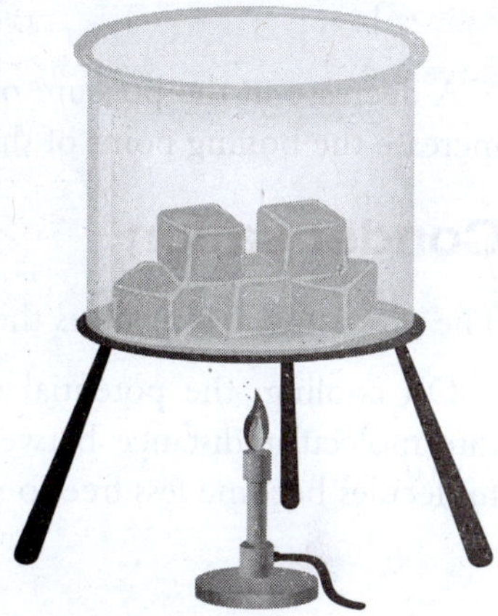

Figure 2.1 Melting of Ice

Examples:

Solids which expand on melting: Paraffin wax; copper etc.

The melting point of copper increases with increase in pressure.

Solids which contract on melting: Ice; Brass; Bronze; Cast iron

The melting point of ice decreases with an increase in pressure.

Evaporation and Boiling

The slow process involving the change of matter from liquid to gas from the surface of the liquid is called **evaporation**.

The temperature at which a liquid changes into a gas on heating at normal atmospheric pressure is called the boiling point of that liquid and the phenomenon is called **boiling**.

The heat energy which is supplied to the liquid is absorbed by the molecules of the liquid and helps the molecules to overcome the intermolecular forces of attraction almost completely. As a result, the molecules move far apart from each other and start moving in all directions at random. Thus, the liquid attains the molecular arrangement of a gas.

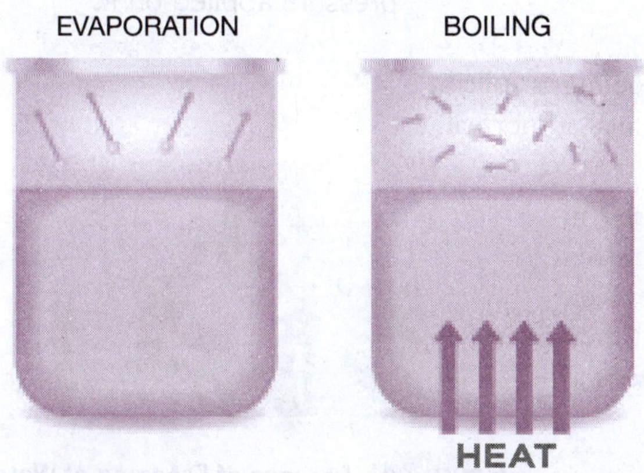

Figure 2.2 Process of Evaporation and Boiling

Konnect

The majestic Himalayan glaciers, which serve as a freshwater resource for millions in India, are also a colossal example of the interconversion of states of matter. When these glaciers melt due to increasing global temperatures, they demonstrate the transformation from solid (ice) to liquid (water).

Table 2.2 Comparative study of evaporation and boiling

Evaporation	Boiling
Slow process	Fast process
Surface phenomenon	Bulk phenomenon
Can occur at any temperature	Occurs at a fixed temperature depending on the nature of liquid and external pressure

A decrease in the pressure on the surface of a liquid decreases its boiling point. Soluble impurities present in a liquid increase the boiling point of the liquid.

Condensation

The process which involves the change of matter from gas to liquid on cooling is called **condensation**.

On cooling, the potential energy of the gas molecules is released in the form of heat energy. Consequently, the intermolecular distance between the gas molecules decreases and the intermolecular force increases. As a result, the molecules become less free to move about. Thus, the gas attains the molecular arrangement of a liquid.

Figure 2.3 Process of Condensation

Since the gases are highly compressible, they can be liquefied by the application of pressure provided the temperature of the gas is equal to or below its critical temperature, and this process is called **liquefaction**.

For every gas, there is a specific critical temperature. The gaseous state of matter below its critical temperature is called **vapour**.

> **Konnect**
>
> **Critical temperature** is the temperature above which the liquefaction of the gas is impossible whatever be the pressure applied on it.

Solidification

The process involving the change of matter from liquid to solid on cooling is called **solidification** or **freezing**. The temperature at which freezing occurs at normal atmospheric pressure is called **freezing point** of that liquid.

On cooling, the potential energy of the liquid molecules is released in the form of heat energy. Consequently, the intermolecular distance decreases and intermolecular force of attraction increases. The molecules lose their translatory movement, rotatory movement, and they only vibrate about their fixed mean position. Thus, the molecules of the liquid attain the molecular arrangement of a solid.

Figure 2.4 Process of Freezing of Water

Sublimation

The process by which some solid substances directly change into the vapour state on heating without passing through the intermediate liquid state is called **sublimation**.

The solid obtained on cooling the vapour is called **sublimate** and the vapour formed is called **sublime**. For example, camphor and iodine.

Kinetic energy of the molecules at the surface of the sublimable substance is high. On the application of external heat and in some cases at normal temperature, the molecules at the surface gain energy and overcome the intermolecular force of attraction. Hence, they directly get converted from solid to vapour states from the surface.

Figure 2.5 Process of Sublimation

EXAMPLE 2.4 How is boiling point related to the vapour pressure of the liquid?

SOLUTION

When the vapour pressure of a liquid becomes equal to the atmospheric pressure, the liquid starts boiling. Hence, the higher the vapour pressure, the lower is the boiling point.

EXAMPLE 2.5 Two beakers A and B contain the same amount of alcohol and water at the same temperature, respectively. What is the change in temperature in these two liquids after some time?

SOLUTION

Both alcohol and water evaporate. Alcohol, being more volatile, evaporates more by taking up more amount of heat from the bulk. Thus, the temperature of alcohol is found to be less than that of water.

EXAMPLE 2.6 Why do glasses fog up when entering a warm room from the cold outside?

SOLUTION

When wearing glasses and entering a warm room from the cold outside, the temperature of the glasses is initially lower than the room's temperature. The warm air in the room contains moisture in the form of water vapour. When this warm, moist air comes into contact with the cold surface of the glasses, it cools down rapidly, causing the water vapour to condense into tiny water droplets on the surface of the glasses. These tiny water droplets scatter light, giving the glasses a foggy appearance. As the glasses gradually warm up to room temperature, the fogging dissipates since the conditions for condensation are no longer present.

EXAMPLE 2.7 When a liquid is placed in a closed container, the level of the liquid initially decreases but eventually becomes constant. Give reasons. solution.

SOLUTION

When a liquid is placed in a closed container, initially there is evaporation, and thus, the volume of the liquid decreases. But as time passes, there is an equilibrilium attained between the liquid and the vapour, and hence, no further decrease in level of liquid is observed.

EXAMPLE 2.8 Salt is often spread on roads and walkways during snowy and icy conditions. Explain the reasoning behind this practice.

SOLUTION

Adding salt to ice lowers its freezing point, a phenomenon known as freezing point depression. When salt is spread on snowy or icy roads, it causes a portion of the ice to melt by lowering the temperature at which water freezes. As the ice melts, the resulting brine solution (salt-water mixture) further depresses the freezing point, causing more ice to melt. This chain reaction continues until most of the ice has melted or the salt is diluted to a point where it's less effective. By lowering the freezing point of ice, salt helps to prevent the formation of ice layers on roads and walkways, making them safer for vehicles and pedestrians.

The parameters of various states of matter and their interconversion from one state to the other deal with the study of matter at the molecular level. The study of matter with respect to the molecular composition requires its classification into elements, compounds and mixtures.

Classification of Matter on the Basis of Chemical Composition

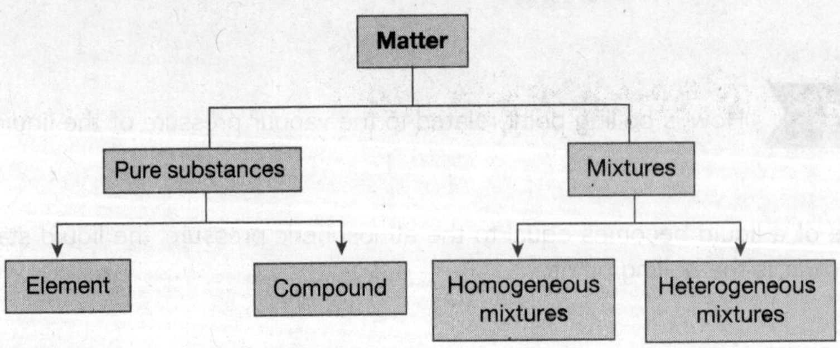

Figure 2.6 Classification of matter based on the chemical composition

Pure Substances

Substances which are homogeneous in nature and contain particles (molecules) of only one kind are called **pure substances**. A pure substance is homogeneous in nature and has definite set of properties. The composition of pure substances cannot be changed by physical methods. Pure substances can be further classified as elements and compounds.

Elements

Pure substances in which molecules are composed of only one kind of atoms are called **elements.**

Examples: Silver, iron, oxygen, nitrogen, etc.

Atomicity of an Element

The number of atoms present in the molecule of an element is called its **atomicity**. Based on the atomicity, the elements are classified into three types as listed hereunder.

1. **Monoatomic Elements**: The elements each of whose molecules contains only one atom.

   Examples: Cu, Ag and He

2. **Diatomic Elements**: The elements each of whose molecules contains two atoms.

   Examples: H_2, O_2 and N_2

3. **Polyatomic Elements**: The elements each of whose molecules contains more than two atoms.

   Examples: O_3, P_4 and S_8

Classification of Elements

It was found that there was a wide variation in the properties of elements. Hence, these were further classified into three categories, i.e., metals, non-metals and metalloids, based on the properties they exhibit.

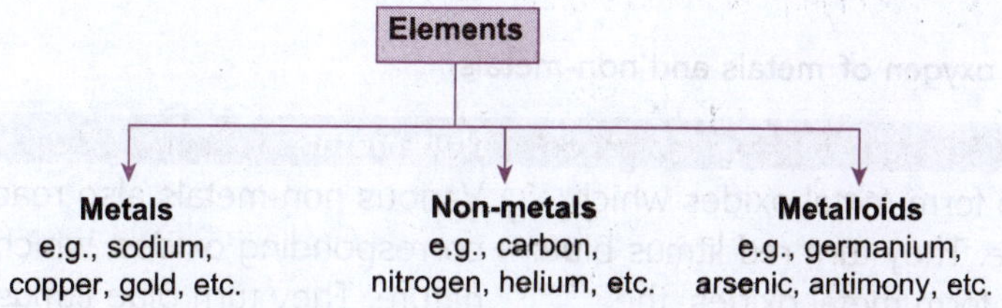

Figure 2.7 Classification of elements based on the properties

Table 2.3 Comparative study of physical properties of metals and non-metals

Parameters	Metals	Non-metals
State	Solids at room temperature. **Exceptions:** Hg and Ga are liquids.	Mostly gases. **Exceptions:** Some of the solid non-metals are C, S, P, I_2, whereas bromine is a liquid non-metal.
Melting and boiling points	Very high melting and boiling points. **Exceptions:** Na, K, Hg have low melting and boiling points. Ga has a low melting point but a high boiling point.	Low melting and boiling points. **Exceptions:** C, Si and B have high melting and boiling points.
Hardness	Generally hard. **Exceptions:** Na and K are soft.	Solid non-metals are brittle. **Exception:** Diamond is the hardest naturally occurring substance.
Density	Have high density. **Exception:** Li, Na and K have density lower than water (1 g/cm^3).	Have low density. **Exception:** Diamond
Conductivity	Good conductors of heat and electricity. **Exceptions:** Bi and W are poor conductors of electricity.	Bad conductors of heat and electricity. **Exception:** Graphite and gas carbon are good conductors of electricity.
Lustre	Have lustre.	No lustre. **Exceptions:** I_2 and graphite.
Tensile strength	High tensile strength. **Exception:** Zn has very less tensile strength.	Do not have tensile strength. **Exception:** Carbon fibre, a recently developed allotrope of carbon.
Malleability and ductility	Generally malleable and ductile. **Exception:** Zinc is not malleable and ductile.	Non-malleable and non-ductile. **Exception:** Carbon fibres are ductile.
Sonorousness	Sonorous.	Non-sonorous.
Occurrence	Found in a combined state. Only noble metals are found in free state.	Found in free state as well as in the combined state.

Table 2.4 Comparative study of chemical properties of metals and non-metals

Property	Metals	Non-metals
Number of electrons in the valence shell	Have 1 to 3 electrons in their valence shells	Have 4 to 7 electrons in their valence shells **Exceptions:** Hydrogen has one electron in its valence shell because the first shell is its valence shell.
Formation of ions	Lose electrons from their valence shells to form stable cations.	Accept electrons to from stable anions.

Table 2.5 Reaction with oxygen of metals and non-metals

Metals	Non-metals
Metals react with oxygen to form metal oxides which are generally basic in nature. They turn red litmus blue. Though most of the metals form metal oxides, the metals differ in their re-activities with oxygen. *Examples:* **(a) Sodium and potassium:** Both react with oxygen vigorously and form oxides at room temperature. $4Na + O_2 \rightarrow 2Na_2O$ $4K + O_2 \rightarrow 2K_2O$	Various non-metals also react with oxygen to give their corresponding oxides, which are generally acidic in nature. They turn blue litmus ored. *Examples:* **(a) Carbon:** Red hot charcoal when burnt with oxygen produces CO_2 gas with the evolution of a large amount of heat. $C + O_2 \rightarrow CO_2$ + Heat Due to the evolution of large amount of heat in this reaction, charcoal, coal, coke, etc. are used as fuels.
(b) Magnesium: Magnesium reacts with oxygen on heating slightly to form corresponding oxide. $2Mg + O_2 \rightarrow 2MgO$	**(b) Sulphur:** Sulphur when burnt with oxygen produces SO_2 gas. $S + O_2 \rightarrow SO_2$.
Reactions of oxide with water Metallic oxides give bases on reacting with water. Bases turn red litmus blue $Na_2O + H_2O \rightarrow 2NaOH$ $K_2O + H_2O \rightarrow 2KOH$ $MgO + H_2O \rightarrow Mg(OH)_2$ $CaO + H_2O \rightarrow Ca(OH)_2$ + Heat	**Reactions of oxide with water** Non-metallic oxides give acids on reacting with water. Acids turn blue litmus to red. $SO_2 + H_2O \rightarrow H_2SO_3$ $CO_2 + H_2O \rightarrow H_2CO_3$ $2NO_2 + H_2O \rightarrow HNO_2 + HNO_3$

Table 2.6 Reaction with water of metals and non-metals

Metals	Non-metals
(a) Potassium: Potassium reacts with cold water. It even reacts with moisture (water vapour). $2K + 2H_2O \rightarrow 2KOH + H_2$	Non-metals generally do not react with water. **(a) Carbon**: When super-heated steam is passed over red-hot coke, a mixture of carbon monoxide and hydrogen called **water gas** is produced. It is a good fuel and reducing agent. $C + H_2O \rightarrow CO + H_2$ (water gas)
(b) Sodium: The reaction takes place in cold water. $2Na + 2H_2O \rightarrow 2NaOH + H_2$ It even reacts with moisture (water vapour).As the reactivity of sodium and potassium is vigorous with water hence they are stored in kerosene.	**(b) Chlorine:** When chlorine gas is passed through water, hydrochloric acid and hypochlorous acid are produced. $Cl_2 + H_2O \rightarrow HCl + HOCl$
	(c) Phosphorus: Though phosphorus catches fire on exposure to air, it has no reaction with water. Hence, it is stored in water.

Table 2.7 Reaction with acids of metals and non-metals

Metals	Non-metals
(a) HCl (i) *Cold dilute:* All active metals like Mg, Al, Fe react, liberating hydrogen gas with pop sound. **Example:** $Mg + 2HCl \rightarrow MgCl_2 + H_2$ (ii) ***Hot concentrated:*** All active metals react more vigorously giving the same products.	Very few non-metals (S, C) react with acids.
(b) H_2SO_4 (i) *Cold dilute:* Active metals like Mg, Al, Fe liberate H_2 gas **Example:** $Zn + H_2SO_4 \rightarrow ZnSO_4 + H_2$ (ii) ***Hot concentrated:*** Most of the metals including Cu, Ag, Hg, Pb liberate SO_2 gas **Example:** $Cu+2H_2SO_4 \rightarrow CuSO_4+SO_2+2H_2O$	Both C and S reacts with Conc. H_2SO_4. $C + 2H_2SO_4 \rightarrow CO_2 + 2H_2O + 2SO_2$ $S + 2H_2SO_4 \rightarrow 3SO_2 + 2H_2O$.

Table 2.8 Reaction with bases of metals and non-metals

Metals	Non-metals
Metals like Al and Zn react with concentrated bases liberating hydrogen gas. $2Al + 2NaOH + 2H_2O \rightarrow 2NaAlO_2 + H_2$	Reactivity of non-metals with bases is complex.

Metalloids

Metalloids are elements which show the properties of both metals and non-metals.

Examples: Germanium, arsenic, antimony, selenium and tellurium

Table 2.9 Some metalloids and their properties

Metalloids	Metallic properties	Non-metallic properties
Germanium	It acts as a semiconductor with rise in temperature	GeO_2 is acidic in nature
Arsenic	Metallic grey arsenic is a fair conductor of electricity	Yellow arsenic forms a hydride, (AsH_3), a weak base
Antimony	Grey-coloured antimony conducts electricity	Yellow antimony forms stibine (SbH_3), a weak base
Selenium	Good conductor of electricity at 475 K	It exists in one non-metallic allotropic form
Tellurium	Low electrical conductivity	It resembles sulphur in chemical properties

Location of Metals, Non-metals and Metalloids on Periodic Table

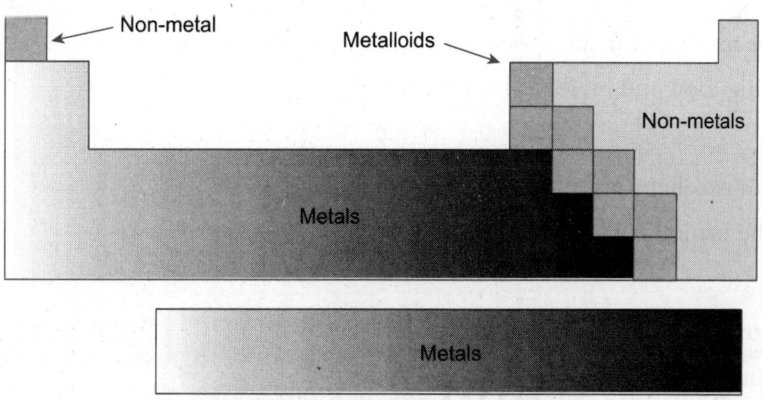

Figure 2.8 Periodic table chart

Uses of Metals

Iron (Fe)

1. Iron is mainly used in the form of steel, an alloy in which the major component is iron.
2. Steel is used for making buckets, drain pipes, chains, etc., as it is extremely tough and it can withstand stress and has a high melting point.

Lead (Pb)

1. It is used for making containers for corrosive liquids and protective screens for X-ray and other harmful radiations as it is unaffected by impure water, steam or dilute mineral acids and has a low melting point (327.5°C).
2. It is used in the automobile batteries.

Magnesium (Mg)

1. It is used in fireworks because it burns with a dazzling white flame.
2. It is used as a reducing agent in the extraction of metals.

Aluminium (Al)

1. Due to its light weight, it is used for the manufacture of aircrafts and automobiles.
2. It is used to make electric transmission cables.
3. It is used for making utensils and novelty articles.

Zinc (Zn)

1. It is used for galvanizing iron to protect it from rusting.
2. It is used as a cathode container in making dry cells.

Copper (Cu)

1. It is used in electric transmission wires and electrical goods.
2. It is used in electroplating and electrotyping.
3. It is used for making printed circuit boards and electronic devices.
4. Copper salts are largely used as insecticides.

Uses of Non-metals

Oxygen (O_2)

1. It helps in the process of respiration and combustion.
2. It has medical and industrial uses.

Nitrogen (N_2)

1. It dilutes the activity of oxygen in air.
2. It is used in preserving food and biological specimens.

Sulphur (S_8)

1. Sulphur powder is an excellent insecticide and fungicide.
2. It is used to make the natural rubber hard for making tyres.

Iodine (I_2)

1. Iodides are used in medicine and photography.
2. It is used in the manufacture of tincture of iodine.

Hydrogen (H_2)

1. It is an excellent non-polluting fuel.
2. It is used to fill weather-observation balloons and gas bags for airships.

Uses of Noble Metals

Gold (Au)

1. It is used for covering the mainframe of artificial satellites.
2. It is used for making ornaments and coins.

Silver (Ag)

1. Silver halides are used for making photographic films.
2. It is used for making ornaments and coins.

Platinum (Pt)

1. It is used as a catalyst in many chemical reactions.
2. It is used in making jewellery.

Titanium (Ti)

1. It is completely inert to human body fluids, making it ideal for medical replacement structures, such as, hip and knee implants.
2. Titanium forms a very tenacious surface oxide layer which is an outstanding corrosive inhibitor.
3. If profit made on selling an article is represented by a positive number, then loss incurred on selling an article is represented by a negative number.

Compounds

Pure substances in which two or more elements combine chemically in a fixed proportion by weight are called **compounds**.

For example, water (H_2O) is considered a pure substance even though it consists of two kinds of atoms, as it has a fixed number of hydrogen and oxygen atoms combined together chemically in a definite proportion by weight. Hydrogen and oxygen combine in a fixed ratio, 1 : 8 by weight, to form water.

Mixtures

The systematic study of elements is done by categorizing them as metals, non-metals and metalloids. The different elements combine with each other to form compounds. The formation of compounds from elements results in change in the molecular composition. Two or more substances, either elements or compounds, can be mixed together in any proportion. The resultant substances are called **mixtures**. Since the formation of a mixture involves only physical process, there is no change in the molecular composition.

Table 2.10 Comparative study of properties of compounds and mixture

Compounds	Mixtures
Constituent atoms combine chemically	Constituent substances are mixed physically
Constituents can be separated by chemical methods	Constituents can be separated by physical methods
These are homogeneous	They can be either homogeneous or heterogeneous
It involves significant energy changes	No significant change in the energy

Classification of a Mixture

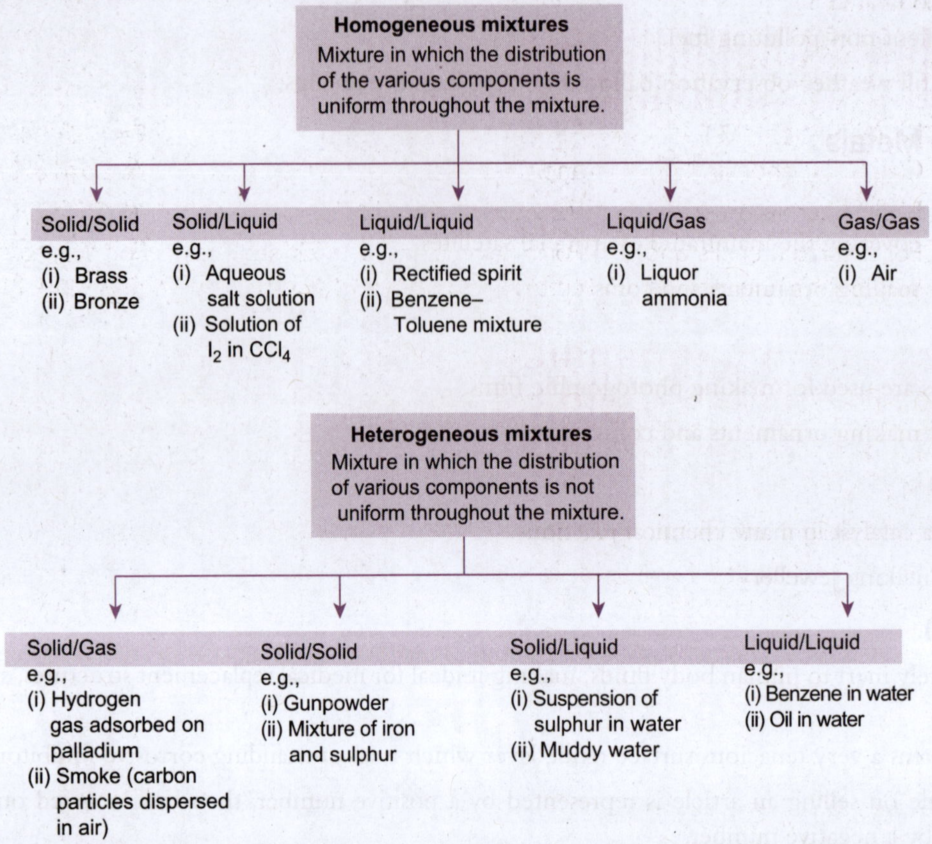

Figure 2.9 Classification of homogeneous mixtures and heterogeneous mixtures

Alloys and Their Uses

Among the various types of a mixture, alloys occupy the most significant position in view of the wide range of applications they find in industry as well as in day-to-day life.

Alloy is a homogeneous mixture of two or more metals or a non-metals. Some important alloys, their composition and uses are listed in the following table:

Table 2.11 Important alloys and their composition

Major component → Copper (Cu)					
Parameters	**Brass**	**Bronze**	**Gun metal**	**German silver**	**Bell metal**
Composition	Cu (60–80%) and Zn (20-40%)	Cu (80%), Zn (10%) and Sn (10%)	Cu (88%), Sn (10%), Zn (1%) and Pb (1%)	Cu (30–60%), Zn (20–30%) and Ni (15–20%)	Cu (80%) and Sn (20%)
Properties	Lustrous, more malleable and ductile than copper	Hard but brittle, resistant to corrosion, takes very high polish	Very hard, gives a very good cast	White like silver, malleable and ductile	Hard and brittle, produces sonorous sound
Uses	For making shells of ammunition, utensils, electrical switches, statues	For making shells, statues, coins and utensils	For making barrels of guns, gears and bearings	For making imitation silver jewellery, utensils, etc.	For making bells

(Continued.)

Table 2.11 Continued

Major component → Iron (Fe)			
Parameters	Stainless steel	Manganese steel	Tungsten steel
Composition	Fe (83%), C (1%), Cu (15%) and Ni (1%)	Fe (84%), Mn (15%) and C (1%)	Fe (79–84%) W(20–15%), C(1%)
Properties	Resists corrosion	Very tough and hard	Very very hard
Uses	For making utensils and surgical instruments	For making safes, armour and rock cutter	For making high-speed tools

Major component → Aluminium (Al)		
Parameters	Duralumin	Magnalium
Composition	Al (95%), Cu (4%), Mn (0.5%), Mg (0.5%)	Al (95%) and Mg (5%)
Properties	Light weight and as strong as steel	Light weight, strong, resistant to corrosion
Uses	For making aircraft frames, rockets, speed boats and automobiles	For making aeroplanes, house appliances, mirrors and scientific instruments

Major component → Nickel (Ni)	
Alloy	Monel metal
Composition	Cu (28%), Ni (67%) and Fe (5%)
Properties	Resistant to corrosion, malleable and ductile
Uses	Used for making sinks, doors and window screws

EXAMPLE 2.9 Why are coins often made of an alloy instead of pure metals like gold or silver?

SOLUTION

Pure metals like gold or silver are relatively soft and can wear out, bend, or get scratched easily. By alloying them with other metals, their hardness and durability are enhanced. This ensures that the coins retain their shape, design, and legibility for a longer time even with frequent handling and circulation. Moreover, using an alloy can also be cost-effective and prevent the coin from being melted down for its intrinsic metal value. Thus, coins are often made of alloys to ensure their longevity and practicality in daily use.

EXAMPLE 2.10 Copper is used in the form of alloys, like, brass and bronze for making statues and decorative articles, but it is used in the pure form for making electric transmission cable. Give reasons.

SOLUTION

In alloys the physical properties of the metals change to some extent. The properties of copper vary in the alloys, like, brass and bronze. The alloy is harder, stronger and has more shine than the pure metal and due to these properties it is used for making statues and decorative articles. While in electric transmission cables, the property exploited is its electrical conductivity and ductility. Both these properties are more prominent in the pure metal than the alloys. Pure copper is, thus, used in making electric transmission cables.

EXAMPLE 2.11 Aluminium melts and burns easily whereas alumina is used as a refractory material for making heat-resistant bricks. Explain.

SOLUTION

Alumina (Al_2O_3) is a compound of aluminium. It is a compound, and hence, its properties are different from that of aluminium. The melting point of alumina is much higher than that of aluminium and it is highly chemical resistant, hence, it is used as a refractory material.

EXAMPLE 2.12 Why is mercury used in thermometer?

SOLUTION

Mercury is used in thermometer because of the following reasons:

(i) It is a shiny viscous liquid.

(ii) It has low thermal expansion, that is, with the increase in temperature, the increase in volume of mercury is less compared to other liquids.

(iii) It does not stick to the glass surface because of weak adhesive force between glass and mercury.

Separation of a Mixture

In a mixture, the individual components retain their original properties. This is exploited to separate the mixture into individual components.

Konnect

The age-old method of separating grain from chaff in India, known as 'winnowing,' uses the principle of differences in weight. The lighter chaff is blown away by the wind, leaving the heavier grain behind. Science has roots in traditional practices too.

Principles Involved

The difference in one or more of the following physical properties of the constituents is utilized to separate the components of a mixture.

1. Physical state
2. Density
3. Melting and boiling points
4. Solubility
5. Magnetic properties
6. Diffusion
7. Ability to sublime
8. Volatility

Separation of a Solid–Solid Mixture

Table 2.12 Techniques and principles involved in separation of solid–solid mixtures

Techniques	Principles involved	Examples
Solvent extraction	One component of the mixture is soluble and the other is insoluble in a given solvent	(i) Mixture of sulphur (soluble) and sand (insoluble) Solvent: Carbon disulphide (CS_2) (ii) Mixture of NH_4Cl (soluble) and I_2 (insoluble) Solvent: water
Magnetic separation	One component of the mixture is a magnetic substance	(i) Mixture of iron ore (magnetic) and sand (ii) Mixture of cobalt (magnetic) and lead
Gravity method	One of the components is heavier and the another one is lighter than the given liquid	(i) Mixture of sand (heavier) and sawdust
Sublimation	One of the components sublimes on heating	(i) Mixture of I_2 (sublimes) and sand (ii) Mixture of NH_4Cl (sublimes) and sand
Fractional crystallization	Difference in the change in solubility in a specific range of temperature	(i) Mixture of KNO_3 (Decrease in solubility with the decrease in temperature is significant) and NaCl (Decrease in solubility with the decrease in temperature in insignificant)

Separation of a Solid–Liquid Mixture

Table 2.13 Techniques and principles involved in separation of solid–liquid mixtures

Techniques	Principles	Examples
Sedimentation and decantation	The solid component is insoluble and heavier than the liquid component	(i) Mixture of sand and water
Filtration	Separation of insoluble solid component by passing through a porous material, like, filter paper	(i) Mixture of AgCl and H_2O (ii) Mixture of chalk and H_2O
Evaporation	Separation of the mixture by evaporating the liquid component. The solid should be soluble in the liquid and should not sublime	(i) Mixture of NaCl and H_2O (ii) Mixture of sulphur and CS_2
***Distillation**	Separation of mixture containing a soluble solid by evaporation followed by condensation. The solid should not sublime	(i) Mixture of NaCl and H_2O

*Distillation is carried out in a special type of apparatus.

Example: Separation of KCl from a solution of KCl and water.

Procedure

The KCl solution is taken in a distillation flask (X).

The flask is carefully heated; the solvent evaporates and the water vapour condenses in Liebig's condenser (Y). KCl remains in the distillation flask and the water is collected in the receiver flask.

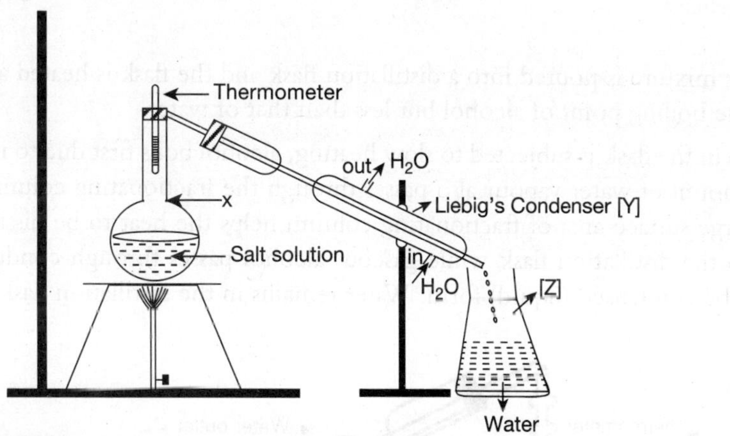

Figure 2.10 Separation of components of KCl solution by distillation

Separation of a Liquid–Liquid Mixture

Separating Funnel

Principle: Separation of immiscible liquid components using a separating funnel where liquids separate out due to different densities.

Example: Separation of petrol (lighter) from water (heavier).

Procedure

1. The liquid–liquid mixture is poured into a separating funnel clamped vertically and the mixture is allowed to stand. Clear layers of the liquids are formed as the liquid with higher density settles down at the bottom of the flask.
2. The nozzle tap is opened slowly and the heavier component is allowed to trickle down. The lighter component remains in the flask.

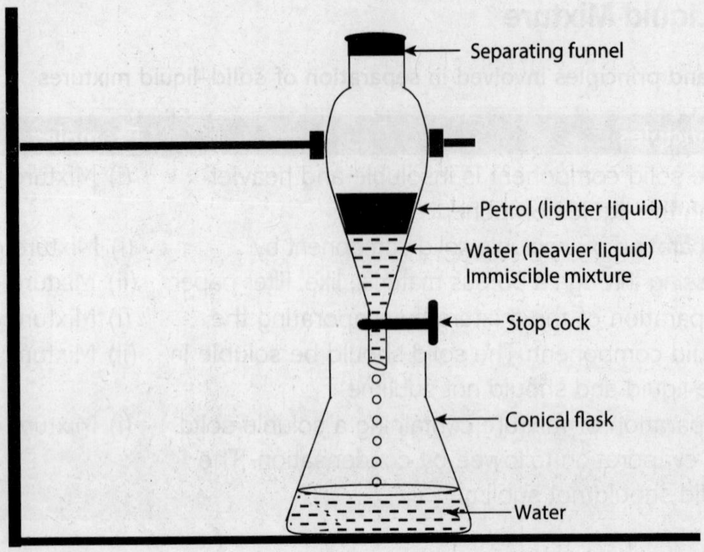

Figure 2.11 Separation of immiscible liquids by separating funnel

Fractional Distillation

Principle: Separation of two miscible liquid components using a distillation flask with a fractionating column using the difference in boiling points (more than 10K) of the liquid components.

Example: Laboratory separation of methanol from water.

Procedure

1. The alcohol–water mixture is poured into a distillation flask and the flask is heated at a temperature which is equal to or more than the boiling point of alcohol but less than that of water.
2. When the mixture in the flask is subjected to slow heating, alcohol boils first due to its lower boiling point than that of water. Some amount of water vapour also passes through the fractionating column along with the gaseous state of alcohol. The large surface area of fractionating column helps the heat to be dissipated and hence water vapour condenses back to the distillation flask while gaseous alcohol passes through condenser and gets collected in the receiving flask in the condensed (liquid) form. Water remains in the distillation flask.

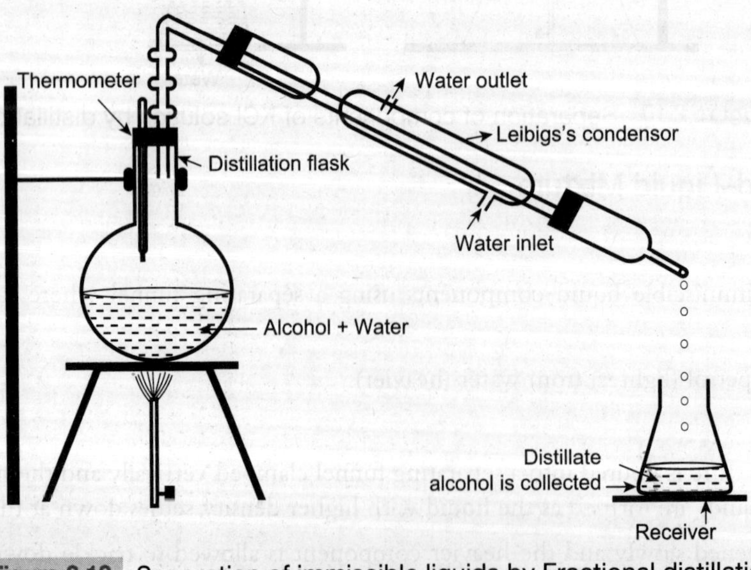

Figure 2.12 Separation of immiscible liquids by Fractional distillation

Separation of a Gas–Gas Mixture

Based on the physical properties of gases, different physical methods are adopted.

Diffusion

Diffusion is the spontaneous movement of gas molecules from a region of higher concentration to a region of lower concentration till the concentration becomes almost equal.

Principle: Difference in densities of gaseous components. Lighter gases diffuses faster than the heavier gases.

Examples:

CO_2 and H_2

SO_2 and N_2

Dissolution in Suitable Solvents

Principle: When one constituent is soluble in a liquid or reacts chemically with a liquid, it is dissolved in that solvent, from which it can be recovered by a chemical reaction.

Examples:

N_2 (insoluble) and CO_2 (soluble) in KOH

NH_3 (soluble) and N_2 (insoluble) in H_2O

SO_2 (soluble) and O_2 (insoluble) in KOH

Preferential Liquefaction

Principle: Employed industrially for the separation of a homogeneous mixture of two gases, having wide difference in critical temperature. The gas having higher critical temperature liquefies under high pressure, when they are allowed to expand suddenly.

Example:

A mixture of H_2 and NH_3 under very high pressure is allowed to expand suddenly. NH_3 gets liquefied and gets separated from H_2.

Fractional Evaporation

Principle: This process can be adopted when a mixture of two gases having different boiling points (more than 10 K) is liquefied by allowing it to expand suddenly under extremely high pressure, followed by evaporating the mixture at the respective boiling points of the constituent gases.

Examples:

N_2 and O_2 (N_2 boils off)

Separation of a Liquid – Gas Mixture

The solution of a gas in a liquid is called **liquid – gas mixture.**

Heating

Principle: The solubility of a gas in a liquid decreases with the rise in temperature.

Example:

1. The liquid–gas mixture (e.g., water–CO_2) is filled in a flask and heated gently so that the solution does not boil.
2. On heating, the solubility of the gas decreases and the dissolved gas is evolved and collected.

Releasing Pressure

Principle: The solubility of a gas in a liquid can be increased by increasing external pressure and is decreased with the decrease in external pressure.

Example:

CO_2 gas is dissolved in water by applying pressure in aerated drinks and this CO_2 gas comes out with a fizzing sound when the pressure is released.

Chromatography

Chromatography is a technique used for the separation and identification of dissolved constituents of a mixture by adsorbing them over an appropriate adsorbent material.

Principle: This process is based on the difference in adsorption of constituents by a surface of an appropriate adsorbent material or solid medium **(stationary phase)**. The rate of adsorption of a particular constituent depends upon its solubility in the solvent **(moving phase)** and its affinity for the adsorbing material.

Example:

Separation of coloured constituent in a mixture of ink by paper chromatography.

Procedure

1. A spot of ink is placed at the centre of a base line on a strip of filter paper.
2. The spot is dried and the paper is hung in a glass jar with its lower end immersed in solvent.
3. The solvent flows over the spot and carries the components to distances along the paper indicated by colour spots, which is characteristic of each constituent in the mixture.

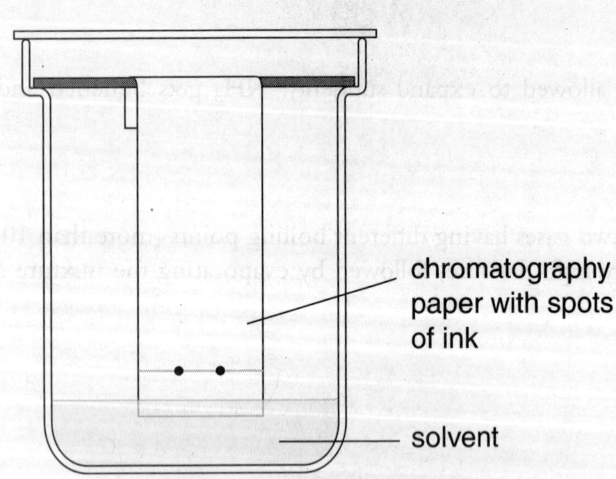

Figure 2.13 Separation of components of Ink by paper chromatography

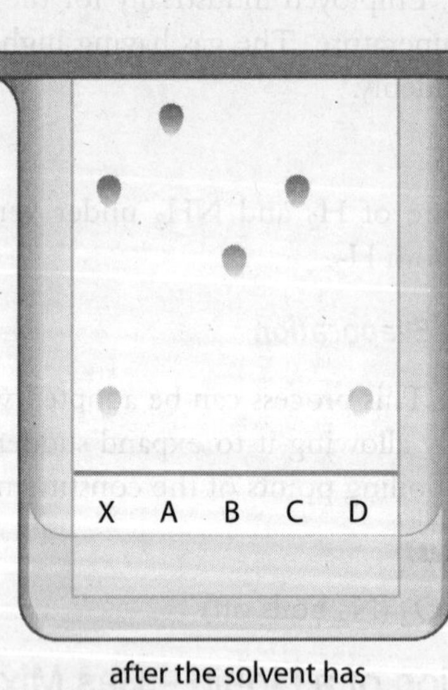

Figure 2.14 Chromatogram

Application of Separating Techniques

The various methods of separation of mixtures find applications in various fields of industry. One of the most important applications is in metallurgy where different methods of separation have been employed to remove impurities from the ores.

Separation techniques, like, distillation and fractional distillation are utilized in the refining of petroleum, alcohol industry, pharmaceutical and food industry, etc. Solvent extraction is also widely used in the manufacture of medicines.

Chromatography finds applications in research laboratories for the identification of new compounds.

EXAMPLE 2.13 A mixture of iron and sulphur is taken and heated strongly. Explain what happens if a magnet is brought near it after heating.

SOLUTION

When iron and sulphur are strongly heated, they combine to from a compound called **iron sulphide** (FeS). This compound, FeS does not have the individual properties of iron or sulphur. Thus, the magnetic property of iron is lost and when this is exposed to a magnet, it is not attracted by the magnet.

EXAMPLE 2.14 How can a gaseous mixture of CO_2, SO_2 and H_2 be separated?

SOLUTION

The molecular weight of H_2 is much less than CO_2 as well as SO_2. Hydrogen gas can be separated from CO_2 and SO_2 by diffusion. Under low-temperature and high-pressure conditions, CO_2 converts to dry ice, a solid, and thus, can be separated. So, under these conditions, SO_2 converts to liquid state and can be separated.

EXAMPLE 2.15 Give the working principle involved in chromatography.

SOLUTION

The particles of a mixture or dye, like, ink are soluble in water. As the water rises on the filter paper, it takes along with it the dye particles. Usually, a dye is a mixture of two or more colours. The coloured components that are more soluble in water and lower ability to be adhered to the adsorbent material, reach to a greater height and in this way the colours get separated.

POINTS TO REMEMBER

- On the basis of the forces of attraction existing between the molecules of a substance, matter can be classified as solids, liquids and gases.
- Matter can also be classified on the basis of chemical composition into three major categories, namely, elements, compounds and mixtures.
- Molecules are the constituent particles of matter and the characteristics of these molecules and their arrangement in the various states of matter were explained by the kinetic molecular theory of matter.
- The change of matter from one state to another that occurs as a result of a change in external conditions, like, temperature or pressure is called interconversion of states of matter or phase transition.
- The process which involves the change in state of matter from solid to liquid by heating is called melting or fusion.
- The temperature at which a solid change into a liquid on heating at normal atmospheric pressure is called the melting point of that solid.
- The slow process involving the change of matter from liquid to gas from the surface of the liquid is called evaporation.
- The temperature at which a liquid change into a gas on heating at normal atmospheric pressure is called the boiling point of that liquid and the phenomenon is called boiling.
- The process which involves the change of matter from gas to liquid on cooling is called condensation.
- Since the gases are highly compressible, they can be liquefied by the application of pressure provided the temperature of the gas is equal to or below its critical temperature, and this process is called liquefaction.
- Critical temperature is the temperature above which the liquefaction of the gas is impossible whatever be the pressure applied on it.
- The process involving the change of matter from liquid to solid on cooling is called solidification or freezing.
- The temperature at which freezing occurs at normal atmospheric pressure is called freezing point of that liquid.
- The process by which some solid substances directly change into the vapour state on heating without passing through the intermediate liquid state is called sublimation.
- Substances which are homogeneous in nature and contain particles (molecules) of only one kind are called pure substances.
- Pure substances in which molecules are composed of only one kind of atoms are called elements.
- The number of atoms present in the molecule of an element is called its atomicity.
- Pure substances in which two or more elements combine chemically in a fixed proportion by weight are called compounds.
- Two or more substances, either elements or compounds, can be mixed together in any proportion. The resultant substances are called mixtures.
- Alloy is a homogeneous mixture of two or more metals or a non-metals.
- Chromatography is a technique used for the separation and identification of dissolved constituents of a mixture by adsorbing them over an appropriate adsorbent material.
- There are various methods of separation which can be used to separate the components of a mixture. The method of separation depends on the differential properties of the components in that mixture.

PRACTICE QUESTIONS CLASSROOM WING

Very Short Answer Type Questions

Direction for question 1:

1. **Define the following terms:**
   (i) Melting point
   (ii) Boiling point
   (iii) Liquefaction
   (iv) Freezing point
   (v) Critical temperature
   (vi) Matter
   (vii) Pure substance
   (viii) Mixture
   (ix) Element
   (x) Compound
   (xi) Metal
   (xii) Non-metal
   (xiii) Metalloids
   (xiv) Alloy
   (xv) Noble metals

Directions for questions from 2 to 11:
Fill in the blanks.

2. An element is a good conductor of electricity, lustrous, and it is used as an electrode in electrometallurgical processes due to its high resistance to heat and chemicals. The constituent atom of the element is ______.
3. The process due to which some solid substances directly vaporise on heating and solidify on cooling without becoming a liquid is called ________.
4. In chromatography, the component which has more affinity for the stationary phase appears at the _______ of the paper.
5. The kinetic energy of the molecules is ________ in solids than in liquids.
6. Certain gases dissolve in water by the application of ________.
7. The intermolecular forces of attraction between molecules are called _________ and different molecules are called __________.
8. The molecules of a liquid possess______ types of motions.
9. Under the normal conditions of temperature and pressure, the metal mercury remains in a __________ state.
10. Thermal expansion in solids is ________ than liquids and gases.
11. The temperature at which a liquid changes into a gas on heating at normal atmospheric pressure is called _________ of that liquid.

Directions for questions from 12 to 30:
Answer the following questions.

12. Some amount of water is kept in a vacuum chamber. In which state will the water exist in the chamber?
13. When we exhale air from our mouth on a winter morning, it appears foggy. Which interconversion of states of matter takes place here?
14. Ice is kept in a vacuum chamber. In which state will it exist?
15. Which interconversion of states of matter is involved in filling up of LPG cylinder?
16. Give two examples for the following types of a mixture:
    (i) Solid: solid homogeneous
    (ii) Solid: liquid homogeneous
    (iii) Liquid: gas homogeneous
    (iv) Liquid: liquid homogeneous
    (v) Gas: gas homogeneous
    (vi) Solid: solid heterogeneous
    (vii) Solid: liquid heterogeneous
    (viii) Liquid: liquid heterogeneous
17. Write the products obtained in the following reactions:
    (i) $Na_2O + H_2O \rightarrow$ (ii) $CO_2 + H_2O \rightarrow$
    (iii) $CO + H_2O \rightarrow$ (iv) $SO_2 + H_2O \rightarrow$
18. What is the principle involved in the following methods of separation of mixtures?
    (i) fractional crystallization
    (ii) magnetic separation

(iii) gravity method
(iv) separating funnel method
(v) distillation
(vi) fractional distillation
(vii) preferential liquefaction
(viii) chromatography
(ix) fractional evaporation

19. Mention the allotropic forms of the following metalloids:
(i) arsenic
(ii) antimony
(iii) selenium

20. What is a supernatant liquid?

21. What is the role of platinum in a catalytic converter?

22. Which property of german silver makes it useful for making imitation jewellery?

23. State one property of germanium which shows its acidic nature.

24. Name the phenomena causing the following events:
(i) formation of dew
(ii) disappearance of naphthalene balls
(iii) drying of wet clothes
(iv) formation of snow
(v) formation of cloud

25. Which metal is used in chemical industries for extracting metals?

26. What is meant by the atomicity of an element?

27. What type of ions do the following form?
(i) a metal
(ii) a non-metal

28. Give two examples of substances which can be separated by the following methods.
(i) fractional crystallization
(ii) sublimation
(iii) magnetic separation
(iv) gravity method
(v) filtration
(vi) distillation
(vii) diffusion
(viii) solvent extraction
(ix) dissolution in a suitable solvent

29. For the following properties listed below, arrange solids, liquids and gases either in the increasing or decreasing order
(i) diffusibility
(ii) intermolecular spaces
(iii) thermal expansion
(iv) intermolecular force of attraction

30. Establish antimony as a metalloid on the basis of its metallic property.

Short Answer Type Questions

31. Why is diamond a very good conductor of heat?

32. A and B are two gases taken in two different cylinders at 45°C. Their critical temperatures are 40°C and 50°C, respectively. Which of the gases can be liquified and how?

33. A pressure cooker decreases the cooking time. Why?

34. State the uses of the following non-metals:
(a) oxygen (b) chlorine
(c) sulphur

35. (a) Explain the procedure for separation of sand water into sand and water.

(b) Two samples of water are taken. One is pure water and another one is sea water. Both are subjected to cooling. Which sample of water freezes first? Justify.

36. Give examples of noble metals. Why are they called noble metals?

37. Explain the following according to the kinetic molecular theory.
(a) melting (b) boiling
(c) condensation (d) freezing

38. Give the characteristics of the following:
(a) elements (b) compounds
(c) mixture

39. Give the uses of the following metals:
(a) Fe (b) Pb
(c) Cu (d) Zn

40. Explain the separation of charcoal from sulphur.

41. Complete the following table:

Comparative study of the properties of solids, liquids and gases			
Parameters	Solids	Liquids	Gases
Mass	Have definite mass		
Volume		Have definite volume	Do not have definite volume
Shape	Have definite shape		
Density	High density		Least density
Compressibility		Slightly compress-ible	
Rigidity	Rigid (cannot flow)		Fluid (can flow)
Free surfaces			No free surfaces
Thermal expansion diffusion		Higher than solids	
			Gases diffuse spontaneously and rapidly

42. Complete the following table:

Comparative study of molecular arrangement in solid, liquid and a gas			
Parameters	Solids	Liquids	Gases
Packing of molecules	Closely packed		Very loosely packed
Intermolecular space		More space than in solid	Huge inter-molecular Space
Intermolecular force of attraction	Huge inter-molecular force of attraction		
Molecular movement		Molecules possess translatory and rotatory motion in addition to vibratory motion	
Kinetic energy	Molecules have least kinetic energy		

43. Solids have a definite volume and a shape. Explain.

44. How is KNO_3–$KClO_3$ mixture separated by fractional crystallization?

45. Explain how the following types of a mixture are separated:

(a) NH_4Cl–$NaCl$ mixture

(b) Sand–sawdust mixture

(c) Chalk–water mixture

Essay Answer Type Questions

46. What is the method of separation of

(a) N_2–CO_2 mixture

(b) H_2–O_2 mixture

(c) NH_4Cl, KCl and sand mixture

(d) Ink–water mixture

47. Compare solids, liquids and gases on the basis of their properties.

48. (a) Name the metalloids and state the reasons why they are categorised as metalloids.

(b) Mercury when spilled on the floor, beads as droplets while water spreads on the floor and forms a film. Justify this on the basis of kinetic molecular theory of matter.

49. Write the main postulates of the kinetic molecular theory.

50. Compare metals and non-metals based on their physical properties.

PRACTICE QUESTIONS COMPETITION WING

Level 1: Apply Your Concepts

Direction for question from 1 to 5:
Define the following

1. Melting or fusion
2. Evaporation
3. Condensation
4. Solidification
5. Sublimation

Directions for questions from 6 to 12:
State whether the following statements are true or false.

6. Smoke is a homogeneous mixture.
7. Sodium is a soft metal.
8. Brass is a homogeneous mixture.
9. Gas carbon is a good conductor of electricity.
10. Distillation is the method used for separation of petrol from water.
11. Glucose–water mixture can be separated by the method of evaporation.
12. Metals form basic oxides or amphoteric oxides.

Directions for questions from 13 to 19:
Fill in the blanks.

13. We blow air to cool a hot liquid in order to ______.
14. Rate of evaporation is increased by increasing ________ and ________.
15. ________ acts as a catalyst during the hydrogenation of vegetable oils.
16. Liquid ________ is used to preserve biological specimens
17. N_2 is ________ in KOH solution while CO_2 is ________.
18. Tincture of iodine is a mixture of ______ and ________.
19. Gases cannot be liquefied above a certain temperature called ________.

Directions for question 20:
Match the entries in Column A with the appropriate ones in Column B.

20. Match the statements of Column A with those of Column B.

Column A (Types of Mixtures)	Column B (Examples)
(i) Solid–solid homogeneous mixture	(a) Coconut oil and water
(ii) Solid-liquid homogeneous mixture	(b) Petrol and diesel
(iii) Liquid-liquid heterogeneous mixture	(c) Bronze
(iv) Liquid-liquid homogeneous mixture	(d) Finely powdered charcoal in water
(v) Solid-liquid heterogeneous mixture	(e) Saline water

Directions for questions from 21 to 44:
For each of the questions, four choices have been provided. Select the correct alternative.

21. **Assertion (A):** Metals are good conductors of electricity.
Reason (R): Metal atoms have completely filled valence shells.
(a) Both A and R are true and R is the correct explanation of A.

(b) Both A and R are true, but R is not the correct explanation of A.

(c) A is true and R is false.

(d) A is false and R is true.

22. **Assertion (A):** Metals have lustre.
Reason (R): Metals have loosely bound electrons.

(a) Both A and R are true and R is the correct explanation of A.

(b) Both A and R are true, but R is not the correct explanation of A.

(c) A is true and R is false.

(d) A is false and R is true.

23. **Assertion (A):** Steel is more resistant to corrosion.
Reason (R): Alloying makes the constituent metal less reactive.

(a) Both A and R are true and R is the correct explanation of A.

(b) Both A and R are true, but R is not the correct explanation of A.

(c) A is true and R is false.

(d) A is false and R is true.

24. **Assertion (A):** Duralumin is as strong as steel.
Reason (R): A metal becomes more malleable when it is converted to an alloy.

(a) Both A and R are true and R is the correct explanation of A.

(b) Both A and R are true, but R is not the correct explanation of A.

(c) A is true and R is false.

(d) A is false and R is true.

25. _______ is used for making photographic films.

(a) $AgNO_3$ (b) KNO_2
(c) AgO (d) AgCl

26. Silver tarnishes due to the formation of _____.

(a) oxide layer (b) sulphide layer
(c) nitride layer (d) hydride layer

27. Which among the pairs are separated by using the principle of dissolution in a suitable solvent?

(a) SO_2 and N_2O_5, KOH as solvent

(b) SO_2 and NO_2, KOH as solvent

(c) SO_2 and N_2O_3, KOH as solvent

(d) SO_2 and NO, KOH as solvent

28. A, B, C and D are four gases. If the order of their critical temperature is as D < B < C < A, then which of the following gases has the highest boiling point?

(a) A (b) B
(c) C (d) D

29. Addition of potassium nitrate to ice results in:

(a) increase in melting point

(b) decrease in melting point

(c) change in colour of ice

(d) both (a) and (c)

30. Identify the heterogeneous mixture among the following.

(a) brine solution (b) duralumin
(c) gun powder (d) liquor ammonia

31. Which of the following is a pure substance?

(a) duralumin (b) magnalium
(c) bell metal (d) magnesium

32. Aluminium foil can be made from aluminium by using:

(a) its thermal and electrical conductivities

(b) its malleable property

(c) its sonorous property

(d) all the above

33. Pickles are not stored in steel or aluminium containers because:

(a) steel has chromium which is poisonous

(b) aluminium takes up oxygen from pickles and spoils it

(c) pickles have acids which can corrode iron and aluminium making pickles poisonous

(d) none of the above

34. The molecular arrangement of a substance depends upon

(a) temperature (b) concentration
(c) pressure (d) all of these

35. Silver, gold and platinum are called noble metals because ________.

(a) these are costly

(b) these are precious

(c) these have very less reactivity

(d) all of these

36. Which of the following statements is true regarding solids?

(a) Solids are highly compressible.
(b) Solids diffuse rapidly.
(c) Solids possess low density.
(d) Solids possess a number of free surfaces.

37. In which of the following substances, intermolecular force of attraction is the maximum?

(a) iron bar (b) water
(c) air (d) nitrogen

38. Which of the following has maximum compressibility?

(a) iron bar (b) petrol
(c) chlorine (d) bromine

39 On heating, the temperature of the melting solid

(a) increases
(b) decreases
(c) remains constant
(d) may increase or decrease depending upon the nature of the solid

40. Which of the following changes directly from solid to gas on heating?

(a) ammonium chloride
(b) sodium chloride
(c) potassium chloride
(d) calcium chloride

41. The process of phase transition from solid to liquid involves the following steps. Arrange them in a proper sequence.

(1) Molecules become free to move, and thus, attain molecular arrangement of liquid.
(2) The energy supplied makes the molecules to vibrate more.
(3) During melting, the molecules overcome the forces of attraction between them.
(4) The molecules acquire rotatory motion, translatory motion in addition to vibratory motion.

(a) 3 4 1 2 (b) 2 3 4 1
(c) 3 4 2 1 (d) none of these

42. A student is carrying out distillation process in a lab. Water is boiling in the distillation flask. Water that is collected in the receiver flask is refrigerated and ice cubes are formed. Ice cubes are then kept outside the refrigerator and they started melting. Arrange the following phases of water in the ascending order of their total (PE + KE) energy considering that the mass of water remains the same.

(1) Water collected in the receiving flask.
(2) Water boiling in the distillation flask.
(3) Steam passing through the delivery tube.
(4) Ice cubes formed in the refrigerator.

(a) 4 3 2 1 (b) 4 1 2 3
(c) 3 4 2 1 (d) 4 1 3 2

43. We blow air to cool a hot liquid in order to ______.

(a) create turbulence in the hot liquid.
(b) provide a larger surface area for the liquid.
(c) provide fresh air above the surface of the liquid.
(d) saturate the air above the liquid with water vapour.

44. In which of the following uses of nitrogen, its characteristic property of inert nature is not exploited?

(a) It is used to preserve biological specimen.
(b) It dilutes the activity of oxygen present in the atmosphere.
(c) It is used to preserve food materials.
(d) Nitrogen is used for the synthesis of ammonia.

Level 2: Review Your Concepts

45. Finely powdered charcoal is added to coconut oil. This mixture is added to the glucose solution. How will you separate them?

46. In which of the following case(s), change of state of matter take place due to the application of pressure?

(a) Skating on ice
(b) Formation of snow
(c) Filling up of cooking gas (LPG) cylinder

47. The same amount of three gases ‘A’, ‘B’ and ‘C’ is taken in three different cylinders. All the cylinders are fitted with movable pistons and the gases are kept at room temperature and normal pressure. Then, external pressure is applied on each piston. The critical temperature of which gas is the highest and why?

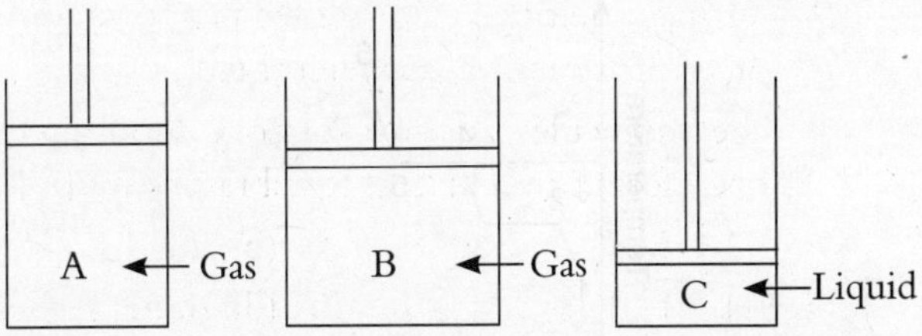

48. A standard chromatogram of the constituents of a food colour is given below.

Four chromatograms (A, B, C and D) shown below represent four different brands of food colours available in the market.

Identify which chromatogram contains which food colour?

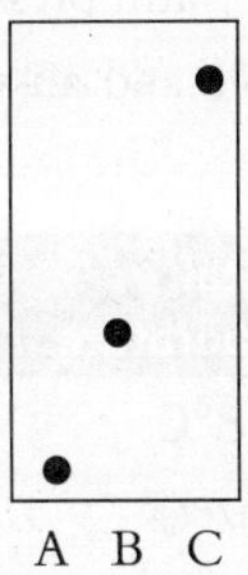

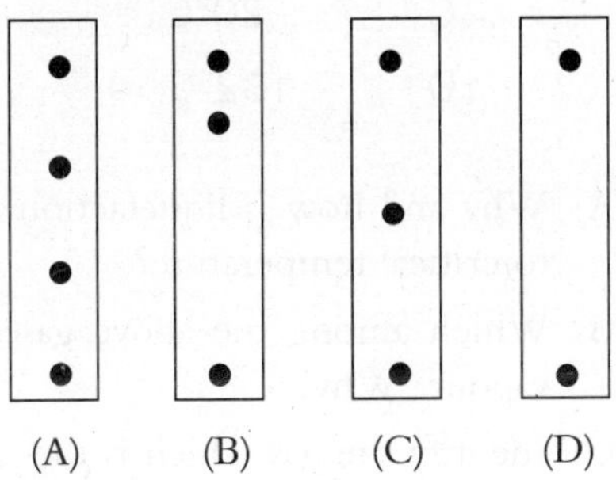

49. (a) Explain the effect of temperature on the electrical conductivity of metals.

(b) Same amount of hot liquid is taken in three containers given below. The liquid in which container gets cooled the fastest and why?

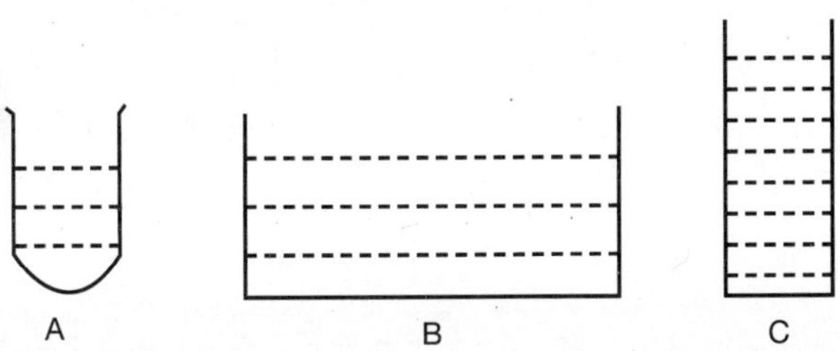

50. Why do naphthalene and camphor sublime under normal conditions of temperature and pressure?

51. Two ice cubes can be joined by pressing them together and then by releasing pressure. How do you account for this?

52. Copper in copper oxide does not liberate SO_2 gas while copper in bronze evolves SO_2 gas with conc. H_2SO_4. However, for making statues, copper is used in the form of bronze but not metallic copper or copper oxide. Explain why the same copper has such varied properties.

53. Why are ornaments prepared by using an alloy of Ag with Cu and not by pure Ag?

54. Perfect moulds can be made by using wrought iron but not by using molten copper. Give reasons.

55. In spite of supplying heat, the temperature of the melting solid does not change. Explain with reasons.

56. During the process of soldering, the metal surfaces are cleaned using dilute acids. What purpose does this serve and which separation technique is involved in this?

57. Explain the methods by which the constituents in gunpowder can be separated.

58. Redistillation of nitric acid is carried out in a ferrosilicon vessel but not in an iron vessel. Explain.

59. Deepa and her family on their house-warming ceremony received many bouquets which they kept at the corner of the drawing room. After some time, they felt the fragrance of the flowers all over the drawing room. What could be the reason behind this? Explain with a suitable reason.

60. When a perfume is poured on a palm, a cooling sensation is perceived. Name and explain the phenomenon associated with it.

61. How does liquefaction of a gas depend on critical temperature?

62. What is the principle involved in using brine solution to remove the ice piled on roads in cold regions?

63. Explain why the snow on the mountain peaks does not melt at a temperature slightly above 0°C.

64. A mixture is formed by two kinds of matter, the molecules of which possess only vibratory motion. If the change in solubility of two substances in a given solvent differs widely with the change in temperature, how can these two solids be separated from the solvent?

65. Give the working principle involved in chromatography.

66. (a) When Shashi went to Vizag with his parents, he noticed that all the fishermen store their fish inside a thermally insulated container which is filled with ice and salt. Can you give an explanation for this?

(b) Explain how and why usage of pressure cooker affects the cooking process.

67. Study the following graph and based on that answer the questions with a suitable reason. The graph represents the various stages involved in step-wise change of ice to steam.
   (a) Identify the stages associated with increase in temperature. Give a reason.
   (b) In which stages, the temperature is constant? Why so?

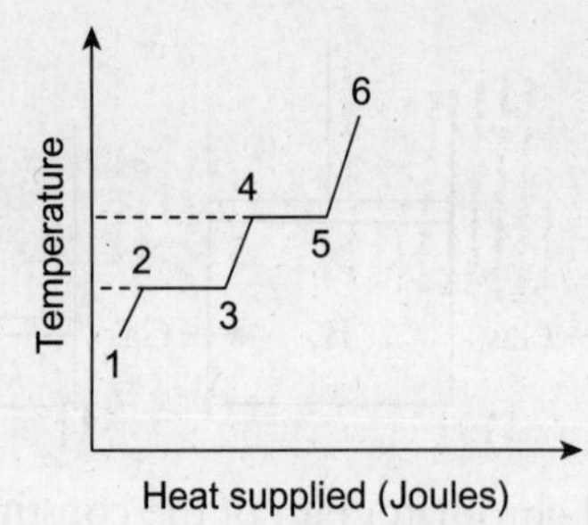

Level 3: Assess Your Concepts

68. What is the shape of the meniscus observed when water and mercury are taken in two different capillary tubes and why?

69. Evaporation can take place at any temperature, but boiling takes place at a fixed temperature. Give appropriate reasons.

70. Vapour pressure of a liquid A is more that of B. Which of these liquids has higher critical temperature in their gaseous state? Justify.

71. Explain the changes observed when a glass of water is placed on the surface of moon.

72. The surface of the electric bulb with a tungsten filament becomes greyish black after being used for a long period of time. Explain the reason.

73. A test tube filled with water is dipped up to its neck in a boiling water bath. Does the water inside the test tube boil? Justify.

74. Skating on ice is almost impossible at very low temperatures say at around −30°C. Why?

75. How is milk powder made from milk? Explain the principle involved.

76. (a) Discuss the change in energy and arrangement of molecules on increasing the temperature of ice from −5°C to 10°C at 1 atm pressure.
   (b) Analyse the given table and answer the following questions.

Gas	Critical temperature
A	−118°C
B	−147°C
C	20°C
D	132°C

   (A) Why and how is liquefaction of a gas related to critical temperature?
   (B) Which among the above gases can be called vapour? Why?
   (C) Identify the gas which is the most difficult to be liquefied. Give reason.

77. If a solution is formed by a combination of solvent A and solid solute B, and decomposition of the solute takes place at the boiling point of solvent; how can we separate these two?

AT

PRACTICE QUESTIONS JEE-NEET SPECIAL WING

Multiple-Answer Type Questions

Directions for questions 1 to 5:

Select one or more correct alternative(s) from the given choices.

1. A metal 'M' reacts with dilute sulphuric acid and liberates hydrogen gas. Another metal 'N' shows no reaction with dilute acid but reacts with concentrated sulphuric acid liberating a gas with pungent odour. Identify the correct sets corresponding to M and N.

	Metals	
	M	N
(a)	Fe	Pb
(b)	Pb	Pt
(c)	Sn	Cu
(d)	Fe	Ag

2. Consider the following sequence of reactions.

   X + Oxygen → Binary compound

   A + Water → Substance B

   Substance 'B' turns blue litmus red. Identify the statements which comply with the given sequence of reactions.

   (a) The substance 'X' can have 6 electrons in its valence shell

   (b) The compound 'A' could be basic or amphoteric

   (c) X can form a negative ion

   (d) X can react with dilute acid to liberate hydrogen gas

3. The boiling points of some gases are given in the table below. If '*x*' atm pressure is required for the liquefaction of gas 'R', at a temperature of '*t*°C, identify the gases which can be liquified by the application of pressure less than '*x*' atm at the same temperature. Assume that t°C is the temperature at which all the given gases can be liquified.

Gas	Boiling point
P	−196°C
Q	−35°C
R	−78°C
S	−233°C
T	−10°C

   (a) P (b) Q

   (c) S (d) T

4. Two non-metals can form two oxides each. These two oxides of each nonmetal can be separated by dissolving the mixture in aqueous solution of potassium hydroxide. Identify the electronic configurations corresponding to those nonmetals mentioned.

   (a) 2,8,5 (b) 2,5

   (c) 2,4 (d) 2,8,6

5. A, B, C and D are four liquids. A and B can be separated by using separating funnel. 'B' remains in the funnel after collecting 'A'. C and D can be separated by using fractional distillation. The liquid 'B' can be separated from the mixture of B, C and D by fractional distillation. 'C' remains in the distillation flask. Identify the statements which comply with these experimental results.

   (a) A and C can be separated by using separating funnel

   (b) 'C' has the highest boiling point among all

   (c) A and D can be separated by using separating funnel

   (d) B and C might form a miscible liquid mixture with water.

Comprehension-Based Questions

Directions for questions 6 to 10:

Read the content given in the following passage and answer the questions given below. Certain hypothetical materials along with their densities are given in the table below.

Substance	Density(g/cc)	
	Solid	Liquid
A	8.94	7.75
B	8.73	8.9
C	19.3	11.1
D	7.13	6.63
E	10.5	9.1
F	9.78	10.1

6. Based on the data given, identify the materials which are not suitable for making perfect moulds.
(a) B (b) B; F
(c) C; E (d) E;F

7. In case of which substances, melting point increases with increase in pressure?
(a) A;B;D (b) B;F
(c) Only C (d) A;C;E

8. Which of the given substances show the phenomenon of regelation shown by ice under suitable conditions?
(a) A (b) E
(c) F (d) C

9. Assertion (A): The melting point of 'E' increases with increase in pressure.

Reason (R): The melting points of all solids show contraction on melting.

(a) Both A and R are correct and R is the correct explanation of A
(b) Both A and R are correct and R is not the correct explanation of A
(c) A is correct and R is wrong
(d) R is correct and A is wrong

10. Ice cube when dropped in water floats on water. Which other substances from the above table fall in the category of ice?
(a) B;F (b) D;E
(c) A;C;F (d) E;B

11. The following curve represents the change in melting point of a substance with change in pressure.

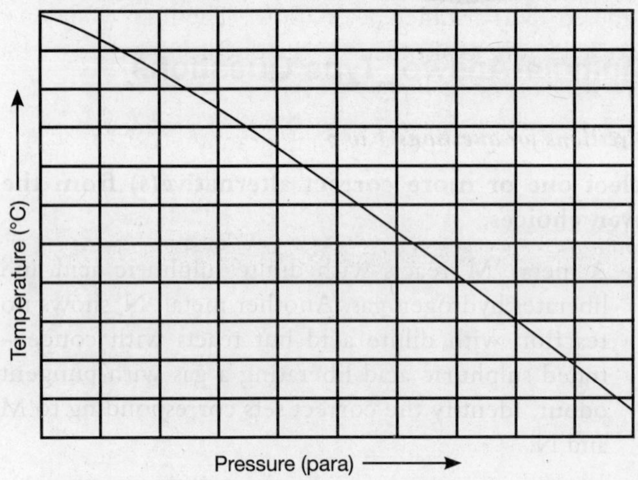

Which among the following statements complies with the same substance?

(a) The substance shows comparable behaviour with the substance 'B' given in the table.
(b) The substance can be used for making statues.
(c) The solid when dropped in its own liquid sinks in it.
(d) The substance melts faster when pressure is applied on it.

Directions for questions 12 to 16:

Read the content given in the following passage and answer the questions given below.

The news headline read--------- 'I took provisional suspension for swift resolution of my doping case: Dipa Karmakar'. The performance enhancing drugs have always been in news. Sometimes, these substances are consumed by the players to enhance their performance in the sports events while sometimes these are consumed to cure a particular disease without being aware of the ban on the particular formulation of drug. World Anti-Doping Agency is the nodal agency which is authorised to issue the list of banned drugs in the sports.

Chromatography is a technique which can be used for identifying presence of such constituents in the urine or blood samples of the participants in the major sports events such as Olympics. Though highly precise and complex methods of chromatography are used for the doping tests, we can understand the basic principle by understanding the most simple method of chromatography that is called paper chromatography.

This technique involves the separation of various coloured components in a mixture by using suitable solvent. Depending on their affinity with the solvent they travel along with the solvent to different distances and form coloured spots at different positions. The ratio of distance travelled by the constituent to the distance travelled by the solvent is known as R_f factor.

Paper Chromatography

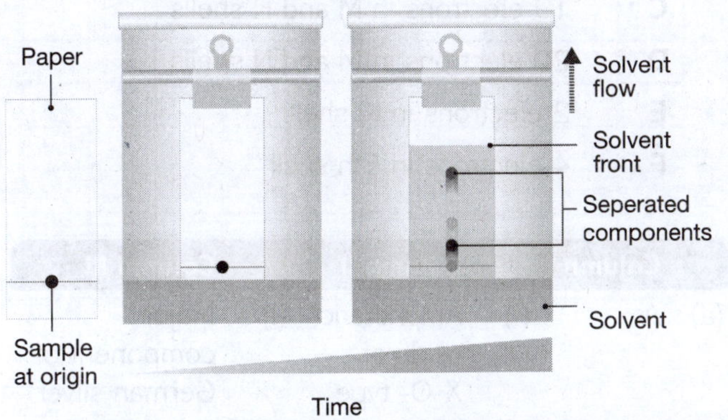

The standard chromatogram of the pure sample shows the Rf factors of the various natural components in that sample. Any additional constituent in the test sample will be having a different Rf value which does not match with any of the natural constituents.

12. The following chromatogram correspond to the urine sample of a healthy human. The major components of urine include urea, creatinine and uric acid apart from water. The Rf value of urea is 0.6. uric acid has maximum affinity with water. What is the Rf value of creatinine?

(a) 0.8 (b) 5
(c) 0.2 (d) 8

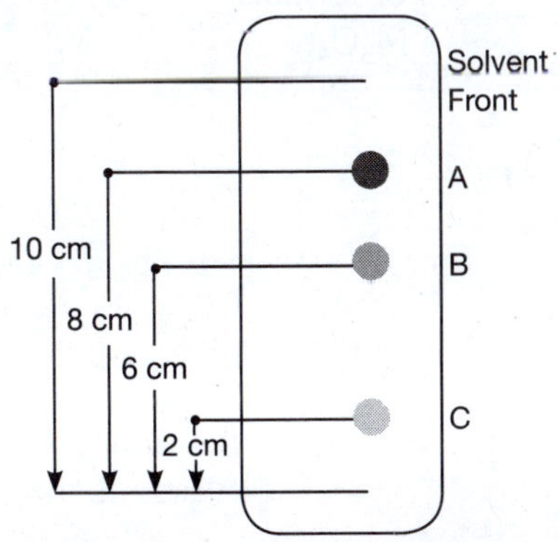

13. The important drugs banned in cricket along with their Rf values are given below. In 2019, Pruthvi Shaw failed in doping test as his urine sample showed the presence of a banned drug which was later found to have been consumed as a constituent of cough syrup. The spot for that drug was found below that for creatinine. Identify the drug mentioned from the data given below.

Banned drug	R_f value
Moduretic	0.9
Nandrolone	0.75
Boldenone	0.3
Terbutaline	0.1

(a) Moduretic (b) Boldenone
(c) Nandrolone (d) Terbutaline

14. The following represents the standard chromatogram of leaf pigments. The distance travelled by the solvent is 9 cm. The distances travelled by the various important pigments are given in the table below.

When the leaf extract is treated with hot ethyl alcohol, chlorophyll a is removed leaving behind the other pigments. The chromatogram is found to be missing the spot corresponding to some R_f value from the original chromatogram. Identify the R_f value of the missing spot.

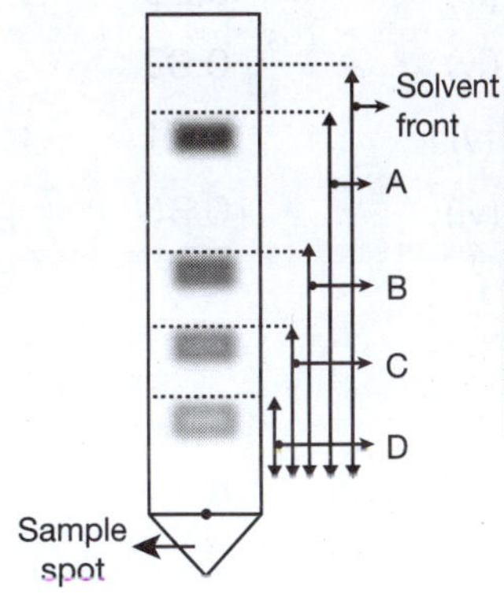

Pigment	Distance
Chlorophyll *a*	6.4 cm
Chlorophyll *b*	5.8 cm
Carotene	8.5 cm
Xanthophyll	4 cm

(a) 0.7 (b) 0.54
(c) 0.44 (d) 0.94

15. **Assertion (A):** The component with the least R_f value is the most soluble in the solvent taken

Reason(R): The R_f value of a component in a mixture is dependent on the affinity of the component with the solvent.

(a) Both A and R are correct and R is the correct explanation of A
(b) Both A and R are correct and R is not the correct explanation of A
(c) A is correct and R is wrong
(d) R is correct and A is wrong

Match The Column

16. Observe the hypothetical chromatogram of a mixture given below and match the entries in column I with those in column II.

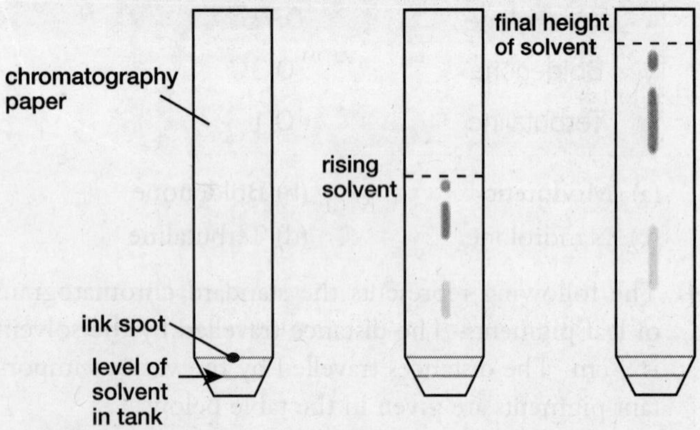

Colour of the spot			R_f value of the component indicated
(a)	Purple	(i)	0.78
(b)	Pink	(ii)	0.87
(c)	Green	(iii)	0.29
(d)	Red	(iv)	0.62
(e)	Blue	(v)	0.71
(f)	Black	(vi)	0.36

17. Based on the data given in the following table match the columns.

Element	Electron distribution
A	13 electrons in M shell
B	3 electrons in M shell
C	19 electrons in M and N shells
D	20 electrons in M and N shells
E	2 electrons in M shell
F	4 electrons in 5th shell

Column I	Column II	Column III
(a) A	(i) Amphoteric oxide of X_2O_3 type	(I) Major component of German silver
(b) B	(ii) Reacts with steam	(II) Best quality alloy in surgical instruments
(c) C	(iii) +2 and +4 ions	(III) Galvanisation
(d) D	(iv) Reacts with NaOH	(IV) Minor component of bell metal
(e) E	(v) +1 and +2 ions	(V) Aircraft frames
(f) F	(vi) Mixed oxide of formula M_3O_4	(VI) Firecrackers

ANSWER KEYS

Crossword

Across

3. Zinc 6. Condensation 7. Bromine 9. Evaporation
12. Solvent 13. Diffusion 14. Sulphur

Down

1. Magnetic 2. Heterogeneous 4. Nickel 5. Molecules
8. Decreases 10. Eight 11. Solid

Classroom Wing

Very Short Answer Type Questions

2. Graphite 3. Sublimation 4. Bottom 5. Less 6. Diffusion
7. Cohesive forces, adhesive forces 8. Translatory, rotatory, vibratory 9. Liquid state
10. Less 11. Boiling point

Competition Wing

Level 1: Apply Your Concepts

6. False 7. True 8. True 9. False 10. False
11. True 12. True 13. 21 14. Temperature and surface area
15. Nickel 16. Nitrogen 17. Insoluble, soluble 18. Iodine and alcohol
19. Critical temperature 20. (i) → (C), (ii) → (E), (iii) → (A), (iv) → (B), (v) → (D)
21. (c) 22. (a) 23. (a) 24. (c) 25. (d)
26. (b) 27. (d) 28. (a) 29. (b) 30. (b)
31. (d) 32. (b) 33. (c) 34. (d) 35. (c)
36. (d) 37. (a) 38. (c) 39. (c) 40. (a)
41. (b) 42. (b) 43. (c) 44. (d)

JEE-NEET Special Wing

Multiple-Answer Type Questions

1. (c) 2. (a, c) 3. (b, d) 4. (b, c) 5. (a, b, c, d)

Comprehension-Based Questions

6. (b) 7. (d) 8. (a) 9. (c) 10. (a)
11. (d) 12. (c) 13. (d) 14. (a) 15. (d)

Match The Column

16. (a) ↔ (iv), (b) ↔ (vi), (c) ↔ (ii), (d) ↔ (v), (e) ↔ (vi)
17. (a)↔ (vi) ↔(II), (b) ↔ (i) ↔(V), (c) ↔ (ii) ↔(I), (d) ↔ (v) ↔(III), (e) ↔ (vi) ↔(VI), (f) ↔ (iii) ↔(IV)

Hints and Explanations

CLASSROOM WING

Very Short Answer Type Questions

1. (i) (a) Temperature
   (b) Solid to liquid state
   (c) Pressure conditions

   (ii) (a) Temperature
   (b) Liquid to vapour state
   (c) Atmospheric pressure

   (iii) Since the gases are highly compressible, they can be liquefied by the application of pressure provided the temperature of the gas is equal to or below its critical temperature and this process is called liquefaction.

   (iv) The temperature at which freezing occurs at normal atmospheric pressure is called freezing point of that liquid.

   (v) Temperature above which a gas cannot be liquefied.

   (vi) Anything that occupies some space and has mass is called matter.

   (vii) Homogenous, contains only one kind of particles

   (viii) Mixing of two or more elements or compounds in any proportion

   (ix) Pure substances in which molecules are composed of only one kind of atoms are called elements

   (x) Pure substances in which two or more elements combine chemically in a fixed proportion by weight are called compounds.

   (xi) Have 1 to 3 electrons in their valence shells. Lose electrons from their valence shells to attain stable structures and form cations.

   (xii) Generally, have 4 to 7 electrons in their valence shells. Accept electrons to attain stable structures and form anions.

   (xiii) Properties of both metals and non-metals

   (xiv) Solid–solid homogenous mixture

   (xv) chemically unreactive

2. It is graphite, and so the constituent atoms are carbon.

3. Sublimation

4. Bottom

5. Less

6. Diffusion

7. Cohesive forces, adhesive forces

8. Translatory, rotatory, vibratory

9. Liquid state

10. Less

11. Boiling point

12. Water will be in a vapour state because there is no external pressure.

13. When we exhale air from our mouth on a winter morning, the warm water vapour present in the exhaled air condenses to form water droplets.

14. Ice kept in a vacuum chamber sublimes and gets converted to the vapour state.

15. Cooking gas (LPG) is liquefied by the application of pressure.

16. (i) Brass, bronze
    (ii) Salt solution, solution of I_2 in CCl_4
    (iii) Soda water. liquor ammonia
    (iv) Water–ethyl alcohol, Benzene-Toluene mixture
    (v) Air
    (vi) Gunpowder, Mixture of iron and sulphur
    (vii) Sand in water, Suspension of sulphur in water
    (viii) Kerosene and water, and benzene in water

17. (i) $Na_2O + H_2O \rightarrow 2NaOH$
    (ii) $CO_2 + H_2O \rightarrow H_2CO_3$
    (iii) $CO + H_2O \rightarrow CO + H_2$
    (iv) $SO_2 + H_2O \rightarrow H_2SO_3$

18. (i) Solubility of solids in a given solvent
    (ii) Magnetic nature of one component
    (iii) Density variations w.r.t. a given solvent
    (iv) Immiscible liquids

(v) Soluble solid in a given liquid
(vi) Difference in boiling points
(vii) Ability of one of the components of gas to liquefy under high pressure
(viii) Adsorption of components of a mixture
(ix) Difference in boiling points of gases

19. (i) Arsenic: Yellow As, Grey As, Black As
(ii) Antimony: White Sb, Yellow Sb, Black Sb
(iii) Selenium: Red Se, Grey Se, Black Se

20. (i) Clear liquid formed
(ii) Solid–liquid solution
(iii) It is the clear liquid that lies above the precipitate or sediment.

21. Increasing rate of reaction

22. Appearance as Ag, malleability, ductility

23. Reactivity of Ge with O_2

24. (i) Condensation of water vapour
(ii) Sublimation of naphthalene balls
(iii) Evaporation of water
(iv) Deposition of water vapour
(v) Condensation of water vapour

25. Sodium (Na).

26. No. of atoms in a molecule

27. (i) Positive
(ii) negative

28 (i) Potassium nitrate and sodium chloride
(ii) Iodine and sand
(iii) Nickel and lead
(iv) Sawdust and sand
(v) Chalk and water
(vi) Salt and water
(vii) Carbon dioxide and water
(viii) Mixture of NH_4Cl (soluble) and I_2 (insoluble) Solvent: water
(ix) N_2 insoluble and CO_2 (soluble) in KOH

29. (i) Increasing order: solids, liquids, gases
(ii) Decreasing order: gases, liquids, solids
(iii) Increasing order: gases, liquids, solids
(iv) Decreasing order: solids, liquids, gases

30. Conduction of electricity by antimony

Short Answer Type Questions

31. Diamond is a very good conductor of heat because of the compact arrangement of small carbon atoms.

32. B can be liquefied by the application of pressure at that temperature, not A.

33 The boiling point of water is directly proportional to the external pressure. The pressure cooker reduces the cooking time by increasing the boiling point of water due to an increase in the external pressure.

34. (i) respiration
(ii) bleaching action
(iii) fungicides

35. (a) Sand is heavier than water. The solid component is insoluble and heavier than the liquid component.
(b) The addition of impurities to any liquid decreases the freezing point of the liquid. As the sea water contains dissolved salts, it has a lower freezing point than the pure water. Therefore, the pure water sample freezes earlier than the sea water sample.

36. Examples of noble metals: Silver, gold and platinum. They are called noble metals because these have very less reactivity, hence are precious.

37. (a) Melting: Any energy that enters a substance causes an increase in the movement of the particles, resulting in melting.
(b) Boiling: Applying more heat allows the water molecules to move even faster, overcoming the attractions between molecules and spreading out as fast-moving molecules.
(c) Condensation: Cooling removes energy from a substance causing a reduction in the movement of the particles. This reduction in movement results in the condensation.
(d) Freezing: If you continue to remove heat from the liquid water, solidification occurs and the water changes to solid ice.

38. (a) Molecules are composed of only one kind of atom.
(b) Two or more elements combine chemically in a fixed proportion by weight
(c) Constituent substances are mixed physically

39. (a) Iron is mainly used in the form of steel, an alloy in which the major component is iron. Steel is used for making buckets, drain pipes, chains, etc.
(b) Lead is used for making containers for corrosive liquids and protective screens for X-ray and other

harmful radiations as it is unaffected by impure water, steam or dilute mineral acids and has a low melting point.

(c) Copper is used in as electric transmission wires and electrical goods.

(d) Zinc is used for galvanizing iron to protect it from rusting.

40. Solvent extraction: One component of the mixture is soluble and the other is insoluble in a given solvent

41. (i) Definite; Definite

(ii) Definite

(iii) no definite shape; no definite shape

(iv) Moderate

(v) Negligible; Easily compressible

(vi) Less rigid

(vii) Any number of free surfaces, only one free surface

(viii) Less; highest Least; Moderate

42. (i) Loosely packed in comparison to solids

(ii) Very less

(iii) Moderate; minimum

(iv) Vibratory motion; translatory, rotatory and vibrartory

(v) Higher kinetic energy than solids; very high kinetic energy

43. The molecules are closely packed, and therefore, solids have a definite shape, definite volume, high density and negligible compressibility

44. KNO_3–$KClO_3$ mixture is separated by fractional crystallization. In this method, two components should be soluble in one solvent, but the solubility should be different. When we add this mixture to water and heat it, the less soluble component, $KClO_3$ crystallizes, leaving out the more soluble KNO_3 behind. Then again the solution is heated and cooled down to get KNO_3 crystals.

45. (a) Sublimation

(b) Gravity method

(c) Filtration

Essay Answer Type Questions

46. (a) suitable solvent

(b) molecular weight

(c) sublimation, suitable solvent

(d) suitable adsorbent

47. (i) mass

(ii) volume

(iii) shape

(iv) density

(v) compressibility

(vi) free surface

(vii) thermal expansion

(viii) diffusion

48. (a) Metalloids are elements which show the properties of both metals and non-metals.

Examples: germanium, arsenic, antimony, selenium and tellurium

(b) Mercury is a metal and there are strong forces of attractions between the mercury atoms. That means, the cohesive forces between mercury atoms are stronger than the adhesive forces between mercury atoms and the particles of floor. Therefore, mercury beads as droplets when spilled on the floor. Water is a polar substance and has stronger adhesive forces between the molecules of water and those of floor. Therefore, water forms a film on the floor.

49. (i) Every form of matter is composed of small particles called molecules.

(ii) The empty space (gaps) that exists in between the molecules is called intermolecular space.

(iii) Molecules exert attractive forces, called intermolecular forces of attraction, upon one another. These forces decrease with an increase in the distance between the molecules. The force of attraction between similar molecules is called cohesive force and that between dissimilar molecules is called adhesive force.

(iv) The molecules possess kinetic energy due to their motion and their movement is ceaseless.

50. (i) state

(ii) melting and boiling points

(iii) conductivity

(iv) tensile strength

(v) malleability and ductibility

(vi) lustre

Competition Wing

Level 1: Apply Your Concepts

1. Solid to liquid state
2. Liquid to vapour state
3. Gas to liquid state
4. Liquid to solid state
5. Solid to vapour state
6. False. Smoke is not a homogeneous mixture.
7. True. Sodium is a soft metal.
8. True. Brass, being an alloy of copper, is a homogeneous mixture.
9. True. Gas carbon is a good conductor of electricity.

13. We blow air to cool a hot liquid in order to provide fresh air above the surface of the liquid.

20. (i) → (C) Solid-solid homogeneous mixture → Bronze
 (ii) → (E) Solid-liquid homogeneous mixture → Saline water
 (iii) → (A) Liquid-liquid heterogeneous mixture → Coconut oil and water
 (iv) → (B) Liquid-liquid homogeneous mixture → Petrol and diesel
 (v) → (D) Solid-liquid heterogeneous mixture → Finely powdered charcoal in water.

21. Metals are good conductors of electricity because of the presence of free electrons. Metal atoms have generally 1 or 2 or 3 electrons in their valence shell.
 Hence, the correct option is (c).

22. Metals have lustre because of the transition of loosely bound electrons.
 Hence, the correct option is (a).

23. Steel is more resistant to corrosion because alloying makes the constituent metal less reactive.
 Hence, the correct option is (a).

24. Duralumin is as strong as steel because it is an alloy of aluminium, and alloying improves the mechanical properties of metal. Alloying reduces the malleability of the metal.
 Hence, the correct option is (c).

36. Due to close packing of molecules in solids, they possess definite shape due to which they have many number of free surfaces.
 Hence, the correct choice is (d).

37. Iron bar is solid, and hence, intermolecular force of attraction is maximum.
 Hence, the correct choice is (a).

38. Since chlorine is a gas at room temperature, it can be compressed to the maximum.
 Hence, the correct choice is (c).

39. During melting the temperature of a solid remains constant, as the external heat energy is utilised to overcome the forces of attraction between the molecules.
 Hence, the correct choice is (c).

40. Ammonium chloride is a sublimable substance which changes directly from solid to gas on heating.
 Hence, the correct choice is (a).

41. (2) The energy supplied makes the molecules to vibrate with more speed.
 (3) During melting, the molecules overcome the forces of attraction between them.
 (4) The molecules acquire rotatory motion, translatory motion in addition to vibratory motion.
 (1) Molecules become free to move, and thus, attain the molecular arrangement of a liquid.
 Hence, the correct choice is (b).

42. (4) Ice cubes formed in the refrigeration
 (1) Water collected in the receiving flask
 (2) Water boiling in the distillation flask
 (3) Steam passing through the delivery tube.
 Hence, the correct choice is (b).

43. We blow air to cool a hot liquid in order to provide fresh air above the surface of the liquid.
 Hence, the correct choice is (c).

44. Nitrogen reacts with hydrogen to form ammonia. Its inert nature is not suitable for this process.
 Hence, the correct choice is (d).

Level 2: Review your Concepts

45. At first, charcoal should be separated by filtration. Then coconut oil can be separated by using a separating funnel and glucose can be obtained by evaporation.

46. During skating, pressure is applied on ice and it melts, and during filling up of the cooking gas cylinder also, pressure is applied to liquefy the cooking gas.
 Hence, in cases (a) and (c), the change of state of matter takes place due to the application of pressure.

47. A critical temperature of C is the highest because it can only be liquefied at that temperature.

48. Chromatogram (A) contains A, B, and two other components. Chromatogram (B) contains A, C, and another component. Chromatogram (C) contains A, B, and C. Chromatogram (d) contains A and C.

49. (a) (i) The cause of electrical conductivity in metals.
(ii) The effect of temperature on kinetic energy of metal atoms.
(iii) The effect of temperature on direction of species, conducting electricity.
(iv) Effect of these on conductivity.
(b) The rate of evaporation is directly proportional to the surface area of the container in which the liquid is taken. The container with maximum surface area has maximum rate of evaporation. The greater the rate of evaporation, the faster the cooling of the liquid is. The liquid in the container B get cooled the fastest than those in the containers A and C.

50. (i) High vapour pressure.
(ii) The effect of high vapour pressure on sublimation.
(iii) Comparison of the kinetic energy of surface molecules.

51. (i) Effect of pressure on the melting point.
(ii) Changes in the melting point of ice with pressure.
(iii) The application of this in joining two ice cubes.

52. (i) Composition of bronze
(ii) Comparison of chemical properties of constituents of bronze and CuO.
(iii) Comparison of physical properties of constituents of bronze with CuO and Cu.

53. (i) Physical properties of Ag.
(ii) Strength of ornaments made of pure silver.
(iii) Change in properties on the addition of Cu.

54. (i) Generally density in a solid state is higher than that in a liquid state.
(ii) Requisites for a good mould.
(iii) Comparison of the change in volumes on the solidification of iron and copper.

55. (i) At the melting point, molecules of a solid move apart.
(ii) Different energies possessed by molecules.
(iii) Energy which is affected while heating.
(iv) Energy which is affected during change in phase.

56. (i) The phenomenon of soldering.
(ii) Composition of metal surface.
(iii) Effect of addition of acid to metals.
(iv) Process of separation.

57. (i) Composition of gunpowder.
(ii) Identification of suitable solvents.
(iii) Extraction of the components from respective solutions.

58. Nitric acid is a strong oxidizing agent. It reacts with iron to form ferric oxide. Ferrosilicon, an alloy of iron is less reactive when compared to iron and does not react with nitric acid. Thus, the redistillation process is carried out in a ferrosilicon vessel.

59. The molecules which cause fragrance diffused into the air from the bouquets and that's how travel from one corner of the room to another. So, Deepa and her family after sometime felt the fragrance of the flowers all over the room.

60. Perfume is a highly volatile liquid. When it rapidly evaporates from the palm, it absorbs heat energy from the palm. This gives a cooling sensation.

61. Liquefaction of a gas by application of pressure is possible only at or below critical temperature. At low temperature the intermolecular forces of attractions are considerably high. This makes the conversion of gaseous state to liquid state feasible on application of pressure.

62. The ice piled on roads in the cold regions is removed by melting process. For this process brine solution is used because this decreases the melting point of ice. Thus, ice melts below 0°C and can be removed.

63. The atmospheric pressure on the mountain peaks is low. As ice contracts on melting, with the decrease in pressure its melting point increases. Thus, the snow does not melt slightly above 0°C.

64. Solids possess the molecules which have only vibratory motion. Thus, both the substances are solids. As their change in solubility in a particular solvent differs in a particular range of temperature, they can be separated by fractional crystallization.

65. The particles of a mixture or dye, like, ink are soluble in water. As the water rises on the filter paper, it takes along with it the dye particles. Usually, a dye is a mixture of two or more colours. The coloured components that are more soluble in water and low tendency of getting adhered to the adsorbent material, reach to a greater height and in this way the colours get separated.

66. (a) Salt added to ice (freezing mixture) is a better refrigerant than ice as adding some impurity

(salt) to the ice decreases its melting point. During melting of ice, it takes away a lot of heat from the substance(s) which is in contact with it. That's why the fishermen store their fish inside a thermally insulated container which is filled with ice and salt. This mixture can maintain a very low temperature.

(b) The water taken in the pressure cooker vessel vaporises to produce steam when the cooker is subjected to heating. Due to the steam accumulated inside the cooker, the pressure increases. The boiling point of water taken as the cooking medium increases as the external pressure increases. As a result of this, the water can be heated to a higher temperature than in the normal vessel without getting vapourised. At higher temperature, the reactions involved in the cooking process take place at a faster rate. Therefore, the usage of pressure cooker reduces the cooking time.

67. (a) In the graph, parts 1 to 2, 3 to 4 and 5 to 6 show heating of solid, liquid and gas, respectively which increases kinetic energy, and hence, there is rise in temperature.

(b) The parts 2 to 3 and 4 to 5 represent melting of solid and boiling of liquid. At these points the heat energy supplied is utilised for decreasing the intermolecular force of attraction, and hence, there is no change in temperature.

Level 3: Assess Your Concepts

68. (i) Type of forces between Hg molecules and Hg–glass molecules.

(ii) Type of forces between water molecules and water–glass molecules.

(iii) Effect of these forces on the shape of meniscus.

69. (i) Differences between evaporation and boiling.

(ii) Comparison of the part of the liquid from where evaporation and boiling take place.

(iii) Condition at which boiling starts in a liquid.

70. (i) Relation between critical temperature and intermolecular forces of attraction of a gas.

(ii) Relation between vapour pressure and intermolecular forces of attraction.

(iii) Relation between intermolecular force of attraction and boiling point.

(iv) Relation between boiling point and critical temperature.

71. (i) Relative pressure on the surface of the moon.

(ii) Effect of pressure on evaporation of water.

72. (i) Pressure inside the bulb.

(ii) Change in state of tungsten filament.

73. The water in the test tube becomes hot but does not boil. The water in the tube gets the heat from the water outside. As the maximum temperature of water in the container outside is 100°C, the water inside the test tube attains 100°C temperature, but immediately the transmission of heat stops due to thermal equilibrium, and hence, the water inside the test tube cannot boil.

74. Skating on ice is possible because ice contracts on melting. So, on applying pressure, the melting point of ice decreases and the ice below the skates starts to melt and because of the formation of thin water film skating is possible on the ice But when temperature is around −30°C, the pressure exerted by body mass is not sufficient to melt the ice below the skates. Hence, skating on ice is not possible at around −30°C.

75. Milk is heated under low pressure conditions. This decreases the boiling point of milk, and thus, the water present in the milk evaporates. This concentrated milk is then sprayed in a hot dry chamber where the evaporation of the leftover water is instant and concentrated milk turns to milk powder.

76. (a) On heating ice at −5°C, its temperature increases up to 0°C, i.e., the kinetic energy of the molecules increases. At 0°C, the ice starts to melt. During this period the energy supplied is taken up to increase the potential energy of the molecules and the arrangement of molecules changes. Once the ice cube melts, the heat energy supplied is again used to increase the temperature of water due to increase in kinetic energy of the molecules. However, from 0°C to 4°C, the molecules of water come closer and above 4°C the molecules move farther away.

(b) (A) In gaseous state, the molecules possess high kinetic energy and there are negligible intermolecular forces of attraction. In liquids, the molecules possess lower kinetic energy and there are greater intermolecular forces of attraction. For the gas to get liquified, the kinetic energy of the molecules should be decreased to a certain extent. This happens only when the gas is cooled to certain minimum temperature which is called critical temperature. Only then, application of pressure can result in the liquefaction of the gas. The gases which have appreciable intermolecular forces of attraction have critical temperatures close to room temperatures. The gases which have very low intermolecular forces of attraction have very low critical temperatures. The liquefaction of such gases is difficult.

(B) The gases which have critical temperatures above room temperatures are considered as vapours because in these cases, the liquid and gaseous states coexist under normal conditions. Among the given gases, gas D has critical temperature of 132°C which is much above the room temperature. Hence, it is called vapour.

(C) Gas B is the one which is most difficult to be liquefied because it has the least value of critical temperature that is –147°C.

77. At the temperature at which solvent A boils, the solute B decomposes. Hence, it is not possible to separate the solute B from solvent A by distillation under normal atmospheric pressure. As the pressure decreases, the boiling point decreases. Thus, by decreasing the external pressure in the above distillation processes, the boiling point of solvent A can be decreased. At this temperature solute B does not decompose and can be separated from the liquid.

JEE-NEET Special Wing

Multiple-Answer Type Questions

1. Metal 'M' could be tin while metal 'N' could be copper. This is because tin is present above hydrogen in the metal reactivity series and hence liberates hydrogen with dilute acids. Copper is present below hydrogen and does not liberate hydrogen on reaction with dilute acids.

2. 'B' should be an acid and 'A' should be acidic oxide of 'X'. Therefore, 'X' should be a nonmetal. A nonmetal is characterised by the presence of 4 to 6 electrons in the valence shell of its atom. It can form a negative ion.

3. The gases having critical temperatures higher than R can be liquified by applying a pressure less than 'x' atm. Q and T are the gases.

4. Nitrogen and carbon can form both acidic and neutral oxides. Acidic oxides can dissolve in potassium hydroxide solution while neutral oxides do not. 2,5 and 2,4 are the electronic configurations of nitrogen and carbon.

5. All the given statements are in compliance with the given experimental results.

Comprehension-Based Questions

6. B and F are the materials which show contraction on melting and expansion on solidification. This is because for these two substances, the density of liquid state is higher than that in solid state. These can form perfect moulds.

7. Increase in pressure always leads to contraction. The melting point of the materials which contract on melting decreases with increase in pressure. The melting point of the materials which expand on melting increases with increase in pressure.

8. 'A' shows similarity in behaviour to ice because it undergoes expansion on melting. The density of liquid state is less than that of solid state. Hence, it is likely to show regelation.

9. A is correct and R is wrong.

10. B and F are substances which show increase in density during melting. Hence, the solid substances are likely to float on liquid instead of being submerged in it.

11. The graph shows decrease in melting point with increase in pressure. That means, the substance expands on melting. It melts faster when pressure is applied on it.

12. The component B corresponds to urea since it has R_f value equal to 0.6. The component 'A' should be uric acid. The component 'C' corresponds to creatinine. Its R_f value is 0.2

13. Terbutaline has the R_f value lower than that of creatinine and hence it is the one mentioned in the description.

14. Among the given R_f values, R_f value of 0.7 corresponds to chlorophyll a which would correspond to the missing spot in the chromatogram.

15. The component with the least R_f value is the least soluble in the solvent taken.

16. Match The Column

	Colour of the spot		R_f value of the component indicated
(a)	Purple	(iv)	0.62
(b)	Pink	(vi)	0.36
(c)	Green	(ii)	0.87
(d)	Red	(v)	0.71
(e)	Blue	(v)	0.78
(f)	Black	(iii)	0.29

17.

Column I			Column II		Column III	
(a)	A	Fe	(vi)	Mixed oxide of formula M_3O_4	(II)	Best quality alloy in surgical instruments
(b)	B	Al	(i)	Amphoteric oxide of X_2O_3 type	(V)	Aircraft frames
(c)	C	Cu	(v)	+1 and +2 ions	(I)	Major component of German silver
(d)	D	Zn	(iv)	Reacts with NaOH	(III)	Galvanisation
(e)	E	Mg	(ii)	Reacts with steam	(VI)	Firecrackers
(f)	F	Sn	(iii)	+2 and +4 ions	(IV)	Minor component of bell metal

CHAPTER

3

Language of Chemistry and Transformation of Substances

Remember

Before beginning this chapter, you should be able to:

- explain the interconversion of states of matter.
- classify matter based upon physical and chemical properties.

Key Ideas

After completing this chapter, you should be able to:

- learn Berzelius system of writing symbols of elements and formulae of elements and compounds.
- know the naming of binary compounds, acids, bases and salts.
- understand valencies of elements with respect to hydrogen, chlorine and oxygen.
- learn trial and error method, for balancing chemical equations.
- study classification of chemical reactions based on the nature of reaction, the energy changes and oxidation–reduction reactions.

Scientific Crypt

A Tribute to Lavoisier (1743 – 1794)

Antoine Lavoisier was born on August 26, 1743 in an elite family of Paris. At the age of 25, he became the elected member of French Academy of sciences. His scientific excellence and brilliant experimental capabilities brought a revolutionary change in the field of chemistry. He is considered as the father of modern chemistry because of his remarkable contributions to chemistry.

Lavoisier derived the theory of combustion, demonstrated the role of oxygen in respiration and introduced a quantitative approach in his experiments because of which a paradigm change was observed in chemistry. Based on his quantitative experimental observations he stated the first version of law of conservation of mass. He also deduced the chemical composition of water and air. He proved experimentally that air is a mixture.

His contribution was not only restricted to the field of chemistry, it enriched biological science also. Unfortunately at the age of 50 Lavoisier was convicted for his association with Ferme General, a tax collecting company, put on trial and beheaded on 8 May, 1794. Later French government realised that he was falsely convicted.

FUN TIME

CROSSWORD

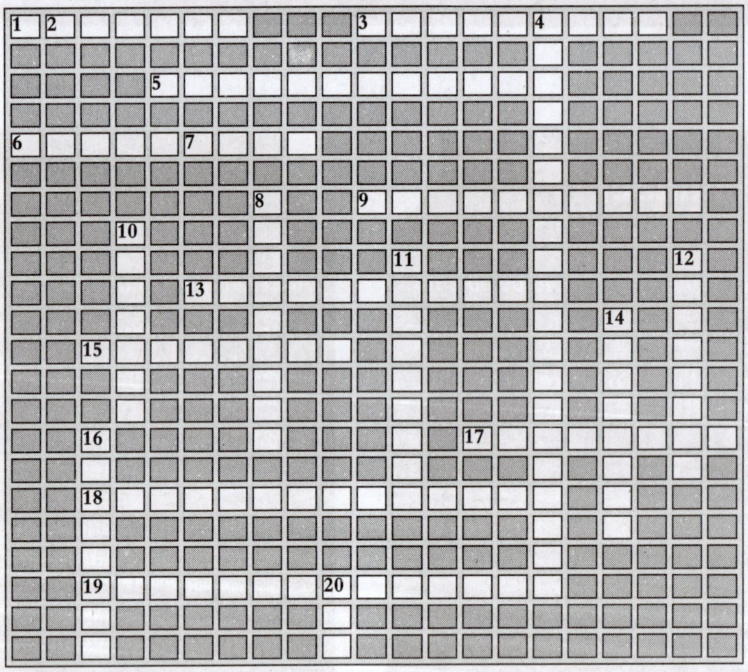

Across

1. The combining capacity of an atom
3. Oxidizing agent undergoes ______.
5. Molecular mass in grams
6. Element – element combination
9. Decomposition of the compound in the presence of light
13. Combustion of nitrogen is (in terms of change in energy)
15. Atomic mass in grams
17. In endothermic reaction energy is ______.
18. Atomic mass of an elements is expressed in ______.
19. Reaction between acid and base.

Down

2. Decomposition of the compound into its constituent elements is called
4. Decomposition of the compound in the presence of heat.
7. Combustion of carbon.
8. Reducing agent undergoes ______.
10. Latin name of tungsten is ______.
11. Symbols and formulae were suggested by ______.
12. In exothermic reaction energy is ______.
14. The most reactive halogen.
16. In metal reactivity series, gold is more reactive than.
20. Suffix used in naming binary compounds.

INTRODUCTION

The branch of science that deals with the study of matter is known as **Chemistry**. The study of matter can have different aspects, like preparation, composition, properties and many more. But the study of composition of matter is of prime importance because preparation and properties of a substance invariably depend on the composition of the matter. On the basis of composition, the matter can be classified into elements, compounds and mixtures. In nature, every substance has an inherent tendency to undergo transformation which may or may not be associated with the change in composition, and hence, properties.

Physical and Chemical Changes

The transformations which are associated with the change in the properties of the matter are considered as chemical changes in contrast to the physical changes in which the matter retains its identity. The innumerable chemical changes occurring in nature can conveniently be represented in the form of chemical equations. For the sake of convenience and universal application, the 118 elements discovered so far have been assigned unique symbols. The molecules formed by the combination of the various elements are represented by distinct formulae. The study of symbols, formulae and chemical equations comes under the purview of language of chemistry.

The transformation which involves a change in the structure or composition of a substance is called **chemical change**. The transformation which does not involve any change in molecular composition is known as a **physical change.**

Table 3.1 Comparative study of characteristics of physical and chemical changes

Physical change	Chemical change
No change in molecular composition takes place. Hence, no new substances are formed. *Example:* When water is cooled to 0°C, it changes to solid form, i.e., ice but no new product is formed in this process. $\underset{\text{(liquid } H_2O)}{\text{Water}} \xrightarrow{0^\circ C} \underset{\text{(solid } H_2O)}{\text{Ice}}$	Molecular composition changes. Hence, new substances are formed. *Example:* When calcium carbonate is heated, calcium oxide and carbon dioxide are formed. $CaCO_3 \rightarrow CaO + CO_2$
Physical change is temporary and easily reversible. *Example:* Water on cooling to 0°C is converted to ice. Hence, Ice on heating can be converted back to water. $\underset{\text{(Liquid)}}{\text{Water}} \underset{\text{heating}}{\overset{\text{cooling}}{\rightleftharpoons}} \underset{\text{(solid)}}{\text{Ice}}$	Chemical change is permanent and not easily reversible. *Example:* Sugar on heating is converted to carbon (black residue) and steam, but the sugar cannot be obtained by cooling the products. $\text{Sugar} \xrightarrow{\Delta} \text{Carbon} + \text{Steam}$
There is no net gain or loss of energy. *Example:* In the conversion of 5 g of water to water vapour some energy is absorbed, and the same amount is released in converting back to water. $\text{Water} \underset{\text{Energy released}}{\overset{\text{Energy absorbed}}{\rightleftharpoons}} \text{Water vapour}$	There is a gain or loss of energy in the form of heat, light or electricity, etc. *Example:* During the formation of ammonia from nitrogen and hydrogen, there is a loss of 22 kcal of energy.
Examples: (i) Conversion of water into steam (ii) Magnetization of an iron bar (iii) Liquefaction of any gas (iv) Melting of ice	*Examples:* (i) Rusting of iron (ii) Formation of curd from milk (iii) Burning of paper (iv) Blackening of silverware

Table 3.2 Processes involving both physical and chemical changes

Processes	Physical changes involved	Chemical changes
Heating of ammonium chloride	Ammonium chloride sublimes	Decomposition to ammonia and hydrogen chloride
Heating of sodium nitrate	Sodium nitrate melts	Decomposition to sodium nitrite and oxygen

Representation of Chemical Changes

Every chemical change can be conveniently represented in the form of a chemical equation. This is because describing a chemical change with the names of the substances becomes cumbersome. The elements and compounds are, therefore, given shorthand notations of symbols and formulae.

Symbols are the shorthand notations representing a single atom of an element and generally consist of a letter or combination of letters derived from the name of the element.

Konnect

In ancient times, alchemists, including some in India, represented chemical changes with symbols and illustrations. This was before the use of chemical equations.

Ions or Radicals

Atom is the smallest particle of matter which takes part in a chemical reaction. Atoms of most of the elements do not exist independently as they are less stable or unstable. They try to attain stability by losing or gaining or sharing electrons.

If an atom loses one or more electrons, it forms a **positive ion** or **cation**. The charge of the ion depends on the number of electrons lost by an atom to form the ion.

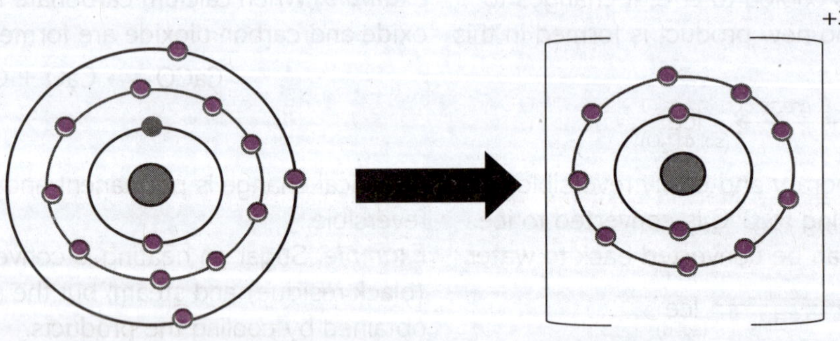

Aluminium atom

Aluminium ion (Al^{3+})

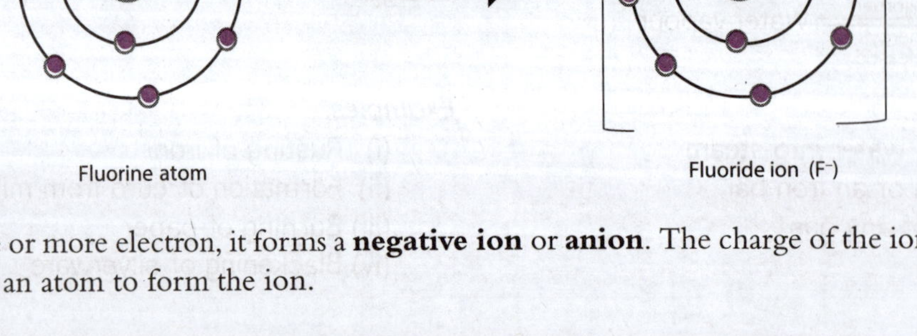

Fluorine atom

Fluoride ion (F^-)

If an atom gains one or more electron, it forms a **negative ion** or **anion**. The charge of the ion depends on the number of electrons gained by an atom to form the ion.

Sometimes, a group of atoms together lose or gain electrons to form an ion. Such ions are called **radicals** or **polyatomic ions**.

Examples: NH_4^+ ; SO_4^{2-}

An ion or radical is classified as monovalent, divalent, trivalent or tetravalent when the number of charges over it is 1, 2, 3 or 4, respectively. A list of ions and their charges is given below:

Table 3.3 Positive radicals

Radical	Nature
Sodium (Na^+)	Monovalent
Potassium (K^+)	Monovalent
Lithium (Li^+)	Monovalent
Ammonium (NH_4^+)	Monovalent
Hydrogen (H^+)	Monovalent
Barium (Ba^{2+})	Divalent
Calcium (Ca^{2+})	Divalent
Zinc (Zn^{2+})	Divalent
Magnesium (Mg^{2+})	Divalent
Nickel (Ni^{2+})	Divalent
Cobalt (Co^{2+})	Divalent
Aluminium (Al^{3+})	Trivalent
Chromium (Cr^{3+})	Trivalent

Some metallic elements show variable valency (more than one valency) and form positive ions with different charges. In that case, the ion with lower charge gets **'–ous'** suffix and the ion with higher charge gets **'–ic'** suffix or the value of charge of an ion is shown by Roman numerals (such as, I, II, III, IV, etc.) in parentheses which is followed by the name of the metal.

Table 3.4 Metallic elements with variable valency

Elements	Cations formed	Names
Copper	Cu^+	Cuprous or copper (I)
	Cu^{2+}	Cupric or copper (II)
Iron	Fe^{2+}	Ferrous or iron (II)
	Fe^{3+}	Ferric or iron (III)
Tin	Sn^{2+}	Stannous or stannum (II)
	Sn^{4+}	Stannic or stannum (IV)
Mercury	Hg^+	Mercurous or mercury (I)
	Hg^{2+}	Mercuric or mercury (II)
Lead	Pb^{2+}	Plumbous or lead (II)
	Pb^{4+}	Plumbic or lead (IV)

Table 3.5 Negative radicals

Radicals	Nature
Hydride (H^-)	Monovalent
Hydroxide (OH^-)	Monovalent
Bisulphite (HSO_3^-)	Monovalent
Bisulphate (HSO_4^-)	Monovalent
Fluoride (F^-)	Monovalent
Chloride (Cl^-)	Monovalent
Hypochlorite (ClO^-)	Monovalent
Chlorite (ClO_2^-)	Monovalent
Chlorate (ClO_3^-)	Monovalent
Perchlorate (ClO_4^-)	Monovalent
Bromide (Br^-)	Monovalent
Dihydrogen phosphate ($H_2PO_4^-$)	Monovalent
Nitrate (NO_3^-)	Monovalent
Nitrite (NO_2^-)	Monovalent
Iodide (I^-)	Monovalent
Oxide (O^{2-})	Divalent
Peroxide (O_2^{2-})	Divalent
Sulphide (S^{2-})	Divalent
Sulphite (SO_3^{2-})	Divalent
Sulphate (SO_4^{2-})	Divalent
Biphosphate (HPO_4^{2-})	Divalent
Phosphate (PO_4^{3-})	Trivalent
Phosphide (P^{3-})	Trivalent
Nitride (N^{3-})	Trivalent

Derivation of Formulae of Compounds

Chemical formulae of the compounds are derived by considering the number of charges on ions. Certain basic rules are followed for writing formulae of compounds as listed hereunder:

RULE 1. The positive radical or cation is written first and then it is followed by the negative radical or anion.

RULE 2. The molecule of any compound being electrically neutral, the total positive charge on the positive radical or cation should be equal to the total negative charge on the negative radical or anion.

Formation of few types of compounds are discussed below:

1. **To form a Compound Between A^+ and X^-:** To form a neutral compound with A^+ and X^-, the total number of positive charges should be equal to the total number of negative charges. As the number of charges on A and X is the same, one atom of A combines with one atom of X to form the neutral compound AX.

   Example: Compound with Na^+ and Cl^-.

   Molecular formula of the compound is NaCl.

2. **To form a Compound Between A^+ and X^{2-}:** To make a neutral compound by combining these two, two atoms of A compensate the two negative charges on X. The compound formed is of the kind A_2X.

   Example: Compound with H^+ and S^{2-}

   Molecular formula is H_2S.

3. **To form a Compound Between A^{2+} and X^{3-}:** One atom of A cannot compensate for all the negative charges of X. Two atoms of A have a total of +4 charges while X has only −3.Two atoms of X have a total of 6 charges which are to be compensated by 3 atoms of A. The compound formed is A_3X_2.

   Examples:

$$Al^{3+}SO_4^{2-} \longrightarrow Al_2(SO_4)_3$$

$$Si^{4+}O^{2-} \longrightarrow SiO_2$$

$$Ca^{2+}CO_3^{2-} \longrightarrow CaCO_3$$

The above methods for writing formulae of a compound can be simplified with the help of criss-cross method.

Criss-cross Method

Step I

The symbol of the cation or positive radical is written on the left side and the symbol of the anion or negative radical on the right side.

Examples:

1. HS   2. CaF

Step II

The number of charges on the ion or radical is indicated.

Examples:

1. H^+S^{2-} 2. $Ca^{2+}F^-$

Step III

The value of the charge on the ion or radical is interchanged and shifted to the lower right side of the ion or radical (the values of the charges are criss-crossed).

Examples:

1. $H^+S^{2-} \longrightarrow H_2S$ 2. $Ca^{2+}F^- \longrightarrow CaF_2$

If the charge on any one ion or radical or both the ions and radicals is 1, then no number is required to be written after they are interchanged and shifted to the lower right side.

Examples:

1. $K^+Cl^- \longrightarrow KCl$ 2. $NH_4^+Cl^- \longrightarrow NH_4Cl$

In case the charge on both the ions or radicals is the same, no number is needed to be written.

Examples:

1. $Fe^{2+}\ O^{2-} \longrightarrow FeO\downarrow$

2. $Al^{3+}\ N^{3-} \longrightarrow AlN\downarrow$

> ***Info Bytes!***
>
> The criss-cross method, which is used to determine the formula of a compound, is akin to a dance where two partners (ions) come together in perfect harmony.

If one of the combining species or both the combining species are polyatomic, then the radical(s) is/are written within parentheses in case the number of radical(s) present in one molecule of the compound is more than 1.

Examples:

1. $Ca^{2+}NO_3^- \longrightarrow Ca(NO_3)_2$
2. $NH_4^+SO_4^{2-} \longrightarrow (NH_4)_2SO_4$

In case the charge of both the ions or radicals has some highest common factor (greater than 1), then both these numbers have to be divided by the highest common factor and the value of the quotient is used.

Examples:

1. $Si^{4+}O^{2-} \longrightarrow SiO_2$
2. $Mn^{4+}O^{2-} \longrightarrow MnO_2$

Naming of Binary Compounds

The compounds that are formed by the combination of two elements are called **binary compounds**.

In naming of the binary compounds, the electropositive atom (generally metal) is specified first by giving its ordinary English name. The name of the second element which is generally a non-metal is obtained by adding the suffix **'–ide'** to its name.

Examples:

$MgCl_2$	Magnesium chloride
$CaCl_2$	Calcium chloride
BaO	Barium oxide
H_2S	Hydrogen sulphide

In case of metals showing **variable valency**, it is necessary to specify which of the positive ions are present.

Examples:

FeO	Ferrous oxide or iron (II) oxide
Fe_2O_3	Ferric oxide or iron (III) oxide
$CuCl$	Cuprous chloride or copper (I) chloride
$CuCl_2$	Cupric chloride or copper (II) chloride

Info Bytes!

The name 'oxygen' means 'acid-producer'? It was incorrectly believed that oxygen was a necessary component for acids.

For binary covalent compounds, generally formed by two **non-metallic elements**, it is required to specify the number of atoms of **more electronegative element** with the help of a meaningful **prefix**.

Table 3.6 Prefixes on the basis of number of atoms

Number of atoms	Prefix
One	Mono
Two	Di
Three	Tri
Four	Tetra
Five	Penta
Six	Hexa
Seven	Hepta
Eight	Octa
Nine	Nona
Ten	Deca

The less electronegative element is specified first, followed by the more electronegative element.

The prefix is generally added to the more electronegative element to specify its number of atoms.

SO_2	Sulphur dioxide
N_2O_5	Dinitrogen pentoxide
SF_6	Sulphur hexafluoride
PCl_3	Phosphorus trichloride
CO	Carbon monoxide

Naming of Acids, Bases and Salts

1. **Binary Acids**: Binary acids are named as hydro……..ic acid.
   The blank should be filled by the name of the corresponding non-metal.

   Examples:

HCl	Hydrochloric acid
HBr	Hydrobromic acid

2. **Oxyacids**: Oxyacids are named without mentioning hydrogen. Often an element (non-metal) is able to form more than one oxyacid. In naming such acids, the one with the greater number of oxygen atom is given the suffix '**−ic**' and the one with the lesser number of oxygen atoms is given the suffix '**−ous**.'

   Examples:

HNO_2	Nitrous acid	HNO_3	Nitric acid
H_2SO_4	Sulphuric acid	H_2SO_3	Sulphurous acid

   When a non-metal forms more than two oxyacids, the prefix '**hypo−**' is used for the acids containing lesser number of oxygen than '**−ous**' acids and '**per−**' is used for acids containing more oxygen atoms than '**−ic**' acids.

   Examples:

HClO	Hypochlorous acid	$HClO_3$	Chloric acid
$HClO_2$	Chlorous acid	$HClO_4$	Perchloric acid

3. **Bases**: For naming bases, the name of the metal (or positive radical) is specified first and then hydroxide due to the presence of hydroxyl radical.

   Examples:

KOH	Potassium hydroxide	$Fe(OH)_3$	Iron (III) hydroxide
$Ca(OH)_2$	Calcium hydroxide	NH_4OH	Ammonium hydroxide
$Fe(OH)_2$	Iron (II) hydroxide		

4. **Salts:**

   - **Salts of binary acids** are written with '**−ide**' suffix, i.e., the name of the metallic radical (or positive radical) is written first and it is then followed by the name of the negative radical.

     Examples:

NaCl	Sodium chloride	$MgBr_2$	Magnesium bromide
K_2S	Potassium sulphide	CaF_2	Calcium fluoride

   - **Salts of oxyacids** are derived from their corresponding oxyacids. The salts which are generated from the oxyacids with '**−ous**' suffix are given the suffix '**−ite**' and those from '**−ic**' suffix are given the suffix '**−ate**.'

Examples:

$ZnSO_3$	Zinc sulphite	$NaOCl$	Sodium hypochlorite
$FeSO_4$	Iron (II) sulphate	$Ca(OCl)_2$	Calcium chlorite
$NaNO_2$	Sodium nitrite	$KClO_3$	Potassium chlorate
$Cu(NO_3)_2$	Copper (II) nitrate	$KClO_4$	Potassium perchlorate

Atomic Weight or Atomic Mass

An individual atom is very small, negligible in weight and cannot be weighed directly. Hence, the mass of the atom is calculated indirectly by comparing its mass with that of hydrogen atom which is taken as the standard atomic mass. Later one-twelfth mass of ${}^{12}_{6}C$ isotope is considered to be the standard for comparing atomic masses of other elements.

The **relative atomic mass** is defined as the number that represents how many times an atom of an element is heavier than one-twelfth of the mass of ${}^{12}_{6}C$ atom.

Table 3.7 Atomic weights of some common elements

Elements	Atomic mass (amu)	Elements	Atomic mass (amu)
Hydrogen	1	Chlorine	35.5
Lithium	7	Potassium	39
Lithium	11	Calcium	40
Carbon	12	Chromium	52
Nitrogen	14	Manganese	55
Oxygen	16	Iron	56
Fluorine	19	Copper	63.5
Sodium	23	Zinc	65.5
Magnesium	24	Bromine	80
Aluminium	27	Silver	108
Phosphorous	31	Tin	119
Sulphur	32	Iodine	127

One-twevlth of the mass of a ${}^{12}_{6}C$ atom is called **atomic mass unit** or **unified mass** abbreviated as amu or *u* respectively. Hence, atomic weights of the elements are expressed in amu.

Example: Atomic weight of oxygen is 16 amu.

The relative atomic mass or atomic weight of an element expressed in grams is called **gram atomic mass** or **gram atom**.

Example: As the atomic weight of oxygen is 16 amu, gram atomic mass of oxygen is 16 g.

Molecular Weight

Molecular weight is calculated by adding the atomic weights of all the constituent atoms.

Examples:

1. Molecular weight of $NaHCO_3$
   The atomic weight of Na = 23 amu
   H = 1 amu
   C = 12 amu
   O = 16 amu
   Therefore, the molecular weight of $NaHCO_3 = 23 + 1 + 12 + (16 \times 3) = 84$ amu
2. Molecular weight of $Ca(OH)_2$
   The atomic weight of Ca = 40 amu
   O = 16 amu
   H = 1 amu
   Therefore, the molecular weight of $Ca(OH)_2 = 40 + (16 \times 2) + (1 \times 2) = 74$ amu

The molecular weight expressed in grams is called **gram molecular weight** or **gram molecular mass.**

Example: Molecular weights of O_2 and H_2O are 32 amu and 18 amu, respectively. Hence, gram molecular weights of O_2 and H_2O are 32 g and 18 g, respectively.

EXAMPLE 3.1

Calculate the total negative charge present on the negative radicals in the following compounds:

(a) Aluminium chloride (b) Potassium sulphate
(c) Barium oxide (d) Lithium carbonate

SOLUTION

(a) Aluminium chloride $\rightarrow Al^{3+}\ Cl^- \Rightarrow AlCl_3$
   ∴ Total negative charge is −3.
(b) Potassium sulphate $\rightarrow K^+\ SO_4^{2-} \Rightarrow K_2SO_4$
   ∴ Total negative charge is −2.
(c) Barium oxide $\rightarrow Ba^{2+}\ O^{2-} \Rightarrow BaO$
   ∴ Total negative charge is −2.
(d) Lithium carbonate $\rightarrow Li^+\ CO_3^{2-} \Rightarrow Li_2CO_3$
   ∴ Total negative charge is −2.

EXAMPLE 3.2

An oxyacid contains two hydrogen atoms, one sulphur atom, and four oxygen atoms.

(a) Name the acid.
(b) Name the different salts that can be formed by the acid on reaction with potassium hydroxide.
(c) Calculate the molecular masses of the above salts.

SOLUTION

(a) The acid is sulphuric acid (H_3SO_4).
(b) $KHSO_4$ → Potassium hydrogen sulphate (or Potassium bisulphate)
   K_2SO_4 → Potassium sulphate
(c) Molecular mass of $KHSO_4 = 39 + 1 + 32 + 64 = 136$
   Molecular mass of $K_2SO_4 = 78 + 32 + 64 = 174$.

EXAMPLE 3.3 The valency of a non-metal 'N' is 3 and its gram atomic mass is 14 g. Calculate the gram molecular masses of its:

(a) nitride (b) oxide (c) phosphide

SOLUTION

The valency of non-metal N is 3 and the gram atomic mass is 14 g.

(a) Formula of nitride of non-metal is N^{3-} ⇒ Gram Molecular mass = 3 × 14 = 42 g

(b) Formula of non-metal oxide is NO_2 ⇒ Gram Molecular mass = 14 + 3 × 16 = 62 g

(c) Formula of non-metal phosphide is NP ⇒ Gram Molecular mass = 14 + 31 = 45 g.

EXAMPLE 3.4

(a) In an acid-base neutralization reaction, the salt produced contains one metal atom (M), two nitrogen atoms and four oxygen atoms. Give the formulae of the acid and the base.

(c) A molecule of a binary salt contains two metal atoms and one sulphur atom. Determine the number of metal atoms present in one molecule of the binary salt formed by that metal and nitrogen? Give reasons in support of your answer.

SOLUTION

(a) The salt produced from the acid-base neutralization reaction is $M(NO_2)_2$

Thus, the valency of metal is 2 as valency of NO^-_2 radical is 1.

The acid used for the formation of this salt is HNO_2 and the base is $M(OH)_2$.

$M(OH)_2 + 2HNO_2 \longrightarrow M(NO_2)_2 + 2H_2O$

(b) A molecule of a binary salt contains two metal atoms and one sulphur atom. Hence, the formula of the salt is M_2S and valency of the metal is 1. Valency of nitride is 3. According to criss-cross method, the formula of binary salt containing metal and nitrogen is M_3N. The number of metal atoms present in one molecule of the binary salt formed is 3.

Chemical Equations

By using various symbols and formulae, it is possible to present a chemical change by means of a chemical equation.

The substances (elements, compounds or both) which take part in the chemical change are called **reactants**.

The new substances (elements, compounds or both) which are formed from the reactants during the reaction are called **products**.

The reactants are written on the left-hand side and the products on the right-hand side of the arrow.

Examples:

$$2NaOH + H_2SO_4 \longrightarrow Na_2SO_4 + 2H_2O$$

$$2KClO_3 \longrightarrow 2KCl + 3O_2$$

All the chemical reactions are bound by certain laws, which are called **laws of chemical combination**.

Laws of Chemical Combination

Law of Conservation of Mass

This states that mass can neither be created nor destroyed. This law is found applicable to all chemical reactions. This means that during a chemical reaction, no change in the mass of the substances takes place. The total mass of the reactants is always equal to the total mass of the products.

Example:

$$Na_2SO_3 + CuCl_2 \longrightarrow 2NaCl + CuSO_3$$

$$\text{Mol. wt of } Na_2SO_3 = 126 \text{ g Mol. wt of } NaCl = 58.5 \text{ g}$$

$$\text{Mol. wt of } CuCl_2 = 134.5 \text{ g} \quad \text{Mol. wt of } CuSO_3 = 143.5 \text{ g}$$

$$\text{Total mass of reactants} = 260.5 \text{ g}$$

$$\text{Total mass of products} = 117 + 143.5 = 260.5 \text{ g}$$

Law of Definite Proportions

When two or more elements combine to form a compound, they combine in a fixed ratio of their weights irrespective of the method of preparation.

Example:

Carbon dioxide can be obtained by three processes as listed hereunder:

(a) By the decomposition of metallic carbonates.

(b) By burning carbon.

(c) By the reaction of metallic carbonates with acids.

When the three samples of CO_2 produced by the three different methods are analysed, the ratio by weight of carbon and oxygen has been found to be the same, i.e., 12 : 32 or 3 : 8.

Law of Multiple Proportions

When two elements combine in different ratios to give more than one type of a product, the ratio of the masses of the element that combines with a fixed weight of the other element always bears a simple integral ratio.

Example: Nitrogen and oxygen combine, and form compounds, such as, N_2O, NO, NO_2, etc.

N_2O: 28 g of nitrogen combines with 16 g of oxygen

Therefore, 14 g of nitrogen combines with 8 g of oxygen

NO: 14 g of nitrogen combines with 16 g of oxygen

NO_2: 14 g of nitrogen combines with 32 g of oxygen

If we analyse the ratio of oxygen that is combining with fixed mass of nitrogen in all the three compounds, it bears a simple integral ratio, i.e., 1 : 2 : 4.

Konnect

A quantitative relationship exists between the reactants and products in a chemical reaction. If specific amount of reactants are taken, then definite quantity of products are formed. Hence, It Is required to balance all the chemical equations with respect to the number of atoms of various elements involved in the equation.

Balanced Chemical Equation

A **balanced chemical equation** is the one in which the number of atoms of each element of the reactants which are there on the left-hand side of the reaction is equal to that of atoms of each element of the products present on the right-hand side of the reaction.

The number of molecules of the reactants and that of the products is written as coefficients.

Examples:

$$2NaOH + H_2SO_4 \longrightarrow Na_2SO_4 + 2H_2O$$

$$2KClO_3 \longrightarrow 2KCl + 3O_2$$

Balancing a Chemical Equation (Trial and Error Method)

Steps involved in the balancing of a chemical equation:

(i) The chemical change is written in words.

(ii) The words are replaced by formulae and symbols and the chemical equation obtained is known as skeletal equation.

(iii) Frequency of number of times (that is number of places at which an element appears on the reactant side and the product side of the equation) is counted and is known as f-number.

(iv) The element which appears the least number of times is balanced first.

(v) The other elements are balanced in the increasing order of their frequency.

(vi) In case two or more elements have the same frequency, the metallic element is balanced first in preference to the non-metallic element.

(vii) In case two or more elements have the same frequency and they are metallic, they are balanced in the increasing order of atomic mass.

Example 1:
Skeleton equation: $KI + H_2SO_4 + MnO_2 \rightarrow KHSO_4 + MnSO_4 + H_2O + I_2$

Element	K	I	H	S	O	Mn
f-number	2	2	3	3	5	2

Step 1: Balancing iodine

$2KI + H_2SO_4 + MnO_2 \rightarrow KHSO_4 + MnSO_4 + H_2O + I_2$

Step 2: Balancing potassium

$2KI + H_2SO_4 + MnO_2 \rightarrow 2KHSO_4 + MnSO_4 + H_2O + I_2$

Step 3: Balancing sulphur

$2KI + 3H_2SO_4 + MnO_2 \rightarrow 2KHSO_4 + MnSO_4 + H_2O + I_2$

Step 4: Balancing oxygen and hydrogen

$2KI + 3H_2SO_4 + MnO_2 \rightarrow 2KHSO_4 + MnSO_4 + 2H_2O + I_2$

The steps of Trial and Error method are discussed below by taking some examples.

Example 2:

Skeleton equation:

$Fe_2O_3 + C \longrightarrow Fe + CO$

Process of balancing:

$Fe_2O_3 + C \longrightarrow 2Fe + CO$

$Fe_2O_3 + C \longrightarrow 2Fe + 3CO$

$Fe_2O_3 + 3C \longrightarrow 2Fe + 3CO$

Balanced equation:

$Fe_2O_3 + 3C \longrightarrow 2Fe + 3CO$

Example 3:

Skeleton equation:

$HNO_3 + S \longrightarrow H_2SO_4 + NO_2 + H_2O$

Process of balancing:

$4HNO_3 + S \longrightarrow H_2SO_4 + NO_2 + H_2O$

$4HNO_3 + S \longrightarrow H_2SO_4 + 4NO_2 + H_2O$

$6HNO_3 + S \longrightarrow H_2SO_4 + 6NO_2 + 2H_2O$

Balanced equation:

$6HNO_3 + S \longrightarrow H_2SO_4 + 6NO_2 + 2H_2O$

Example 4:

Skeleton equation:

$K_2Cr_2O_7 + HCl \longrightarrow KCl + CrCl_3 + H_2O + Cl_2$

Process of balancing:

$K_2Cr_2O_7 + HCl \longrightarrow 2KCl + 2CrCl_3 + H_2O + Cl_2$

$K_2Cr_2O_7 + 2HCl \longrightarrow 2KCl + 2CrCl_3 + H_2O + Cl_2$

$K_2Cr_2O_7 + 14HCl \longrightarrow 2KCl + 2CrCl_3 + 7H_2O + Cl_2$

Balanced equation:

$K_2Cr_2O_7 + 14HCl \longrightarrow 2KCl + 2CrCl_3 + 7H_2O + 3Cl_2$

EXAMPLE 3.5 Two oxides of a metal contain 25.8% and 41.02% of oxygen by weight, respectively. Find the ratio of weights of metal combining with fixed weight of oxygen.

SOLUTION

Assume that the weight of each oxide is 100 g.

	Weight of metal	Weight of oxygen
Oxide - I	74.2	25.8
Oxide - II	58.98	41.02

25.8 g of oxygen reacts with 74.2 g of metal.

1 g of oxygen reacts with $= \dfrac{1 \times 74.2}{25.8} = 2.87$ g of metal

41.02 g of oxygen reacts with 58.98 g of metal.

1 g of oxygen reacts with $= \dfrac{1 \times 58.98}{41.02} = 1.437$ g of metal

$\therefore$ The ratio of weight of the metal in the two oxides is 2.87 : 1.437 = 2 : 1 (approx)

EXAMPLE 3.6

For each of the following reactions identify the products formed and balance the reaction.

(a) $BaCl_2 + Na_2SO_4 \longrightarrow$ (b) $2CuS + 3O_2 \longrightarrow$

(c) $Na + H_2O \longrightarrow$ (d) $2KI + Cl_2 \longrightarrow$

SOLUTION

(a) $BaCl_2 + Na_2SO_4 \longrightarrow BaSO_4 + 2NaCl$

(b) $2CuS + 3O_2 \longrightarrow 2CuO + 2\,SO_2$

(c) $2Na + 2H_2O \longrightarrow 2NaOH + H_2$

(d) $2KI + Cl_2 \longrightarrow 2KCl + I_2$

Writing a balanced chemical equation does not necessarily imply that the reaction takes place inevitably at all conditions. For every chemical reaction to take place, certain specific conditions are required.

Conditions Required for A Chemical Reaction

1. **Physical Contact:** Chemical reaction takes place only when the reactants are brought in contact with each other.
Example:

$$CaO + H_2O \longrightarrow Ca(OH)_2$$

Calcium hydroxide is formed only when calcium oxide comes in contact with water.

2. **Solution:** Some chemical reactions take place only when the reactants are taken in the form of solutions.

Example: There is no reaction between silver nitrate and sodium chloride when they are in solid state. Reaction takes place only when they are dissolved in water.

$$AgNO_3 + NaCl \longrightarrow AgCl + NaNO_3$$

3. **Heat:** A large number of chemical reactions take place by the absorption of heat. These are called **thermochemical reactions**. The chemical reactions accompanied by the net absorption of heat are called endothermic reactions and those with the release of heat are said to be exothermic reactions.
Example:

$$2KClO_3 \xrightarrow{\Delta} 2KCl + 3O_2$$

$$Fe + S \xrightarrow{\Delta} FeS$$

On simple mixing of iron fillings and sulphur, no reaction takes place; they combine and form iron sulphide only on heating.

4. **Light:** There are certain reactions which take place only in the presence of light. These are called **photochemical reactions**.
Example: Photosynthesis

$$6CO_2(g) + 6H_2O(l) \xrightarrow{\text{sunlight}} C_6H_{12}O_6(s) + 6O_2(g)$$

Photosynthesis does not take place in the absence of light.

5. **Electricity:** Some reactions take place only by the passage of electric current. These are called **electrochemical reactions**.
Example:

(a) Decomposition of water into hydrogen and oxygen:

$$2H_2O \xrightarrow{\text{Electric current}} 2H_2 + O_2$$

(b) Decomposition of molten Al_2O_3 into aluminium and oxygen:

$$2Al_2O_3 \xrightarrow{\text{Electric current}} 4Al + 3O_2$$

6. **Sound:** Certain reactions take place by the absorption of sound energy.

Example:

Decomposition of acetylene into carbon and hydrogen:

$$C_2H_2 \xrightarrow{\text{Sound energy}} 2C + H_2$$

7. **Pressure:** Certain chemical reactions take place only when pressure is applied.

Example:

Formation of ammonia from nitrogen and hydrogen takes place at high pressure:

$$N_2 + 3H_2 \xrightarrow{\text{pressure}} 2NH_3$$

8. **Catalyst:** A chemical substance which alters the rate of reaction without undergoing any net change in its chemical composition at the end of the chemical reaction is called **catalyst.**

The rates of some chemical reactions are influenced by the catalysts and such reactions are called **catalytic reactions.**

- **Positive Catalyst:** The catalyst which accelerates the rate of a reaction is called **positive catalyst.**

Example: The rate of decomposition of $KClO_3$ is more in the presence of MnO_2:

$$2KClO_3 \xrightarrow{MnO_2} 2KCl + 3O_2$$

- **Negative Catalyst or Inhibitor:** The catalyst which retards the rate of reaction is called **negative catalyst.**

Example: The rate of decomposition of hydrogen peroxide decreases in the presence of alcohol or ether:

$$2H_2O_2(l) \xrightarrow[\text{(or) ether}]{\text{Alcohol}} 2H_2O(l) + O_2(g)$$

Since the number of chemical reactions is large, the study of these reactions can be made easier by classifying them. All the chemical reactions are classified into four broad categories depending on the way the product is formed.

Limitations of Chemical Equations

A chemical equation can be equipped with different information like the physical state of the reactants and the products, conditions required for the reaction to take place, change in energy during the occurrence of the reaction. But certain information regarding a chemical reaction cannot be reflected in the chemical equation.

1. A chemical equation does not reflect the rate of the chemical reaction or the time taken for the chemical reaction to occur.
2. If the reactants or the products are in gaseous state or in aqueous solution state, the chemical equation does not represent the actual concentration of them.
3. The chemical equation does not reflect the nature of the reaction that is the chemical reaction is spontaneous, explosive etc.

Classification of Chemical Reactions

All chemical reactions can be broadly classified into four types depending upon the nature of the reaction.

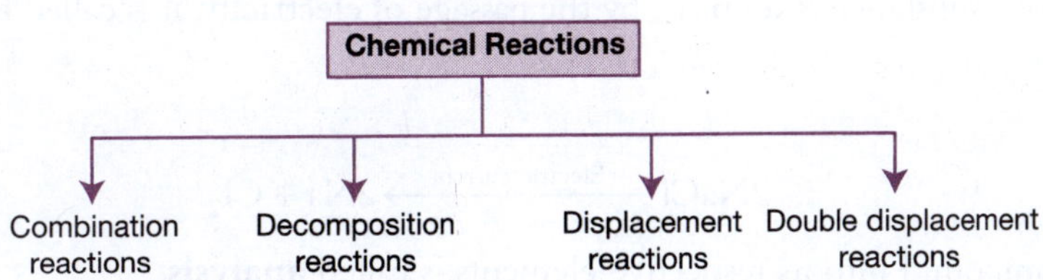

Figure 3.1 Classification of reactions based on nature

Combination Reaction

A chemical reaction in which two or more substances combine to form a single new substance is called **combination reaction.**

Representation: $A + B \longrightarrow AB$

Types of Combination Reaction

(a) Element–element combination reaction.

$$H_2 + Cl_2 \longrightarrow 2HCl$$

(b) Element–compound combination reaction.

$$2CO + O_2 \longrightarrow 2CO_2$$

$$2NO + O_2 \longrightarrow 2NO_2$$

(c) Compound–compound combination reaction.

$$CaO + CO_2 \longrightarrow CaCO_3$$

Info Bytes!

The formation of a compound from its constituent elements is called synthesis.

Decomposition Reaction

The reaction in which a single compound splits into two or more simpler substances is known as **decomposition reaction.**

Representation: $AB \longrightarrow A + B$

Examples:

(a) $2Pb(NO_3)_2 \longrightarrow 2PbO + 4NO_2 + O_2$

(b) $2Al_2O_3 \longrightarrow 4Al + 3O_2$

Types of Decomposition Reaction

- If the decomposition of a substance takes place by the absorption of heat, it is called **thermal decomposition.**

Examples:

$$CaCO_3 \xrightarrow{\Delta} CaO + CO_2$$

$$2HgO \xrightarrow{\Delta} 2Hg + O_2$$

- If the decomposition of a substance takes place in the presence of light, it is called **photolytic decomposition (photolysis).**

Example:

$$2HOCl \xrightarrow{\text{Sunlight}} 2HCl + O_2$$

- If the decomposition of a substance takes place by the passage of electricity, it is called **electrolytic decomposition (electrolysis).**

Example:

$$2NaCl \xrightarrow{\text{Electric current}} 2Na + Cl_2$$

Decomposition of the compound into its respective elements is called **analysis.**

Displacement Reaction

In a displacement reaction, the more reactive element displaces the less reactive element from its compound.

Since the displacement reaction depends on the relative reactivities of various metals, they are arranged in the decreasing order of reactivity.

Representation:

$$AB + C \longrightarrow CB + A$$
$$2XY + Z \longrightarrow 2XZ + Y$$

The ability of an element to displace another element is known by its relative position in the reactivity series.

Metal Reactivity Series

The arrangement of metals along with hydrogen in the decreasing order of reactivity is called **metal reactivity series.**

Table 3.8 Metal reactivity series

Potassium	K	(most reactive metal)
Sodium	Na	
Calcium	Ca	
Magnesium	Mg	
Aluminium	Al	
Zinc	Zn	Reactivity decreases
Iron	Fe	
Nickel	Ni	
Tin	Sn	
Lead	Pb	
Hydrogen	H	
Copper	Cu	
Mercury	Hg	
Silver	Ag	
Gold	Au	
Platinum	Pt	↓ (least reactive metal)

The more reactive metal displaces the less reactive metal from its compound.

Example:

$$Fe + \underset{\text{(copper sulphate)}}{CuSO_4} \longrightarrow \underset{\text{(ferrous sulphate)}}{FeSO_4} + Cu$$

As iron is more reactive than copper, it displaces copper from copper sulphate solution, thereby forming ferrous sulphate.

Halogen Reactivity Series

Non-metals do not show such regular trend in reactivity like metals. But halogens show such gradation in reactivity from fluorine to iodine. This is known as **halogen reactivity series.**

	Reactivity ↓
F_2	(Most reactive halogen)
Cl_2	
Br_2	
I_2	(Least reactive halogen)

The more reactive halogen displaces the less reactive halogen from its compound.

Example:

$$2NaBr + Cl_2 \longrightarrow 2NaCl + Br_2$$

Chlorine is more reactive than bromine, hence, it displaces bromine from sodium bromide and a reddish brown bromine gas is formed.

Double Decomposition or Double Displacement Reaction

The chemical reaction in which two reactants (compounds) combine to form two new substances by exchanging their radicals is called **double decomposition**.

Representation: $AB + CD \longrightarrow AD + CB$

Examples:

$$2NaNO_3 + CuSO_4 \longrightarrow Na_2SO_4 + Cu(NO_3)_2$$

$$NaOH + HCl \longrightarrow NaCl + H_2O$$

$$K_2SO_4 + Cu(NO_3)_2 \longrightarrow 2KNO_3 + CuSO_4$$

Few of the following are various reactions that involve double decomposition reaction:

- If the reaction takes place between an acid and a base, it is called **neutralization reaction**. Salt and water are formed in this reaction.

Examples:

$$NaOH + HCl \longrightarrow NaCl + H_2O$$

$$2NH_4OH + H_2SO_4 \longrightarrow (NH_4)_2SO_4 + 2H_2O$$

- In a double decomposition reaction, if one of the products gets precipitated, the reaction can be called **precipitation reaction.**

Examples:

$$KCl + AgNO_3 \longrightarrow KNO_3 + AgCl \downarrow$$

$$BaCl_2 + Na_2SO_4 \longrightarrow 2NaCl + BaSO_4 \downarrow$$

All the chemical reactions that take place fall under any one of the above categories.

In addition to the above categories, some chemical reactions are categorized as redox reactions as they involve oxidation and reduction reactions.

Oxidation

Oxidation is defined as addition of oxygen or electronegative element or removal of hydrogen or electropositive element from a compound.

Examples:

$Mg + O_2 \rightarrow MgO$	Addition of oxygen to Mg	$HgO \rightarrow Hg + O_2$	Removal of oxygen from HgO
$Mg + Cl_2 \rightarrow MgCl_2$	Addition of chlorine to Mg	$HI \rightarrow H_2 + I_2$	Removal of hydrogen from HI

Reduction

Reduction is defined as the addition of hydrogen or electropositive element or removal of oxygen or electronegative element from a compound.

Examples:

$H_2 + Cl_2 \rightarrow HCl$	Addition of hydrogen to chlorine	$PCl_5 \rightarrow PCl_3 + Cl_2$	Removal of chlorine from PCl_5
$Na + Cl_2 \rightarrow NaCl$	Addition of sodium to chlorine	$H_2O_2 \rightarrow H_2O + O_2$	Removal of oxygen from H_2O_2

Redox Reaction

Oxidation and reduction are simultaneous processes taking place in a reaction. That is why those reactions are called **redox reactions**. In a redox reaction, one substance undergoes oxidation and the other substance undergoes reduction.

The substance which undergoes oxidation by itself is called **reducing agent** and the substance which undergoes reduction by itself is called an **oxidizing agent**.

Example:

$$H_2S + Cl_2 \longrightarrow 2HCl + S$$

H_2S loses hydrogen, and hence, is said to undergo oxidation. Hydrogen is added to chlorine, and hence, chlorine is said to undergo reduction. Therefore, H_2S is called reducing agent and chlorine an oxidizing agent.

Example:

$$2HgCl_2 + SnCl_2 \longrightarrow Hg_2Cl_2 + SnCl_4$$

A more electropositive element, mercury, is added to $HgCl_2$. It is, therefore, said to be reduced. A more electronegative element (chlorine) is added to $SnCl_2$. It is, therefore, said to be oxidized. $HgCl_2$ acts as the oxidizing agent and $SnCl_2$ acts as the reducing agent.

Chemical reactions can also be classified on the basis of energy changes associated with the reactions.

Exothermic Reactions

A chemical reaction associated with evolution of heat energy is called an **exothermic reaction**.

Representation:

Reactants $\longrightarrow$ Products + Q kcal

(or)

Reactants – Q kcal $\longrightarrow$ Products

Q = heat energy released

Example:

$$C + O \longrightarrow CO_2 + 94 \text{ kcal}$$

$$C + O_2 - 94 \text{ kcal} \longrightarrow CO_2$$

For the formation of CO_2 from carbon and oxygen, the bonds between oxygen atoms in oxygen molecules should be broken. For the breaking of this bond, some amount of energy is absorbed. At the same time, some amount of energy is released during the formation of new bonds between carbon and oxygen.

If energy released is more than the energy required during the reaction, the difference in energy is released as heat energy.

Endothermic Reactions

A chemical reaction which proceeds with the absorption of heat energy is called an **endothermic reaction**.

Representation:

Reactants + Q kcal $\longrightarrow$ Products

(or)

Reactants $\longrightarrow$ Products – Q kcal

Q = heat energy absorbed

Example:

$$N_2 + O_2 \longrightarrow 2NO - 44 \text{ kcal}$$

$$N_2 + O_2 + 44 \text{ kcal} \longrightarrow 2NO$$

$$C + 2S + 22 \text{ kcal} \longrightarrow CS_2$$

For the formation of nitric oxide from nitrogen and oxygen, some amount of energy is required to break the bonds between nitrogen and oxygen atoms present in the respective molecules. Some amount of energy is released during the formation of bonds between nitrogen and oxygen. In this case, the energy absorbed is more than the energy released. Hence, the difference in energy is absorbed as heat energy during the reaction.

EXAMPLE 3.7 Nitric acid turns yellow on long standing. Explain.

SOLUTION

On long standing, HNO_3 undergoes photolytic decomposition and gives NO_2 which is a brown coloured gas. Hence, HNO_3 appears yellow.

$$4HNO_3 \xrightarrow{hv} 4NO_2 + 2H_2O + O_2$$

EXAMPLE 3.8 Silverware tarnishes on exposure to polluted atmosphere. Give reason.

SOLUTION

Silverware tarnishes in the polluted atmosphere because of the presence of H_2S gas. Silver reacts with H_2S present in atmosphere to form silver sulphide which is black in colour.

$$4Ag + 2H_2S + O_2 \longrightarrow 2Ag_2S + 2H_2O$$

EXAMPLE 3.9 The complete combustion of a hydrocarbon gives CO_2 and H_2O. In the balanced chemical equation, the coefficients of CO_2 and H_2O are 3 and 4, respectively. Find out the formula of the hydrocarbon.

SOLUTION

Hydrocarbons on complete combustion give CO_2 and H_2O. Coefficients of CO_2 and H_2O are 3 and 4, respectively. The hydrocarbon must contain 3 carbon atoms and eight hydrogen atoms as the hydrocarbon is composed of carbon and hydrogen. Thus, the formula of hydrocarbon must be C_3H_8.

Balanced equation is $C_3H_8 + 5O_2 \longrightarrow 3CO_2 + 4H_2O$

EXAMPLE 3.10 In the welding of railway tracks, a proper proportion of aluminium powder and iron (III) oxide is made to react with each other at high temperature. Explain the type of reaction involved and also identify the reducing and the oxidizing agents.

SOLUTION

At high temperature aluminium reacts with iron (III) oxide.

$$2Al + Fe_2O_3 \longrightarrow Al_2O_3 + 2Fe + Heat$$

It is a displacement and exothermic reaction.

Al acts as reducing agent as it undergoes oxidation while Fe_2O_3 acts as oxidizing agent as it undergoes reduction.

EXAMPLE 3.11 Mercury loses its lusture and sticks to the walls of the glass in the presence of ozone. Write the reasons and the possible reaction for this change.

SOLUTION

When ozone is passed through mercury, the mercury loses its lusture and sticks to the glass tube. This is called **tailing of mercury** and is due to the formation of mercurous oxide.

$$2Hg + O_3 \longrightarrow Hg_2O + O_2$$

POINTS TO REMEMBER

- The transformation which involves a change in the structure or composition of a substance is called chemical change.
- Ions formed by the loss of electron(s) are positively charged and are called cations or positive radicals and the ions formed by the gain of electron(s) are negatively charged and are known as anions or negative radicals.
- Chemical formulae of the compounds are derived by considering the number of charges on ions.
- The compounds that are formed by the combination of two elements are called binary compounds.
- Oxyacids are named without mentioning hydrogen.
- The relative atomic mass is defined as the number that represents how many times an atom of an element is heavier than one-twelfth of the mass of $_{12}^{6}C$ atom.
- One-twelfth of the mass of a $_{12}^{6}C$ atom is called atomic mass unit, abbreviated as amu.
- The relative atomic mass or atomic weight of an element expressed in grams is called gram atomic weight or gram atom.
- Molecular weight is calculated by adding the atomic weights of all the constituent atoms.
- The molecular weight expressed in grams is called gram molecular weight.
- The substances (elements, compounds or both) which take part in the chemical change are called reactants.
- The new substances (elements, compounds or both) which are formed from the reactants during the reaction are called products.
- All the chemical reactions are bound by certain laws, which are called laws of chemical combination.
- Law of Conservation of Mass states that mass can neither be created nor destroyed.
- Law of Definite Proportions states that when two or more elements combine to form a compound, they combine in a fixed ratio of their weights irrespective of the method of preparation.
- Law of Multiple Proportions states that when two elements combine in different ratios to give more than one type of a product, the ratio of the masses of the element that combines with a fixed weight of the other element always bears a simple integral ratio.
- A balanced chemical equation is the one in which the number of atoms of each element of the reactants which are there on the left-hand side of the reaction is equal to that of atoms of each element of the products present on the right-hand side of the reaction.
- A chemical reaction in which two or more substances combine to form a single new substance is called combination reaction.
- The reaction in which a single compound splits into two or more simpler substances is known as decomposition reaction.
- In a displacement reaction, the more reactive element displaces the less reactive element from its compound.
- The chemical reaction in which two reactants (compounds) combine to form two new substances by exchanging their radicals is called double decomposition.
- If the reaction takes place between an acid and a base, it is called neutralization reaction.
- In a double decomposition reaction, if one of the products gets precipitated, the reaction can be called precipitation reaction.
- Oxidation is defined as addition of oxygen or electronegative element or removal of hydrogen or electropositive element from acompound.
- Reduction is defined as the addition of hydrogen or electropositive element or removal of oxygen or electronegative element froma compound.
- In a redox reaction, one substance undergoes oxidation and the other substance undergoes reduction.
- The substance which undergoes oxidation by itself is called reducing agent and the substance which undergoes reduction by itself is called an oxidizing agent.
- A chemical reaction associated with evolution of heat energy is called an exothermic reaction.
- A chemical reaction which proceeds with the absorption of heat energy is called an endothermic reaction.

PRACTICE QUESTIONS CLASSROOM WING

Very Short Answer Type Questions

Directions for questions from 1 to 10:
Fill in the blanks.

1. A trivalent metal forms salts with 'ic' and 'per' acids of chlorine. The number of oxygen atoms in the salts is respectively _____.
2. Limestone on heating gives solid 'X' which on dissolution in water forms 'Y'. Molecular formulas of X and Y are _____ and _____ reactions, respectively.
3. The suffix for salts of 'ous' oxyacids is _____.
4. The compound SF_6 is named as _____.
5. The reaction Fe + S $\longrightarrow$ FeS represents _____.
6. Stibnum is the Latin name of _____.
7. When Fe^{2+} combines with O^{2-}, the compound obtained is _____.
8. $N_2 + 3H_2 \longrightarrow 2NH_3 + X$ kcal/mol, then the formation of NH_3 involves _____ of energy.
9. The symbols of carbon and cobalt are _____ and _____, respectively.
10. The symbol S stands for _____.

Directions for questions from 11 to 30:
Answer the following questions.

11. In the following table some commonly used positive and negative radicals are listed. Use the criss-cross method to obtain the formulae of the compound that is formed using the given radicals. Name the compound, thus, obtained.

S. No.	Positive radicals	Negative radicals	Formulae	Name of the compounds
1.	Al^{3+}	CO_3^{2-}		
2.	K^+	SO_4^{2-}		
3.	NH_4^+	SO_4^{2-}		
4.	Ni^{2+}	S^{2-}		
5.	Al^{3+}	C^{4-}		
6.	Ag^{2+}	Br^-		
7	Ca^{2+}	F^-		
8.	Li^+	H^-		
9.	Al^{3+}	N^{3-}		
10.	Fe^{3+}	O^{2-}		
11.	Na^+	I^-		
12.	K^+	MnO_4^-		
13.	H^+	ClO_3^-		
14.	Ca^{2+}	HSO_4^-		
15.	H^+	NO_2^-		
16.	H^+	SO_3^{2-}		
17.	Ca^{2+}	P^{3-}		
18.	K^+	OH^-		
19.	H^+	NO_3^-		
20.	H^+	SO_4^{2-}		
21.	H^+	S^{2-}		
22.	Cu^+	S^{2-}		
23	Cu^{2+}	Cl^-		
24.	Hg^{2+}	Cl^-		
25.	Na^+	PO_3^{3-}		
26.	Ba^{2+}	PO_4^{3-}		
27.	Ca^{2+}	HCO_3^-		
28.	NH_4^+	OH^-		
29.	NH_4^+	HPO_4^{2-}		
30.	K^+	$H_2PO_4^-$		
31.	H^+	Cl^-		
32.	H^+	ClO^-		
33.	H^+	ClO_4^-		
34.	H^+	ClO_2^-		
35.	K^+	CrO_4^{2-}		
36.	K^+	$Cr_2O_4^{2-}$		
37.	Sn^{4+}	S^{2-}		
38.	Cr^{3+}	SO_4^{2-}		
39.	NH_4^+	$Cr_2O_4^{2-}$		

S. No.	Positive radicals	Negative radicals	Formulae	Name of the compounds
40.	Fe^{3+}	OH^-		
41.	Pb^{4+}	Cl^-		
42.	Mn^{2+}	O^{2-}		
43.	Ba^{2+}	CO_3^{2-}		
44.	Na^+	ZnO_2^{2-}		
45.	Pb^{2+}	NO_3^-		

12. Why is the burning of LPG a chemical change?

13. Balance the following chemical equations:

(i) $As + HNO_3 \longrightarrow NO_2 + H_3AsO_4 + H_2O$

(ii) $Cl_2 + SO_2 + H_2O \longrightarrow H_2SO_4 + HCl$

(iii) $Zn + HNO_3 \longrightarrow Zn(NO_3)_2 + NO_2 + H_2O$

(iv) $NH_3 + Br_2 \longrightarrow N_2 + NH_4Br$

(v) $KI + H_2SO_4 + MnO_2 \longrightarrow KHSO_4 + MnSO_4 + H_2O + I_2$

(vi) $C_3H_8 + O_2 \longrightarrow CO_2 + H_2O$

(vii) $CO_2 + H_2O \longrightarrow C_6H_{12}O_6 + O_2$

(viii) $Fe_3O_4 + H_2 \longrightarrow Fe + H_2O$

(ix) $Pb(NO_3)_2 \longrightarrow PbO + NO_2 + O_2$

(x) $Pb_3O_4 \longrightarrow PbO + O_2$

(xi) $CuO + NH_3 \longrightarrow Cu + H_2O + N_2$

(xii) $HNO_3 + C \longrightarrow CO_2 + H_2O + NO_2$

(xiii) $Na_2O_2 + H_2O \longrightarrow NaOH + O_2$

(xiv) $H_2S + FeCl_3 \longrightarrow FeCl_2 + HCl + S$

(xv) $NaOH + Cl_2 \longrightarrow NaCl + NaClO_3 + H_2O$

(xvi) $K_2Cr_2O_7 + HCl \longrightarrow KCl + CrCl_3 + H_2O + Cl_2$

(xvii) $Ca(OH)_2 + NH_4Cl \longrightarrow CaCl_2 + H_2O + NH_3$

(xviii) $FeCl_3 + SO_2 + H_2O \longrightarrow FeCl_2 + HCl + H_2SO_4$

(xix) $NH_3 + O_2 \longrightarrow NO + H_2O$

(xx) $FeS_2 + O_2 \longrightarrow Fe_2O_3 + SO_2$

(xxi) $Ca_3(PO_4)_2 + SiO_2 + C \longrightarrow CaSiO_3 + P_4 + CO$

(xxii) $KMnO_4 + SO_2 + H_2O \longrightarrow K_2SO_4 + MnSO_4 + H_2SO_4$

(xxiii) $Sn + HNO_3 \longrightarrow Sn(NO_3)_2 + H_2O + NH_4NO_3$

(xxiv) $Al_2(SO_4)_3 + NaOH \longrightarrow Na_2SO_4 + NaAlO_2 + H_2O$

(xxv) $Al_4C_3 + H_2O \longrightarrow Al(OH)_3 + CH_4$

(xxvi) $HI + HIO_3 \longrightarrow I_2 + H_2O$

(xxvii) $Ca_3P_2 + H_2O \longrightarrow Ca(OH)_2 + PH_3$

(xxviii) $S + HNO_3 \longrightarrow H_2SO_4 + NO_2 + H_2O$

(xxix) $I_2 + HNO_3 \longrightarrow HIO_3 + NO_2 + H_2O$

(xxx) $Na_2O_2 + KMnO_4 + H_2SO_4 \longrightarrow Na_2SO_4 + MnSO_4 + K_2SO_4 + H_2O + O_2$

14. What is the difference between photochemical and thermochemical reactions?

15. What is an inhibitor? What is the inhibitor used in the preparation of H_2SO_4?

16. In the following table, some compounds are listed. In each case identify the positive and negative radicals present in the compound.

S. No.	Compounds	Positive radicals	Negative radicals
(i)	SiO_2		
(ii)	CuS		
(iii)	H_2O_2		
(iv)	BaO_2		
(v)	MgS		
(vi)	$NaAlO_2$		
(vii)	MnO_2		
(viii)	LiH		
(ix)	$KMnO_4$		
(x)	$CaSiO_3$		
(xi)	CaF_2		
(xii)	$HOCl$		
(xiii)	$Ca(OCl)_2$		
(xiv)	H_2SO_3		
(xv)	KH_2PO_4		
(xvi)	K_2HPO_4		
(xvii)	H_2S		
(xviii)	H_2SO_3		
(xix)	$Mn(ClO_4)_2$		
(xx)	$Ba(OH)_2$		

17. For each of the following reactions identify the products formed and balance the reaction.

(i) $NaCl + AgNO_3 \longrightarrow$

(ii) $KOH + H_2SO_4 \longrightarrow$

(iii) $H_2CO_3 \xrightarrow{\Delta}$

(iv) $KNO_3 + H_2SO_4 \longrightarrow$

(v) $HgO \xrightarrow{\Delta}$

(vi) $C_4H_{10} + O_2 \longrightarrow$

(vii) $Na_2CO_3 + HCl \longrightarrow$

(viii) $Zn + HCl \longrightarrow$

(ix) $Ca(OH)_2 + H_2CO_3 \longrightarrow$

(x) $AgNO_3 + Cu \longrightarrow$

(xi) $BaCl_2 + Na_2SO_4 \longrightarrow$

(xii) $CuS + O_2 \longrightarrow$

(xiii) $PbSO_4 + Na_2CO_3 \longrightarrow$

(xiv) $Na + H_2O \longrightarrow$

(xv) $KI + Cl_2 \longrightarrow$

(xvi) $CaCO_3 \xrightarrow{\Delta}$

(xvii) $NaBr + Cl_2 \longrightarrow$

(xviii) $NaOH + HCl \longrightarrow$

(xix) $Fe + Cl_2 \longrightarrow$

(xx) $KCl + F_2 \longrightarrow$

18. Arrange the carbonate, sulphate, chlorite, and hydroxide radicals in the correct order of number of oxygen atoms.

19. Both the metals 'X' and 'Y' can form two oxides in which their valencies differ by two units. What could be X and Y?

20. Metal M forms an oxide with the formula M_2O. What is the formula of the compound formed between M and a non-metal A with six electrons in its M shell?

21. What is meant by oxidation and reduction?

22. What is the change that takes place when common salt is dissolved in water?

23. Define an exothermic reaction. Give an example.

24. $Ag + CuSO_4 \longrightarrow Cu + AgSO_4$

Is this reaction possible? Explain.

25. Why do chemical reactions involve loss or gain of energy?

26. Differentiate between oxidation and reduction.

27. What is a displacement reaction?

28. What is chemical decomposition? Give one example.

29. What are catalytic reactions? Give an example.

30. Define an endothermic reaction. Give one example.

Short Answer Type Questions

31. The monovalent positive radical has four hydrogen atoms and a bivalent negative radical has four oxygen atoms. What could be the formula of the salt formed by these two radicals?

32. Both metals 'A' and 'B' can form two oxides, and their valencies differ by one unit. What could be A and B?

33. What is a chemical equation? Write the steps involved in writing a chemical equation.

34. Write the differences between reduction and oxidation.

35. To obtain hydrogen and oxygen from water, what are the conditions to be maintained? What are the different names that can be given to this reaction?

36. Why are the double decomposition reactions also called double displacement reactions?

37. Write the steps in naming a binary compound formed by two non-metallic elements, except hydrogen, with the help of an example.

38. Write the steps in naming a base.

39. $Fe_3O_4 + 4H_2 \longrightarrow 3Fe + 4H_2O$

$2Na + Cl_2 \longrightarrow 2NaCl$. Identify the oxidizing and reducing agents in the given reactions.

40. Photolysis comes under which type of chemical reaction? Explain it with an example.

41. Classify the following equations into combination, displacement, decomposition and double displacement.

(i) $NH_4Cl \longrightarrow NH_3 + HCl$

(ii) $2NO + O_2 \longrightarrow 2NO_2$

(iii) $ZnCO_3 \longrightarrow ZnO + CO_2$

(iv) $Ag_2SO_4 + 2FeSO_4 \longrightarrow Ag + Fe_2(SO_4)_3$

(v) $2NH_3 \longrightarrow N_2 + 3H_2$

(vi) $AgNO_3 + HCl \longrightarrow AgCl + NaNO_3$

(vii) $2SO_2 + O_2 \longrightarrow 2SO_3$

42. (a) Write the characteristics of a chemical reaction.

(b) The ratio of metal atoms to total number of constituents present in the sulphite of a metal is 1:7. Determine the formulae of metal.

(A) hydroxide (B) chloride

(C) sulphide (D) phosphide

43. Classify the following into physical and chemical changes.

(i) freezing of water

(ii) fermentation of alcohol

(iii) burning of coal

(iv) breaking of glass

(v) glowing of an electric bulb

44. Why do we need to use formulae?

45. Write the steps in naming oxyacids:

(i) with greater number of oxygen atoms and

(ii) with less number of oxygen atoms.

Essay Answer Type Questions

46. An acid contains three hydrogen atoms, one non-metal 'X', and four oxygen atoms. What could be the formula of the salt formed when the acid is treated with bivalent metal hydroxide?

47. Give the differences between oxidation and reduction in terms of oxygen, hydrogen, electropositive element and electronegative element.

48. What is a decomposition reaction? Explain different decomposition reactions with equations.

49. What is a chemical combination reaction? Explain the different types of combination reactions.

50. Explain the law of multiple proportions with an example.

51. The percentages of metal in two metal oxides X and Y are 92.6% and 96.2% respectively. Verify the law of multiple proportions.

PRACTICE QUESTIONS COMPETITION WING

Level 1: Apply Your Concepts

Direction for question 1:
Complete the table

1. In the following table some commonly used positive and negative radicals are listed. Use the criss-cross method to obtain the formulae of the compound that is formed using the given radicals. Name the compound, thus, obtained.

S. No.	Positive radicals	Negative radicals	Formulae	Name of the compounds
1.	Na^+	Cl^-		
2.	Na^+	CO_3^{2-}		
3.	Al^{3+}	PO_4^{3-}		
4.	Zn^{2+}	PO_4^{3-}		
5.	Ca^{2+}	NO_3^-		

Directions for questions from 2 to 8:
State whether the following statements are true or false.

2. Formula for potassium biphosphate is $KHPO_4$.
3. The compounds H_2O and D_2O follow law of multiple proportions.
4. A_2X is comprised two divalent negative radicals and one monovalent positive radical.
5. Formation of sodium nitrite and oxygen by thermal decomposition of sodium nitrate involves only a chemical change.
6. The reaction $C + O_2 \longrightarrow CO$, follows the law of conservation of mass.
7. Valency of sulphur in SO_2 is 2.
8. In exothermic reactions, the energy of products is more than the energy of reactants.

Directions for questions from 9 to 15:
Fill in the blanks.

9. Slaked lime turns milky on treatment with carbon dioxide. The reaction is a _____ and _____ reaction.
10. The formula of hydride of non-metal 'X' is XH_3. X can form different oxides in which X exhibits valencies one unit lower and one unit higher than that in XH_3. The formulae of the oxides are _____ and _____, respectively.
11. If the molecular weight of a compound $Na_X\ SO_Y$ is 142, then the values of X and Y are, respectively, _____ and _____.
12. In $Sn + HNO_3 \longrightarrow Sn(NO_3)_2 + H_2O + NH_4NO_3$, the valencies of Sn are _____.
13. In binary compounds, the suffix _____ is added to the second element.
14. The symbol of the element _____ is F.
15. The reverse reaction of neutralization is _____.

Directions for question 16:
Match the entries given in Column A with appropriate ones in Column B.

16. Match the entries of Column A with those of Column B.

Column A (Compound)		Column B Valency of +ve radical	−ve radical
(i) Cupric phosphate	(A)	2	2
(ii) Stannic sulphite	(B)	4	3
(iii) Barium sulphate	(C)	2	3
(iv) Plumbic phosphate	(D)	4	2

Directions for questions from 17 to 40:
For each of the questions, four choices have been provided. Select the correct alternative.

17. **Assertion (A):** The ratio of a number of metal atoms to the total number of atoms in ferric hydrogen phosphate is 1:10.

Reason (R): Ferric hydrogen phosphate contains trivalent positive and monovalent −ve ions.

(a) Both A and R are true and R is the correct explanation of A.
(b) Both A and R are true, but R is not the correct explanation of A.
(c) A is true and R is false.
(d) A is false and R is true.

18. **Assertion (A):** The green colour of the $FeSO_4$ solution fades away when Zn rod is dipped in it but not Ni rod.
Reason (R): The order of reactivity is Ni > Zn > Fe.
(a) Both A and R are true and R is the correct explanation of A.
(b) Both A and R are true, but R is not the correct explanation of A.
(c) A is true and R is false.
(d) A is false and R is true.

19. **Assertion (A):** In a compound, the total positive charge is equal to that of the negative charge.
Reason (R): In a compound, the total number of atoms in a positive ion is always equal to that of a negative ion.
(a) Both A and R are true and R is the correct explanation of A.
(b) Both A and R are true, but R is not the correct explanation of A.
(c) A is true and R is false.
(d) A is false and R is true.

20. **Assertion (A):** Both Al and Zn liberate hydrogen with dilute hydrochloric acid.
Reason (R): Both Al and Zn are more reactive than hydrogen, and the re-activity order is Zn > Al > H.
(a) Both A and R are true and R is the correct explanation of A.
(b) Both A and R are true, but R is not the correct explanation of A.
(c) A is true and R is false.
(d) A is false and R is true.

21. Removal of CO_2 and H_2O from atmospheric air by using KOH and anhydrous $CaCl_2$ is an example of ________ and ________ changes, respectively.
(a) chemical, chemical
(b) physical, physical
(c) chemical, physical
(d) physical, chemical

22. Which of the following reactions is a synthesis reaction?
(a) When steam is passed over red hot coke, a mixture of carbon monoxide and hydrogen is formed.
(b) Sodium reacts with water to form sodium hydroxide and hydrogen.
(c) When the milk of lime (calcium hydroxide) is added to hot sodium carbonate solution, sodium hydroxide is obtained and calcium carbonate separates out as mud.
(d) Stannic chloride is prepared by passing chlorine into molten tin.

23. $Pb(NO_3)_2 + Fe_2(SO_4)_3 \longrightarrow Fe(NO_3)_3 + PbSO_4$
Coefficients of lead sulphate and ferric nitrate in the balanced equation of the above reaction are:
(a) 3, 4 (b) 3, 3
(c) 3, 2 (d) 2, 3

24. Write the names of the salts formed by the reaction of the following.
(i) Ca and HNO_3 and (ii) Ca and H_2SO_3
(a) (i) Calcium nitrate (ii) Calcium sulphate
(b) (i) Calcium nitrite (ii) Calcium sulphite
(c) (i) Calcium nitrate (ii) Calcium sulphite
(d) (i) Calcium nitrite (ii) Calcium sulphate

25. A, B and C are the elements such that A on reaction with air produces a dazzling white flame, B is used in rubber industry for hardening and C acts as a conductor with rise in temperature. Then A, B and C are:
(a) metals
(b) metal, and non-metal, respectively
(c) non-metal, metal and metalloid, respectively
(d) metal, non-metal and metalloid, respectively

26. In the preparation of H_2SO_4 the catalyst and the inhibitor, respectively, are
(a) platinum, molybdenum
(b) iron, arsenic oxide
(c) platinum, arsenic oxide
(d) iron, molybdenum

27. $Fe_2O_3 + 3C \longrightarrow 2Fe + 3CO$, in this reaction
(a) Fe undergoes oxidation and C undergoes reduction
(b) Fe undergoes reduction and C undergoes oxidation
(c) both Fe and C undergo reduction
(d) both Fe and C undergo oxidation

28. Arrange the elements Zn, Sn, Ca and Al in the increasing order of their reactivity for replacing Cu from $CuSO_4$ solution.

(a) Zn > Sn > Ca > Al

(b) Ca > Al > Zn > Sn

(c) Ca > Al > Sn > Zn

(d) Ca > Sn > Zn > Al

29. The valency of sulphate radical is equal to the valency of

(a) phosphate radical

(b) hydrogen phosphate radical

(c) dihydrogen phosphate radical

(d) phosphide radical

30. The ratio of oxygen atoms present in one molecule of cupric nitrite and ferric sulphite is

(a) 4 : 9 (b) 2 : 3

(c) 1 : 2 (d) 1 : 3

31. Which of the following statements is false?

(a) A catalyst is highly specific.

(b) The percentage of yield of products cannot be influenced by a catalyst.

(c) All catalysts have a large surface area.

(d) Composition of a catalyst changes during the reaction.

32. Which one of the following is the salt of a binary acid?

(a) calcium sulphate

(b) magnesium bromide

(c) zinc phosphate

(d) sodium carbonate

33. Which of the following is a salt of 'ous' acid?

(a) Na_2SO_4 (b) $NaNO_3$

(c) $NaClO_2$ (d) $NaClO_4$

34. Arrange the following compounds in the order of valency of a positive radical.

(i) $A(H_2PO_4)_2$ (ii) B_2O

(iii) $C_2(SO_4)_3$

(a) (iii) > (i) > (ii)

(b) (iii) > (ii) > (i)

(c) (ii) > (i) > (iii)

(d) (i) > (ii) > (iii)

35. The valency of nitride ion is same as the valency of ______ ion

(a) ferric (b) plumbic

(c) zinc (d) calcium

36. Both the metals 'X' and 'Y' can form two oxides in which their valencies differ by two units. What could be X and Y?

(a) Cu, Fe

(b) Fe, Pb

(c) Pb, Sn

(d) Sn, Cu

37. Reaction between barium chloride and aluminium sulphate is an example of

(a) neutralization reaction

(b) displacement reaction

(c) precipitation reaction

(d) combination reaction

38. Which among the following salts produces maximum number of metal ions per molecule when dissolved in a suitable solvent?

(a) aluminium phosphate, $AlPO_4$

(b) magnesium phosphate, $Mg_3(PO_4)_2$

(c) sodium biphosphate, Na_2HPO_4

(d) aluminium dihydrogen phosphate, $Al(H_2PO_4)$

39. A series of chemical reactions were carried out in a laboratory in the following way. At first zinc granules reacted with H_2SO_4 to form H_2 gas. Then hydrogen gas reacted with chlorine gas under diffused sunlight to form hydrogen chloride gas. Hydrogen chloride gas produced in this process was dissolved in water to form hydrochloric acid. Hydrochloric acid reacted with sodium hydroxide to form sodium chloride and water. Sodium chloride, thus, produced is first melted and then electricity is passed through it. Due to the passage of electricity through sodium chloride, sodium metal and chlorine gas are obtained.

Rahul was asked to arrange the above reactions in the order of combination, decomposition, displacement and double decomposition.

His answer is given below.

(1) formation of H_2 gas

(2) formation of hydrogen chloride gas

(3) formation of sodium and chlorine from sodium chloride

(4) formation of sodium chloride

Which among the following orders given below is correct, according to you?

(a) 3 4 2 1 (b) 2 3 1 4

(c) 1 2 3 4 (d) 2 3 4 1

40. Arrange the following reactions in the given order, i.e., compound–element combination, compound–compound combination and element–element combination.

(1) Coke is burnt in an inadequate supply of air.

(2) The product formed in the reaction (1) is again burnt in the presence of oxygen.

(3) The product formed in the reaction (2) is treated with water.

(a) 1 3 2 (b) 2 3 1

(c) 2 1 3 (d) 3 1 2

Level 2: Review Your Concepts

41. The formula of hydride of a metal 'X' is XH2. What will be the formula of the compound formed between X and a non-metal 'Y' with five electrons in its M shell?

42. The electronic configuration of a metal 'M' is 2, 8, 18, 1. What could be the formulae of nitrate and nitrides of metal M?

43. The formula of hydrogen phosphate of a metal M is $MHPO_4$. Give the formula of its:

(a) chloride

(b) bicarbonate

(c) sulphite

44. Write the balanced chemical equation for the following:

(i) Potassium bromide on treatment with manganese dioxide and sulphuric acid gives manganese and potassium sulphates, bromine and water.

(ii) In the preparation of phosphate fertilisers, calcium phosphate in phosphate rock is converted into phosphoric acid and calcium sulphate.

(iii) Sodium nitrite is produced by the reaction of the oxides of nitrogen in which nitrogen shows valency 2 and 4 in a solution of sodium carbonate.

45. (a) Nitrogen and oxygen react to produce nitric oxide. What is the weight of oxygen required to convert 4.9 g of nitrogen to nitric oxide?

(b) Calculate amount of potassium chlorate required to give 120 g of oxygen. What kind of chemical reaction takes place in the above process?

46. The salt of an oxyacid of metal M contains two sulphur and six oxygen atoms. What will be the formula of the base formed by the metal and why?

47. The molecular weight of a salt of oxyacid of chlorine of a divalent metal which contains more number of oxygen atoms than its corresponding 'ic' acid is 239. What will be the molecular weights of its.

(i) phosphate, (ii) iodide and (iii) bisulphate?

48. Given below are three chemical equations. Study the equations and identify the elements that show variable valency? Give reasons in support of your answer. ('M' and 'N' stand for different metals.)

(i) $MS + ZnSO_4 \longrightarrow MSO_4 + ZnS$

(ii) $3MCl_2 + N_2(SO_4)_3 \longrightarrow 3MSO_4 + 2NCl_3$

(iii) $NS + H_2SO_4 \longrightarrow NSO_4 + H_2S$

49. Blue-coloured $CuSO_4$ is taken in two test tubes A and B. Zinc granules are added to test tube A and small iron pieces are added to test tube B. Explain the observations in each case by giving reasons.

50. How do you account for the following?

(a) Nitric acid is colourless but on long standing it turns yellow.

(b) Hydrochloric acid can be concentrated by conc. H_2SO_4 but not by phosphorous pentoxide (or) quick lime.

51. In the welding of railway tracks, a proper proportion of aluminium powder and iron (iii) oxide are made to react with each other at high temperature. Explain the type of reaction involved and also identify the reducing and the oxidizing agents.

52. The valency of a metal is 2 and its atomic weight is 24. What will be the molecular weight of its

(a) sulphite (b) chloride

(c) chlorate

53. While balancing a chemical equation, only the coefficients of the formulae are changed, but the subscripts are not changed. Give reasons.

54. The chemical X is a hydroxide of a divalent metal. On treating this hydroxide with CO_2, a milky white precip-

itate of Y is formed. The precipitate turns to colourless solution by the excess passage of CO_2. This colourless solution again gives milky white precipitate Y on heating. Identify X and Y and also give necessary equations.

55. A hydrocarbon on complete combustion produces 176 g of carbon dioxide and 90 g of water. What will x the formula of hydrocarbon be? Also give balanced chemical equation of combustion of hydrocarbon.

56. Heating and subsequent cooling of certain substances are given below. Classify them into either physical or chemical change.
(a) lead nitrate
(b) bluish green copper carbonate
(c) yellow coloured lead oxide
(d) White powdered zinc oxide

57. Arrange the following radicals in the increasing order of total number of constituent atoms present in the respective radicals.
(a) hydroxide (b) nitride
(c) chromate (d) sulphite
(e) dihydrogen phosphate

58. (a) Two beakers A and B contain water. Glucose is added to beaker A and ammonia gas is passed through beaker B. What types of changes (physical or chemical) take place in the beakers? Justify.
(b) Which among the following reactions are possible?
(a) $Cu + 2HCl \rightarrow CuCl_2 + H_2$
(b) $2NaCl + F_2 \rightarrow 2NaF + Cl_2$
(c) $MgSO_4 + Zn \rightarrow ZnSO_4 + Mg$
(d) $Pb(NO_3)_2 + Ni \rightarrow Ni(NO_3)_2 + Pb$
(e) $Zn + CuSO_4 \rightarrow ZnSO_4 + Cu$
(f) $2Al + 3H_2SO_4 \rightarrow Al_2(SO_4)_3 + 3H_2$

59. Oxide of a metal on treatment with water produces a hissing sound and energy. The product (Y) formed on treatment with hydrochloric acid gives a solid X. Identify the oxide, the product (Y) and X. Also write all the balanced chemical equations and calculate molecular masses of the oxide, the product Y and X.

60. A non-metal X forms two oxides, A and B. The ratio of weight of the element X to the weight of oxygen in A and B is 7 : 20 and 7 : 16, respectively. If the molecular mass of the oxide, A is 108, identify A and B.

61. Electrolysis of molten sodium chloride produces sodium and chlorine. Is this reaction a redox reaction? Give reasons in support of your answer.

62. Express the following chemical changes in the form of chemical equations and identify what types of chemical reactions they are.
(a) A copper coin is placed in a solution of corrosive sublimate, mercuric chloride. The products obtained are cupric chloride and mercury.
(b) A piece of (a) sulphur and (b) charcoal burns vigorously when dropped in molten potassium nitrate, because potassium nitrate decomposes to form potassium nitrite and oxygen and this oxygen helps to burn charcoal and sulphur giving out carbon dioxide and sulphur dioxide, respectively.
(c) Aqueous ammonium hydroxide solution is made to react with aqueous copper sulphate solution and a bluish white precipitate of cupric hydroxide and ammonium sulphate are formed.

63. (a) Decomposition reactions are always initiated with the supply of energy. Give appropriate reasons.
(b) Generally, burning or combustion reactions are exothermic. Justify.

64. In the welding of railway tracks, a proper proportion of aluminium powder and iron (III) oxide are made to react with each other at high temperature. Explain the type of reaction involved and also identify the reducing and the oxidizing agents.

Level 3: Assess Your Concepts

65. A non-metal 'X' with electronic configurations 2, 4 forms two oxides in which 'X' shows valencies two and four. Oxide with higher valency is dissolved in water. The acid produced is treated with NaOH to form salt. What could be the formula of the salt?

66. The molecular mass of oxide of a metal M is 40 and the percentage of metal is 60%. What is the molecular mass of perchlorate of the metal?

67. Metal with electronic configurations 2, 8, 14, 2 can form two different hydroxides A and B. Both the hydroxides in reaction with sulphuric acid give two salts 'X' and 'Y'. Identify X and Y.

68. A compound X of silver on treatment with barium chloride gives the respective products Y and Z. X on treatment with sodium hydroxide gives A and B where A can also be obtained when silver is attacked by ozone

and B is the salt of an oxyacid of nitrogen which ends with the suffix 'ate.' Identify and give the chemical formulae of the substances X, Y, Z, A and B.

69. The salt of hypohalous acid is prepared from the respective components, namely, halogen and the corresponding metallic hydroxide. The metal is the one which possesses the number of electrons in the ratio of 1 : 4 : 4 : 1 which corresponds to, namely, K, L, M and N shells, respectively, and the halogen is a greenish-yellow colour gas which can displace bromine from magnesium bromide. Identify the salt and the respective components.

70. (a) The molecular masses of sulphate and hydroxide of a metal M are 142 and 40, respectively. Calculate atomic mass and valency of the metal.

(b) Identify, A, B, C, types of reactions and oxidizing, reducing agents in the following processes.

(A) A mixture of ferric oxide and carbon is strongly heated to form a solid A and gas B.

(B) Gas B is passed on red hot carbon to form gas C.

(C) Gas B can be prepared by the combustion of non-metal.

71. What are the changes observed when moist sugar is treated with anhydrous calcium chloride and concentrated H_2SO_4, respectively?

72. Identify the type of chemical change that silver chloride undergoes in photogrey lenses.

73. Blue-coloured gas X having a characteristic fishy odour, can restore the colour of lead paintings. This gas can also be used for sterilizing water. Identify the gas X. Mention the type of reaction(s) involved.

74. Fluorine is very reactive and attacks all metals but still a copper vessel is used in the preparation of fluorine gas. Why?

AT

PRACTICE QUESTIONS JEE-NEET SPECIAL WING

Multiple-Answer Type Questions

Directions for questions 1 to 6:

Select one or more correct alternative(s) from the given choices.

1. Potassium dichromate reacts with hydrochloric acid to form two solid products A and B along with water and chlorine gas. Identify the facts which comply with the balanced chemical equation for the reaction.
   (a) The coefficient of hydrochloric acid would be 14.
   (b) 6 molecules of chlorine are released when 1 molecule of potassium dichromate reacts with sufficient quantity of hydrochloric acid.
   (c) 2 molecules each of X and Y are obtained as per the balanced chemical equation.
   (d) The total number of molecules on the product side would be equal to those on the reactant side.

2. $2XCl_2 + YCl_2 \rightarrow X_2Cl_2 + YCl_4$. Considering metals in the place of X and Y, identify the true statements which are in accordance with this equation.
   (a) X and Y show same variable valencies
   (b) X could be mercury and Y could be tin
   (c) Both X and Y liberate hydrogen on reaction with dilute acids
   (d) XCl_2 acts as the oxidising agent while YCl_2 acts as the reducing agent.

3. A metal 'M' displaces hydrogen from dilute hydrochloric acid in a slow reaction. This metal cannot displace any other metal present above hydrogen in the metal reactivity series. Identify the incorrect statements regarding the characteristic features of the metal.
   (a) 'M' is present just below hydrogen in the metal reactivity series.
   (b) 'M' exhibits both +2 and +4 valencies
   (c) 'M' is a stronger reducing agent than sodium
   (d) 'M' cannot be used for the preparation of hydrogen by the addition of dilute acids.

4. Nitrogen forms different oxides in which the valency of nitrogen is different. Consider that the mass of oxygen which combines with gram atomic mass of nitrogen is 'x' g in the oxide in which nitrogen shows the valency 4. The masses of nitrogen which combine with 'x' g of oxygen are given below. Identify the correctly matched sets.

	Valency of nitrogen	Mass of nitrogen combining with 'x' g oxygen
(a)	1	56 g
(b)	5	11.2 g
(c)	2	28 g
(d)	3	18.6 g

5. A nonmetal has 7 electrons in its valence 'M' shell. One of its oxyacid has 42% nonmetal. 49 g of the potassium salt of this oxyacid is subjected to thermal decomposition till completion. Identify the data which complies with this activity. The mass of the product in the reaction vessel was measured at the end of the activity.
   (a) The mass of the product measured at the end would be 29.8 g
   (b) The mass of the product measured at the end would be 49 g
   (c) The percentage of apparent loss in weight in the reaction would be around 20%
   (d) The number of molecules of products would be 3 more than the number of molecules of reactants.

6. Mass of 1 atom of an element is 4.67 times the mass of a carbon atom. Which among the following statements comply with this element?
   (a) This element can form two normal oxides and a mixed oxide
   (b) 1Gram molecule of higher oxide = 2.2-gram molecules of lower oxide
   (c) One gram molecule of the higher oxide undergoes reduction with carbon monoxide to form 3-gram molecules of gaseous product.
   (d) The lower oxide is more stable than the higher oxide

Comprehension-Based Questions

Directions for questions 7 to 12:

Read the content given in the following passage and answer the questions given below.

The lower oxyacid of phosphorus has 2 replaceable hydrogens and one nonreplaceable hydrogen. The higher oxyacid has all the three replaceable hydrogens. These two oxyacids form their various radicals.Consider the salts of these negative radicals with the simple divalent positive ion.

7. The names of the radicals are given in column I and the number of atoms per molecule are given in column II. Match the entries in column I with those in column II.

Radical name		No.of atoms per molecule
(a) Biphosphate	(i)	15
(b) Phosphate	(ii)	5
(c) Dihydrogen phosphate	(iii)	6
(d) Phosphide	(iv)	13
(e) Phosphite	(v)	7

8. Consider a salt of ammonium ion and biphosphate radical. Find the number of molecules of acid and base required respectively for the formation of 5 molecules of the salt.
(a) 2.5; 5 (b) 5; 5
(c) 5; 10 (d) 2.5; 10

9. Magnesium reacts with phosphorus to form a binary compound. Identify the correct coefficients of magnesium and phosphorus in the balanced chemical equation.
(a) 1; 2 (b) 2; 3
(c) 3; 2 (d) 3; 1

10. Identify the molecular mass of the ammonium salt of the higher oxyacid of phosphorus formed at the end of complete neutralisation.
(a) 149 (b) 115
(c) 132 (d) 113

11. Find out the percentage of phosphorus in sodium salt of phosphoric acid which can react with 2 molecules of sodium hydroxide.
(a) 56 (b) 12.9
(c) 38 (d) 25.8

12. The formula of the phosphide of a metal is MP. What would be the correct formula of the hydrogen phosphate of that metal?
(a) $M_2(HPO_4)_3$
(b) $M(HPO_4)_3$
(c) $M_3(HPO_4)_2$
(d) $M(H_2PO_4)_3$

Directions for questions 13 to 17:

Read the content given in the following passage and answer the questions given below.

Hydrocarbon	No. of moles of the products formed by the complete combustion of one mole of the hydrocarbon	
	CO_2	H_2O
A	3	4
B	4	3
C	3	2
D	2	1
E	2	3
F	3	3

13. How many moles of oxygen are required for the complete combustion of 1 mole of B?
(a) 11 (b) 6
(c) 4.5 (d) 5.5

14. The hydrocarbon F is subjected to complete combustion utilizing 3 moles of oxygen. Find the number of moles of 'F' taken for combustion?
(a) 1 mole (b) 1.25 mole
(c) 0.67 mole (d) 0.18 mole

15. 2.5 moles hydrocarbon required 6.25 moles oxygen for complete combustion. Predict the hydrocarbon from the above table.
(a) A (b) E
(c) F (d) D

16. **Assertion (A):** For the hydrocarbon of the general formula C_nH_{2n+2} the number of moles of oxygen required for its complete combustion would be equal to $3n$.

Reason (R): The number of moles of oxygen for the combustion of C_xH_y would be equal to $(4x + y)/4$

(a) Both A and R are correct, and R is the correct explanation of A

(b) Both A and R are correct, and R is not the correct explanation of A

(c) A is correct and R is wrong

(d) R is correct and A is wrong

17. Which of the following hydrocarbons will produce the same molar ratio of the products as hydrocarbon 'F' when combusted?

(a) C_4H_8 (b) C_5H_{10}

(c) C_2H_4 (d) All of these

Directions for question 18:

Read the content given in the following passage. Based on the information given in the below passage, answer the question.

The products of combustion of various hydrocarbons are passed through the condenser. Then, the volumes of the gaseous product are measured in each experiment. 1 mole of gaseous product is assumed to occupy 'x' litre volume. In column I, the hydrocarbon is given while in column II, the volume occupied is given.

18. Match the entries in column I with those in column II

Hydrocarbon	Volume occupied
(a) 0.5 mole A	(i) $x/2$
(b) 0.2 mole B	(ii) $8x/3$
(c) 0.25 mole C	(iii) $6x/5$
(d) 0.6 mole D	(iv) $3x/4$
(e) 0.25 mole E	(v) $3x/2$
(f) 0.9 mole F	(vi) $4x/5$

ANSWER KEYS

Crossword

Across

1. Valency 3. Reduction 5. Gram molecule 6. Synthesis
9. Photolysis 13. Endothermic 15. Gram atom 17. Absorbed
18. Atomic mass unit 19. Neutralization

Down

2. Analysis 4. Thermal decomposition 7. Exothermic 8. Oxidation
10. Wolfram 11. Berzelius 12. Released 14. Fluorine
16. Platinum 20. ide

Classroom Wing

Very Short Answer Type Questions

1. $HClO_3$; $HClO_4$ 2. CaO; $Ca(OH)_2$ 3. ite 4. Sulphur hexafluoride
5. Combination, synthesis 6. Antimony 7. FeO 8. evolution
9. C, Co 10. sulphur

Competition Wing

Level 1: Apply Your Concepts

2. False 3. False 4. False 5. False 6. True
7. False 8. False 9. Precipitation; neutralization 10. XO; XO_2
11. 2, 4
12. 0 and 2 13. ide 14. fluorine 15. hydrolysis
16. (i) → (C); (ii) → (B); (iii) → (A); (iv) → (D) 17. (c)
18. (c) 19. (c) 20. (c) 21. (c) 22. (d)
23. (c) 24. (c) 25. (d) 26. (c) 27. (b)
28. (b) 29. (b) 30. (a) 31. (d) 32. (b)
33. (c) 34. (a) 35. (a) 36. (c)
37. (c) 38. (b) 39. (b) 40. (b)

JEE-NEET Special Wing

Multiple-Answer Type Questions

1. (a, c) 2. (b, d) 3. (a, c) 4. (a, b, c, d) 5. (a, c, d)
6. (a, b, c)

Comprehension-Based Questions

7. (a) ↔ (v), (b) ↔ (iv), (c) ↔ (i), (d) ↔ (ii), (e) ↔ (iii) 8. (c)
9. (c) 10. (a) 11. (d) 12. (a) 13. (d)
14. (c) 15. (d) 16. (d) 17. (d)
18. (a) ↔ (v), (b) ↔ (vi), (c) ↔ (iv), (d) ↔ (iii), (e) ↔ (i), (f) ↔ (ii)

Hints and Explanations

CLASSROOM WING

Very Short Answer Type Questions

1. ic and per acids of chlorine are $HClO_3$ and $HClO_4$, respectively.

   ∴ The formulae of salts with trivalent metal are $M(ClO_3)_3$ and $M(ClO_4)_3$. The number of oxygen atoms in these salts, respectively, are 9 and 12.

2. $CaCO_3 \xrightarrow{Heat} CaO + CO_2 - Energy$
   (X)

   $CaO + H_2O \rightarrow Ca(OH)_2 + Energy$
   (Y)

   Formation of X is endothermic and decomposition. Formation of Y is exothermic and compound–compound combination.

3. ite
4. Sulphur hexafluoride
5. Combination, synthesis
6. Antimony
7. FeO
8. evolution
9. C, Co
10. sulphur
11. Criss-cross the valencies of the radicals.
    - $Al_2(CO_3)_3$
    - K_2SO_4
    - $(NH_4)_2SO_4$
    - NiS
    - Al_4C_3
    - $AgBr_2$
    - CaF_2
    - LiH
    - AlN
    - Fe_2O_3
    - NaI
    - $KMnO_4$
    - $HClO_3$
    - $Ca(HSO_4)_2$
    - HNO_2
    - H_2SO_3
    - Ca_3P_2
    - KOH
    - HNO_3
    - H_2SO_4
    - H_2S
    - Cu_2S
    - $CuCl_2$
    - $HgCl_2$
    - Na_3PO_3
    - $Ba_3(PO_4)_2$
    - $Ca(HCO_3)_2$
    - NH_4OH
    - $(NH_4)_2HPO_4$
    - KH_2PO_4
    - HCl
    - HClO
    - $HClO_4$
    - $HClO_2$
    - K_2CrO_4
    - $K_2Cr_2O_4$
    - SnS_2
    - $Cr_2(SO_4)_3$
    - $(NH_4)_2Cr_2O_4$
    - $Fe(OH)_3$
    - $PbCl_4$
    - MnO
    - $BaCO_3$
    - Na_2ZnO_2
    - $Pb(NO_3)_2$
12. (i) Composition of LPG

    (ii) Products obtained on combustion
13. Equal number of atoms of elements of reactants and products on either side of a chemical equation.

14. Reaction in the presence of light and heat, respectively
15. Decreases the rate of reactions
16. Use Criss-cross method
17. (i) Type of reactions
(ii) Different laws
18. Carbonate → CO_3^{-2}, sulphate SO_4^{-2}, chlorite → ClO_2^{-1}, and Hydroxide → OH^-
Hence, the correct order is Hydroxide < chlorite < carbonate < sulphate.
19. Both Pb and Sn form two oxides PbO, PbO_2 and SnO, SnO_2, respectively. In PbO and SnO, the valencies of Pb and Sn are two, and in PbO_2 and SnO_2 the valencies of Pb and Sn are four.
20. The valency of metal M is 1 and metal ion is M^{+1}. Anion formed by non-metal A is A^{-2}.
∴ Formula of the compound is M^{+1}, $A^{-2} \Rightarrow M_2A$.
21. Oxidation is addition of oxygen or electronegative element or removal of hydrogen or electropositive element from a compound.
Reduction is the addition of hydrogen or electropositive element or removal of oxygen or electronegative element from a compound.
22. Physical change
23. A chemical reaction associated with evolution of heat energy is called an exothermic reaction. For example: $C + O \rightarrow CO_2 + 94$ kcal
24. Cu is more electropositive than Ag
25. Energy changes during making or breaking of bonds
26. Oxidation—addition of oxygen, reduction—removal of oxygen
27. More active metal displaces less active metal from its compound.
28. The reaction in which a single compound splits into two or more simpler substances is known as decomposition reaction.
E.g., $2Al_2O_3 \rightarrow 4Al + 3O_2$
29. The rates of some chemical reactions are influenced by the catalysts and such reactions are called catalytic reactions. For example, The rate of decomposition of $KClO_3$ is more in the presence of MnO_2.
30. A chemical reaction which proceeds with the absorption of heat energy is called an endothermic reaction.
E.g., $N_2 + O_2 \rightarrow 2NO$ - 44 kcal

Short Answer Type Questions

31. The monovalent +ve radical with four hydrogen is AH_4^{+1} and the bivalent –ve radical with four oxygen atoms BO_4^{-2}.
∴ The formula of the salt is AH_4^{+1}, $BO_4^{-2} = (AH_4)_2 BO_4$.
32. Copper can form two oxides Cu_2O and CuO in which the valency of Cu is 1 and 2, respectively. Similarly, Hg can form two oxides Hg_2O and HgO in which the valency of Hg is 1 and +2, respectively.
33. (i) representation of a chemical change
(ii) left-hand side reactants, right-hand side products
34. (i) addition of oxygen, removal of hydrogen is oxidation
(ii) removal of oxygen, addition of hydrogen is reduction
35. (i) acidulated water
(ii) electrochemical reaction
36. mutual exchange of radicals
37. (i) less electronegative nonmetal followed by more electronegative nonmetal
(ii) prefix is added to a more electronegative element
38. (i) metal ion
(ii) negative radical
39. (i) substance which loses oxygen
(ii) substance which gains the electrons
40. If the decomposition of a substance takes place in the presence of light, it is called photolytic decomposition (photolysis).
$2HOCl \rightarrow 2HCl + O_2$
41. (i) Decomposition
(ii) Combination
(iii) Decomposition
(iv) Displacement
(v) Combination
(vi) Double Displacement
(vii) Combination
42. (a) (i) new substances formed
(ii) energy changes
(b) Let the metal ion be M^{x+}
∴ Metal sulphite is M^{x+}, $SO_3^{2-} \Rightarrow M_2\,(SO_3)_x$

Given that $\frac{2}{2+4x} = \frac{1}{7}$

$\Rightarrow x = 3$

$\therefore$ Metal ion is M^{3+}

(A) Metal hydroxide is M^{3+}, $OH^- \Rightarrow M(OH)_3$

(B) Metal chloride is M^{3+}, $Cl^- \Rightarrow MCl_3$

(C) Metal sulphide is M^{3+}, $S^{2-} \Rightarrow M_2S_3$

(D) Metal phosphide is M^{3+}, $P^{3-} \Rightarrow MP$

43. (i) Physical change

(ii) Chemical Change

(iii) Chemical Change

(iv) Physical Change

(v) Physical Change

44. (i) used in chemical reactions

(ii) used to save time

45. (i) corresponding prefix

(ii) comparison with other oxyacids

Essay Answer Type Questions

46. The formula of acid is H_3XO_4.

$H_3XO_4 + M(OH)_2 \rightarrow M_3(XO_4)_2 + H_2O$

47. (i) addition or removal of hydrogen (or electropositive element)

(ii) addition or removal of oxygen (or electronegative element)

48. The reaction in which a single compound splits into two or more simpler substances is known as decomposition reaction. If the decomposition of a substance takes place by the absorption of heat, it is called thermal decomposition. If the decomposition of a substance takes place by the passage of electricity, it is called electrolytic decomposition (electrolysis). If the decomposition of a substance takes place in the presence of light, it is called photolytic decomposition (photolysis).

49. A chemical reaction in which two or more substances combine to form a single new substance is called combination reaction.

(i) Element–element combination reaction: The formation of a compound from its constituent elements is called synthesis.

(ii) Element–compound combination reaction

(iii) Compound–compound combination reaction

50. When two elements combine in different ratios to give more than one type of a product, the ratio of the masses of the element that combines with a fixed weight of the other element always bears a simple integral ratio. For example,

N_2O: 28 g of nitrogen combines with 16 g of oxygen. Therefore, 14 g of nitrogen combines with 8 g of oxygen

NO: 14 g of nitrogen combines with 16 g of oxygen

NO_2: 14 g of nitrogen combines with 32 g of oxygen

51.

Metal oxide	% Metal	% oxygen
X	92.6	7.4
Y	96.2	3.8

In X, 92.6 g of metal reacts with 7.4 g of oxygen

100 g of metal reacts with $\frac{100 \times 7.4}{92.6} = 8$ g of oxygen

In Y, 96.2 g of metal reacts with 3.8 g of oxygen

$\therefore$ 100 g of metal reacts with $\frac{3.8 \times 100}{92.6} = 4$ g

$\therefore$ for fixed weight of metal, ratio by weight of oxygen is $8 : 4 \approx 2 : 1$

$\therefore$ Law of multiple proportions is verified.

Competition Wing

Level 1: Apply Your Concepts

1. Criss-cross the valencies of the radicals.

NaCl

Na_2CO_3

$AlPO_4$

$Zn_3(PO_4)_2$

$Ca(NO_3)_2$

9. $Ca(OH)_2 + CO_2 \rightarrow CaCO_3 + H_2O$

Slaked lime turns milky on treatment with carbon dioxide. The reaction is a precipitation and neutralization reaction.

10. Valency of non-metal X in XH_3 with re-spect to H is 3. Given that valencies of X in the two oxides are 2 and 4 with respect to oxygen, and formulae of oxides are XO and XO_2.

16.

(Compound)	Valency of +ve radical	Valency of −ve radical
$Cu_3(PO_4)_2$	2	3
$Sn_2(SO_3)_4 = Sn(SO_3)_2$	4	2
$BaSO_4$	2	2
$Pb_3(PO_4)_4$	4	3

17. The formula of ferric hydrogen phosphate is $Fe_2(HPO_4)_3$.

$$\therefore \text{Ratio} = \frac{2}{2+3+3+12} = \frac{2}{20} = \frac{1}{10} = 1:10$$

The valency of $HPO_4 - 2$ is 2.

Hence, the correct option is (c).

18. More reactive metal displaces less reactive metal from its aqueous solution. The order of reactivity of Zn, Fe, and Ni is Zn > Fe > Ni.

Hence, the correct option is (c).

19. In a compound, the total +ve charge is equal to that of –ve charge, but the total number of atoms in +ve ion may or may not equal to that of –ve ion.

Hence, the correct option is (c).

20. Metals which are more reactive than hydrogen on treatment with dilute acids give hydrogen gas. The order of reactivity of Zn, Al, and H is Al > Zn > H.

Hence, the correct option is (c).

32. Magnesium bromide is a salt formed from magnesium hydroxide ($Mg[OH]_2$) and hydrobromic acid (HBr). Hydrogen bromide is a binary acid. Hence, magnesium bromide is a salt of binary acid.

Hence the correct choice is (b)

33. $NaClO_2$ is the sodium salt of chlorous acid ($HClO_2$).

Hence the correct choice is (c)

34. (i) $A[H_2PO_4]_2$ A^{2+}

(ii) B_2O B+1

(iii) $C_2(SO_4)_3$ C+3

iii > i > ii

Hence the correct choice is (a)

35. Nitride: N^{3-}

Ferric: Fe^{3+}

However, others are Pb^{4+}, Zn^{2+} and Ca^{2+}

Hence the correct choice is (a)

36. Both Pb and Sn form two oxides PbO, PbO_2 and SnO, SnO_2, respectively. In PbO and SnO, the valencies of Pb and Sn are two, and in PbO_2 and SnO_2 the valencies of Pb and Sn are four.

Hence the correct choice is (c)

37. $3BaCl_2 + Al_2(SO_4)_3 \rightarrow 3BaSO_4 + 2AlCl_3$

The above reaction is an example of precipitation reaction because in this case we will get $BaSO_4$ as a precipitate.

Hence the correct choice is (c)

38. Formulae of compounds are

(a) $AlPO_4$

(b) $Mg_3(PO_4)_2$

(c) $Na_2H\,PO_4$

(d) $Al(H_2PO_4)_3$

$Mg_3(PO_4)_2$ will produce maximum number of metal ions by dissolving in a suitable solvent.

Hence the correct choice is (b)

39. $Zn + H_2SO_4 \rightarrow Zn\,SO_4 + H_2$, displacement reaction

$H_2 + Cl_2 \rightarrow 2HCl$ is a combination reaction.

$HCl + NaOH \rightarrow NaCl + H_2O$ is a double displacement reaction.

$2NaCl \rightarrow 2Na + Cl_2$ decomposition reaction

Hence, the order is (b), (c), (a) and (d),

(2) formation of hydrogen chloride gas

(3) formation of sodium and chlorine from sodium chloride

(1) formation of H_2 gas

(4) formation of sodium chloride

Hence the correct choice is (b)

40. $2C$ (coke) + $O_{2\ (inadequate)} \rightarrow 2CO$ is element–element combination

$2CO + O_2 \rightarrow 2CO_2$ is compound–element combination

$CO_2 + H_2O \rightarrow H_2CO_3$ is compound–compound combination

(2) The product formed in reaction (1) is again burnt in the presence of oxygen.

(3) The product formed in reaction (2) is treated with water.

(1) Coke is burnt in an inadequate supply of air.

Hence the correct choice is (b)

Level 2: Review Your Concepts

41. Valency of X in XH_2 is 2 and X can form is X^{+2}. Y is P and it can form P^{-3} ion. The formula is $X^{+2}, P^{-3} \rightarrow X_3P_2$.

42. Cations formed by metal M are M^{+1} and M^{+2}.
Formulae of nitrates are MNO_3, $M(NO_3)_2$.
Formulae of nitrides are M_3N, M_3N_2.

43. (i) valency of M
(ii) identification of the valency of metal M
(iii) derivation of the formula of chloride, bicarbonate and sulphite from its valency

44. (i) reactants on left-hand side and products on right-hand side
(ii) balancing the equations by keeping appropriate coefficients on either side of the reaction.

45. (a) (i) law of definite proportions
(ii) determination of the weight of nitrogen and oxygen which combine to form nitric oxide
(iii) calculation of the weight of oxygen from the weight of nitrogen given
(iv) 5.6 g

(b) $2KClO_3 \rightarrow 2KCl + 3O_2$

3×32g of O_2 is obtained from 2(122.5)g of $KClO_3$

$\Rightarrow$ 96 g of O_2 is obtained from 245 g of $KClO_3$

$\therefore$ 120 g of O_2 is obtained from "x" g of $KClO_3$

$$\therefore x = \frac{120 \times 245}{96}$$

$x = 306.25$ g of $KClO_3$

This is a thermal decomposition reaction.

46. (i) negative radical in an oxyacid
(ii) Identification of the types of negative radicals formed from sulphur and oxygen
(iii) derivation of the formula of the salt
(iv) derivation of the formula of the base formed by the metal

47. (i) identification of negative radical of the given oxyacid
(ii) identification of salt of an oxyacid from the given molecular weight
(iii) calculation of atomic weight of metal and identification of metal
(iv) Writing formulae of the divalent metal with corresponding negative radicals
(v) calculation of molecular weights of the above salts

48. (i) Calculate valency of M and N (metals) present in the reactants and products
(ii) valencies of M and N in their respective equations
(iii) identification of the element with variable valency

49. (i) reactivity series of metals
(ii) reactivity of metals according to metal reactivity series
(iii) reactions taking place
(iv) change in property of the solution due to the reaction

50. (i) changes that take place in nitric acid on long standing
(ii) effect of the product on nitric acid solution
(iii) reactivity of HCl towards concentrated H_2SO_4, P_2O_5 and quick lime

51. (i) Give the formula of iron (III) oxide.
(ii) reaction between Al and iron (III) oxide
(iii) Based on the above chemical reaction, predict the type of reaction.
(iv) Identification of oxidizing and reducing agents.

52. (i) formulae of salts based on valency of metal
(ii) derivation of formulae of the compounds based on the valency of the metal
(iii) calculation of its corresponding molecular weight

53. significance of coefficient and subscripts associated with the formula

54. (i) Identification of X
(ii) Reaction of X with carbon dioxide
(iii) Identification of Y
(iv) Reaction of Y with excess carbon dioxide and identification of the product formed.
(v) Thermal decomposition of the above product.

55. (i) general balanced chemical equation for combustion of hydrocarbon
(ii) calculation of the coefficients of carbon dioxide and water using the formula
(iii) coefficient of

$$CO_2 = \frac{\text{Amount of } CO_2 \text{ produced}}{\text{Molecular weight}}$$

(iv) Coefficient of

$$H_2O = \frac{\text{Amount of } H_2O \text{ produced}}{\text{Molecular weight}}$$

(v) chemical formula of hydrocarbon from the coefficients of carbon dioxide and water

56. Physical changes are heating of yellow coloured lead oxide and white powdered zinc oxide. Chemical changes are heating of lead nitrate and bluish green copper carbonate.

57.

Name of the radicals	Formulae	No. of constituents
Nitride	N^{3-}	1
Hydroxide	OH^-	2
Sulphite	SO_3^{2-}	4
Chromate	CrO_4^{2-}	5
Dihydrogen phosphate	$H_2PO_4^-$	7

58. (a) When glucose is added to beaker A containing water, dissolution takes place. It is a physical change. When ammonia gas is passed through beaker B containing water, formation of NH_4OH takes place. This is a chemical change.

(b) More reactive element displaces less reactive elements. The order of reactivity of metals is Mg > Al > Zn > Ni > Pb > H > Cu. Hence, (b), (d), (e), (f) are possible.

59. Calcium oxide on treatment with water produces hissing sound and energy.

$$CaO + H_2O \rightarrow Ca(OH)_2$$

Product (Y)

$$Ca(OH)_2 + 2HCl \rightarrow CaCl_2 + 2H_2O$$

(X)

Molecular mass of CaO = 40 + 16 = 56

Molecular mass of $Ca(OH)_2$ = 40 + 2(17) = 74

Molecular mass of $CaCl_2$ = 40 + 2(35.5) = 111

60. In 108 g of A, $\frac{7}{27} \times 108 = 28\,g$ of A is present.

Since the valency of oxygen is 2, we can consider the formula of A as $X_2\,O_a$.

$$\therefore\ a = \frac{108 - 28}{16} = 5 \text{ and the formula of A is } X_2O_5.$$

Atomic weight of X = 28/2 = 14

∴ Element X is nitrogen, and A is N_2O_5.

Let the formula of B is N_2O_b Since the ratio of N and O in B is 7 : 16, the number of oxygen atoms present in B is 4 [∴ 28 g of nitrogen combines with 64 g of oxygen].

∴ Formula of B is N_2O_4 (or) NO_2

61. During electrolysis of molten sodium chloride, sodium is deposited at cathode and chlorine is liberated at anode. Since removal of more electronegative element from NaCl gives sodium, the process is called reduction. Since removal of more electropositive element from NaCl gives chlorine, the process is called oxidation. Therefore, the electrolysis of molten sodium chloride is called redox reaction.

62. (a) $Cu + HgCl_2 \rightarrow CuCl_2 + Hg$

Copper displaces mercury from mercuric chloride and forms cupric chloride and mercury. This is a displacement reaction.

(b) $2KNO_3 \rightarrow 2KNO_2 + O_2$ (1)

$S + O_2 \rightarrow SO_2$ (2)

$C + O_2 \rightarrow CO_2$ (3)

The first reaction represents the decomposition of potassium nitrate to form potassium nitrite and oxygen. Oxygen liberated helps burn sulphur and charcoal to give sulphuric dioxide and carbon dioxide as given in reactions (2) and (3). Reaction (1) is a decomposition reaction, whereas reactions (2) and (3) are combination reactions.

(c) $2NH_4OH + CuSO_4 \rightarrow Cu(OH)_2 \downarrow + (NH_4)_2SO_4$

This is a double displacement and precipitation reaction.

63. (a) Since the atoms are bonded within the molecule by certain forces of attraction, energy is required to dissociate the molecules. In a decomposition reaction, breaking of bond takes place. To break bonds, energy is required. Hence, the energy needs to be supplied to initiate most of the decomposition reactions.

(b) Burning or combustion is a combination of a substance with oxygen and new bonds are formed with oxygen. As formation of bonds involves release of energy, combustions are generally exothermic.

64. At high temperature, aluminium reacts with iron (III) oxide.

$$2Al + Fe_2O_3 \longrightarrow Al_2O_3 + 2Fe + Heat$$

It is a displacement as well as an exothermic reaction. Al acts as a reducing agent as it undergoes oxidation while Fe_2O_3 acts as an oxidizing agent as it undergoes reduction.

Level 3: Assess Your Concepts

65. Carbon forms two oxides CO and CO_2, and the valencies of carbon are 2 and 4, re-spectively.

$CO_2 + H_2O \rightarrow H_2CO_3$ carbonic acid

$NaOH + H_2CO_3 \rightarrow NaHCO_3$ (or) Na_2CO_3

66. Given that 100 g of metal oxide contains 60 g of metal.

∴ 40 g of metal oxide contains? g of metal.

$= \frac{40 \times 60}{100} = 24$ g of metal

∴ Atomic weight of the metal is 24 and the metal is Mg.

∴ Molecular weight of $Mg(ClO_4)_2 = 24 + 71 + 128 = 223$

67. Metal with electronic configuration 2, 8, 14, 2 is Fe. Fe can form two hydroxides $Fe(OH)_2$ and $Fe(OH)_3$. The formulae of salts of these hydroxides with sulphuric acid are $FeSO_4$ and $Fe_2(SO_4)_3$.

$Fe(OH)_2 + H_2SO_4 \rightarrow FeSO_4 + H_2O$

$Fe(OH)_3 + 3H_2SO_4 \rightarrow Fe_2(SO_4)_3 + 3H_2O$

68. (i) identification of A from the product formed by the reaction of silver with ozone

(ii) identification of X from B

(iii) identification of Y and Z from X

69. (i) identification of the metal from the given ratio

(ii) identification of halogen based on colour

(iii) identification of chemical formula of salt of oxyacid

70. (a) Let the valency of metal be x and atomic weight be m.

∴ Metal sulphate is $M^{x+}SO_4^{2-} \Rightarrow M_2(SO_4)_x$

∴ Metal hydroxide is $M^{x+}OH_4^{2-} \Rightarrow M(OH)_x$

∴ Molecular weight of metal sulphate is

$$2m + 96x = 142 \rightarrow \quad (1)$$

Molecular weight of metal hydroxide is $m + 17x = 40$

$$\Rightarrow 2m + 34x = 80 \rightarrow \quad (2)$$

From (1) and (2)

$$\Rightarrow 2m + 96x = 142$$
$$\Rightarrow 2m + 34x = 80$$
$$(-) \quad (-) \quad (-)$$
$$62x = 62$$
$$\Rightarrow x = 1$$

∴ From (1) $\Rightarrow 2m + 96(1) = 142$

$\Rightarrow 2m = 142 - 96 = 46 \Rightarrow m = 23$

∴ Valency and atomic weight of the metal are 1 and 23, respectively.

(b) (A) $2Fe_2O_3 + 3C \rightarrow 4Fe + 3CO_2$

(A) (B)

It is a displacement as well as redox reaction. Since Fe_2O_3, loses oxygen it is oxidizing agent and carbon is gaining oxygen, it is reducing agent.

(B) $CO_2 + C \longrightarrow 2CO$

(B) (C)

It is a combination as well as redox reaction. Since CO_2 loses oxygen it is oxidizing agent and carbon is gaining oxygen it is reducing agent.

(C) $C + O_2 \longrightarrow CO_2 + Energy$

(B)

It is a combination, redox and exothermic reaction.

Since oxygen is added to carbon, carbon is reducing agent and oxygen is oxidizing agent.

71. When moist sugar is treated with anhydrous $CaCl_2$, it removes the moisture from the moist sugar due to its deliquescent nature. The chemical composition of sugar does not change in this process. Hence, it is a physical change. When sugar reacts with concentrated H_2SO_4, it is converted to black residue called **sugar charcoal**. Concentrated H_2SO_4, due to its dehydrating nature, removes the hydrogen and oxygen present in the compound as water and the chemical composition of sugar changes. Hence, it is a chemical change.

72. Silver chloride present in the photogrey lenses undergoes photolysis and gives silver and chlorine.

$$2AgCl \xrightarrow{\text{Sunlight}} 2Ag + Cl_2$$

It is a decomposition reaction as well as a redox reaction as silver loses an electronegative element, i.e., chlorine. Silver undergoes reduction while chlorine undergoes oxidation.

73. Since X is a gas which is used in sterilizing water and has a characteristic fishy odour, it is O_3. O_3 combines with black lead sulphide to give lead sulphate. It is a redox reaction.

$$PbS + 4O_3 \rightarrow PbSO_4 + 4O_2$$

74. Fluorine attacks all metals including copper. In the preparation of fluorine gas electrolysis is carried out in the copper vessel. Copper reacts with fluorine to form stable copper fluoride. This copper fluoride so formed acts as a protective layer against further corrosion of copper.

JEE-NEET Special Wing

Multiple-Answer Type Questions

1. The balanced chemical equation for the reaction is $K_2Cr_2O_7 + 14HCl \rightarrow 2KCl + 2CrCl_3 + 7H_2O + 3Cl_2\uparrow$

2. Metal X shows the valencies of 2 and 1, Metal Y shows the valencies of 2 and 4. Mercury shows the valencies of 1 and 2 while tin shows the valencies of 2 and 4. Mercury is below hydrogen in the metal reactivity series and hence does not liberate hydrogen gas.

3. The metal which displaces hydrogen from dilute acids and can not displace any metal above hydrogen should be the one which is placed just above hydrogen in the metal reactivity series. Sodium is a much stronger reducing agent than lead.

4. The oxide of nitrogen in which nitrogen shows the valency of 4 is NO_2. In this, 14 g nitrogen combines with 32 g oxygen. GAM of nitrogen is 14 g.

	Valency of nitrogen	Formula of oxide	Mass of nitrogen combining with 'x' g oxygen
(a)	1	N_2O	56 g
(b)	5	N_2O_5	11.2 g
(c)	2	NO	28 g
(d)	3	N_2O_3	18.6 g

5. The nonmetal is chlorine with electronic configuration 2, 8, 7. The percentage of chlorine in $HClO_3$ is 42%. The potassium salt is $KClO_3$.

   $2KClO_3 \rightarrow 2KCl + 3O_2$

   49 g of potassium chlorate gives 29.8 g solid product that is potassium chloride. That only remains in the reaction vessel. The amount of gaseous product is 19.2 g. Since the gaseous product escapes out into the atmosphere, this mass is considered to be the apparent loss in weight. This is approximately equal to 20%.

6. The element mentioned is iron [$4.67 \times 12 = 56$] Iron can form ferrous oxide, ferric oxide and a mixed oxide that is ferro so, ferric oxide. The gram molecular masses of the lower oxide and higher oxide are 72 g and 160 g respectively. [$72 \times 2.2 \approx 160$]

   $Fe_2O_3 + 3CO \rightarrow 2Fe + 3CO_2$

   Ferric oxide is more stable than ferrous oxide.

Comprehension-Based Questions

7.

Radical name		No.of atoms per molecule
(a) Biphosphate	(v)	7
(b) Phosphate	(i)	13
(c) Dihydrogen phosphate	(i)	15
(d) Phosphide	(ii)	5
(e) Phosphite	(iii)	6

8. $H_3PO_4 + 2NH_4OH \rightarrow (NH_4)_2HPO_4 + 2H_2O$

   5 molecules of acid and 10 molecules of base are required to form 5 molecules of the salt.

9. $3Mg + 2P \rightarrow Mg_3P_2$

10. $(NH_4)_3PO_4$ molecular mass = 149 g

11. NaH_2PO_4 is the salt which can react with 2 more molecules of sodium hydroxide.

    GMM = 120

    Percentage of Phosphorus = 3100/120 = 25.8%

12. The cation should be trivalent since phosphide ion is P^{-3}. Hydrogen phosphate is HPO_4^{-2}.

    $M_2(HPO_4)_3$ is the formula of the salt.

Common Solutions for questions 13 to 17:

The general stoichiometric chemical equation for the combustion of the hydrocarbon C_xH_y is:

$C_xH_Y + (4x + y)/4\ O_2 \rightarrow xCO_2 + y/2\ H_2O$

Hydrocarbon	No.of moles required/produced for the complete combustion of one mole of hydrocarbon		
	O_2	CO_2	H_2O
Alkane- C_nH_{2n+2}	$\frac{3n+1}{2}$	n	$n+1$
Alkene- C_nH_{2n}	$\frac{3n}{2}$	n	n
Alkyne- C_nH_{2n-2}	$\frac{3n+1}{2}$	n	$n-1$

	Hydrocarbon	No.of moles required/produced for the complete combustion of one mole of hydrocarbon		
		O_2	CO_2	H_2O
A	C_3H_8	5	3	4
B	C_4H_6	5.5	4	3
C	C_3H_4	4	3	2
D	C_2H_2	2.5	2	1
E	C_2H_6	3.5	2	3
F	C_3H_6	4.5	3	3

13. One mole of the hydrocarbon 'B' on its complete combustion forming 4 and 3 moles of CO_2 and H_2O respectively.

$\Rightarrow$ A total of 11 moles of oxygen atoms are formed on the product side.

$\Rightarrow$ Same number of moles of oxygen atoms would have been utilized on the reactants side

$\Rightarrow$ 11 moles of oxygen atoms = 5.5 moles of oxygen molecules are required for the complete combustion of 1 mole of the hydrocarbon 'B'.

14. From the given table, 9 moles of oxygen atoms are formed as products of the complete combustion of one mole of the hydrocarbon 'F'

$\Rightarrow$ 9 moles of oxygen atoms = 4.5 moles of oxygen molecules would have been required for the complete combustion of one mole of 'F'

$\Rightarrow$ 3 moles of oxygen will be utilised by----- $\frac{3}{4.5}$ = 0.67 moles of 'F' for its complete combustion.

15. 2.5 moles of hydrocarbon require 6.25 moles of oxygen.

1 mole of hydrocarbon requires -----6.25/2.5 = 2.5 moles of oxygen molecules which equals 5 moles of oxygen atoms.

In any stoichiometric equation, the number of atoms of each element on the reactant side should be equal to that on the product side.

So, among the hydrocarbons given in the options, one mole of hydrocarbon 'D' on combustion produces 2 and 1 mol of CO_2 and H_2O respectively which contains a total of 4 + 1 = 5 moles of oxygen atoms = 2.5 mol of oxygen.

Hence the hydrocarbon should be 'D'.

16. $C_xH_Y + (4x + y)/4\ O_2 \rightarrow xCO_2 + y/2\ H_2O$

For the hydrocarbon of the general formula C_nH_{2n+2} the number of moles of oxygen required for complete combustion would be equal to $(3n + 1)/2$.

17. From the information given in the table, hydrocarbon 'F' on combustion produces 3 moles of CO_2 and H_2O each, i.e., it produces products in a 1 : 1 molar ratio.

All three hydrocarbons given in the options produce CO_2 and H_2O in a 1 : 1 molar ratio when combusted. Hence, the correct answer is all of these.

18.

	Hydrocarbon		Volume occupied
(a)	0.5 mole A	(v)	$3x/2$
(b)	0.2 mole B	(vi)	$4x/5$
(c)	0.25 mole C	(iv)	$3x/4$
(d)	0.6 mole D	(iii)	$6x/5$
(e)	0.25 mole E	(i)	$x/2$
(f)	0.9 mole F	(ii)	$8x/3$

CHAPTER

4

Air and Oxygen

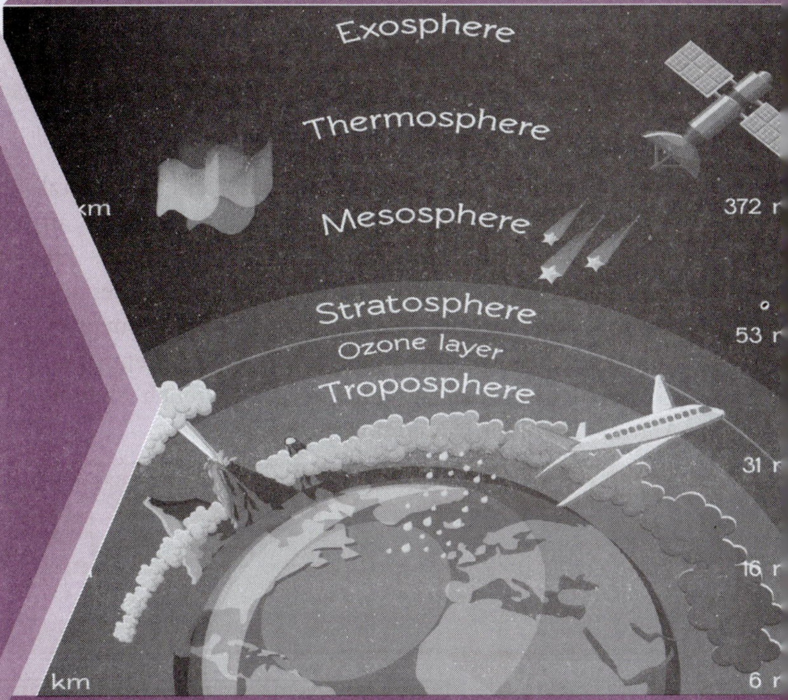

Remember

Before beginning this chapter, you should be able to:

- name different layers of atmosphere.
- understand the importance of common gases in nature and their uses.

Key Ideas

After completing this chapter, you should be able to:

- study about the composition and characteristics of air.
- explain different layers of atmosphere and their importance.
- learn different methods of preparation and properties of oxygen.
- understand the importance of oxygen in nature and its uses.
- study the causes, effects and different measures to curb air pollution.

A Tribute to Joseph Priestley (1733 – 1804)

Joseph Priestley, an English chemist and a natural philosopher discovered the active ingredient of air without which the existence of life is not possible. He described air as a composition of a mixture of gases and dethrone the age old idea about air as an elementary substance. He called the highly reactive ingredient of air as "dephlogisticated air" and the great French chemist Antoine Lavoisier named it as "oxygen".

He invented carbonated water, the rubber eraser and a dozen of key chemical compounds. He was also a maveric theologian. He was forced to flee his homeland, England in 1794 because of his unorthodox religious writings and vocal support for the American and French revolution. Priestley's home in Pennsylvania was designated as National Historic Chemical society, the world's largest scientfic society.

FUN TIME

CROSSWORD

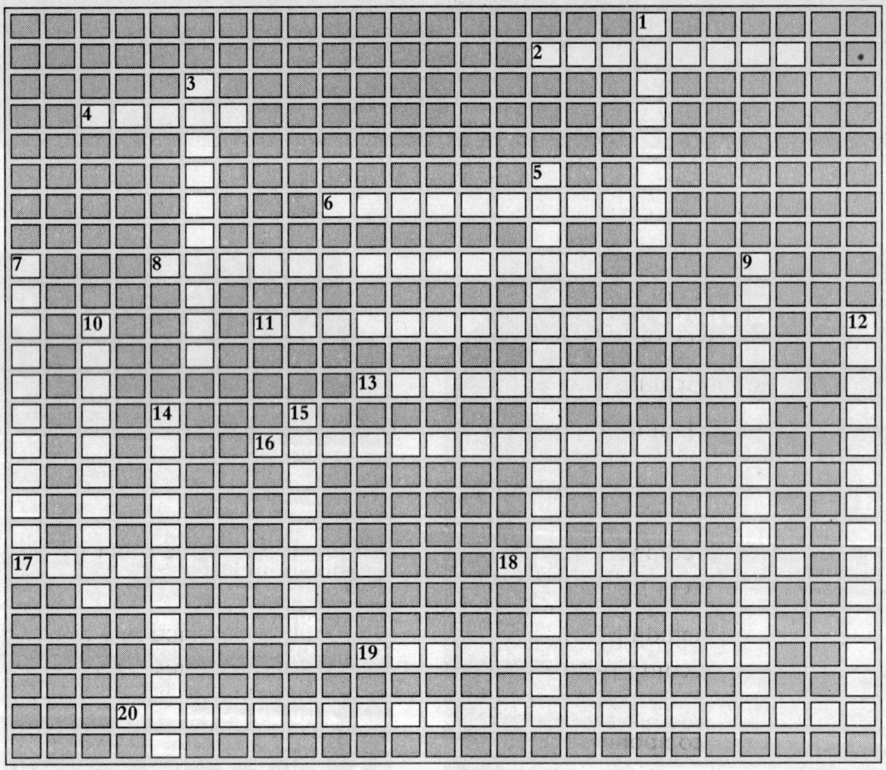

Across

2. Role of MgO_2 in the preparation of O_2 from H_2O_2
4. Homogenous mixture of two or more metals
6. Layer of atmosphere in which meteorites burn
8. Process of coating of iron objects with zinc
11. The zone of flame in which complete combustion takes place
13. Increase in surface temperature of earth leading to the melting of glaciers
16. Gas utilized by plants to prepare their food material
17. Layer of atmosphere containing maximum percentage of biomass
18. Scientist who gave the name oxygen
19. Layer of atmosphere consisting of ozone layer
20. Process of separation of mixture of gases based on the boiling points

Down

1. Mixture of 95% oxygen and 5% carbon dioxide
3. Substances causing pollution
5. Chemical responsible for depletion of ozone layer
7. Radiations from earth that are absorbed by ozone layer
9. Phenomenon of maintenance of earth's temperature by air
10. Process of burning of materials in presence of air
12. Formation of holes in the ozone layer
14. Layer of atmosphere that reflects radio signals
15. Instrument used to measure atmospheric pressure

INTRODUCTION

Air, water, food, etc. almost all the basic necessities are provided to us by nature. Amongst all, air plays the vital role in many processes taking place in the nature. Since all processes in nature are associated with air, we cannot imagine life without air. Being invisible, the presence of air is felt in every activity in nature.

Air

The study of air and its importance dates back to the 15th century until when air was considered to be an element. Later, in 1674, Mayoco for the first time predicted the presence of two components in air, namely, the active component and the inactive component. Since then, air is no more considered to be an element. In the later years, Lavoisier also found the ratio of the active and inactive components of air to be 1 : 4 by volume.

The later studies and experiments have revealed major components to be oxygen and nitrogen, the former being the active component and the latter being the inactive component.

Characteristics of Air as a Mixture

1. Variable composition of air at different places on earth.
2. No heat change is involved in the mixing up of gases in air.
3. No definite boiling point for liquid air.
4. Separation of air into various components can be done by physical methods.
5. The properties of different gases are retained in the air.
6. Air has no definite chemical formula.
7. Air does not exhibit definite chemical properties of its own.

Components of Air

Oxygen and nitrogen are the major components of air. Apart from these two, some other gases, such as, carbon dioxide, water vapour and inert gases are present in the atmosphere.

The various components of air including inert gases can be separated by the fractional distillation of liquid air. This is based on the principle that different components of air boil at different temperatures.

Table 4.1 Boiling points of components of air

Gases	Boiling points
CO_2	–78.5°C
Xe	–108°C
Kr	–153°C
O_2	–183°C
Ar	–186°C
N_2	–196°C
Ne	–246°C
He	–269°C

Every component of air has its own importance and functions. Some of them are listed below.

Table 4.2 Functions of different components of air

Components	Functions
Oxygen [O_2]	Respiration, burning of fuels, fermentation and decomposition of organic matter
Nitrogen [N_2]	Growth of plants and animals. Slows down the activity of oxygen in the atmosphere
Carbon [CO_2]	Photosynthesis and greenhouse effect
Water [H_2O]	Moisture for growth of plants and animals. Prevention of excess evaporation from living cells
Helium [He]	Weather balloons and for diluting oxygen carried by scuba divers
Neon [Ne]	Advertisement sign boards and lighting in aerodromes
Argon [Ar]	Electric bulbs

Composition of Air

Though the composition of air varies from place to place and time to time, the average composition by weight and by volume are determined.

Table 4.3 Composition of air by weight and volume

Components	Percentage by weight	Percentage by volume
Oxygen	23.1	21
Nitrogen	75.5	78
CO_2	0.053	0.03 to 0.04
Water vapour	Variable	Variable (up to a maximum of 4%)
Argon	1.288	0.95%
Other Gases	Trace Amounts	

Apart from these, other gases and dust particles are also present in air in trace amounts.

Atmosphere

The layer of air that surrounds the Earth up to an altitude of 300 km is called **atmosphere**. Above this altitude, the region is absolutely free of air. This region above the atmosphere is called **space**.

> **Info Bytes!**
> The Earth's atmosphere extends to about 10,000 km above the Earth's surface. However, the majority of its mass is found within just 30 km from the surface.

Layers of Atmosphere

The atmosphere is divided into four layers based on the variations in temperature and composition of different regions at different altitudes from the surface of the earth.

Troposphere

The layer of atmosphere which is in contact with the earth's surface is called **troposphere**. The range of temperature in this layer is close to that of the earth since it is just above the earth's surface. In this layer, the temperature decreases with increase in altitude up to about –50°C. It lies between 0 km and 10 km above the earth's surface and contains the maximum percentage of the total mass of the atmosphere.

Stratosphere

The layer of atmosphere above the troposphere is called **stratosphere**. In this layer, temperature range does not alter up to a height of about 25 km. Above this, the temperature gradually decreases up to a range of 0°C–10°C. It lies between 10 km and 50 km above the surface of the earth.

Mesosphere

The layer succeeding the stratosphere is called **mesosphere**. In this layer, the range of temperature is lower than that of the layers below it. It lies between 50 km and 80 km above the surface of the earth.

Thermosphere

This is the topmost layer of atmosphere and it is called **thermosphere** due to the very high temperatures prevailing there. The basic reason for this is that the atmosphere in this layer absorbs intense solar radiation.

Due to the absorption of such high intense radiation, the molecules get ionised. As a result, this layer consists of ions and free electrons. Hence, this layer is also known as **ionosphere.**

Exosphere

The outermost layer of the atmosphere which extends upto 10,000 km above the earth's surface is known as **exosphere** or **magnetosphere**.

The composition of air is not uniform throughout the atmosphere. It varies from one layer to the other layer.

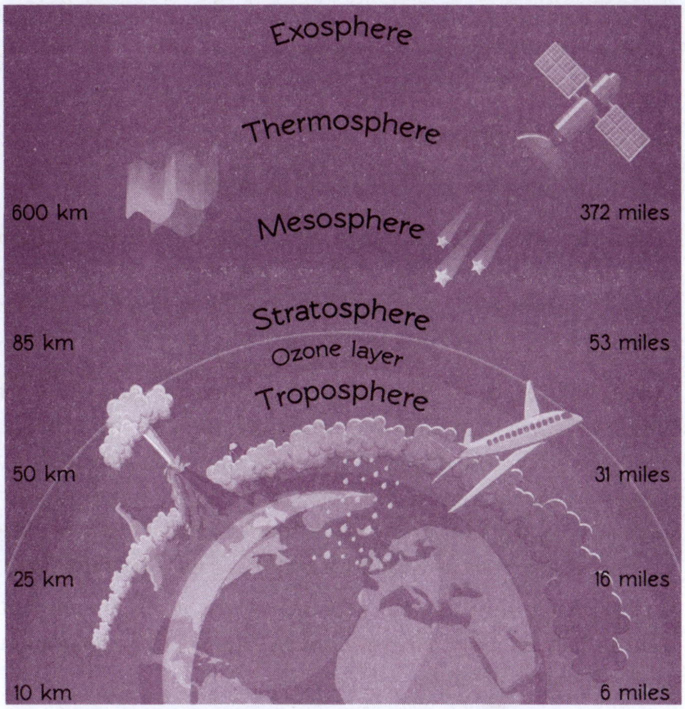

Figure 4.1 Layers of Atmosphere

Significance of Atmosphere

The atmosphere plays an important role in all natural phenomena taking place. These are:

1. Formation of clouds
2. Occurrence of rain
3. Formation of snow
4. Preventing harmful radiations reaching the earth
5. Formation of winds

Since the atmosphere is associated with all these natural processes, the study of atmosphere helps in making weather forecasts regarding cyclones, floods and droughts. They further help in taking proper steps to protect the life from these natural disasters.

Atmospheric Pressure

The atmosphere in any layer is composed of air, which exerts a downward pressure, and this downward pressure exerted by air due to its weight on the surroundings is called **atmospheric pressure**.

Since pressure is defined as the force exerted per unit area, it is expressed in Newton/metre^2 which is called **Pascal**. Hence, the SI unit of pressure is **Pascal (Pa)** or **kilopascal (kPa)**.

Konnect

The barometer, a device to measure atmospheric pressure, was invented in the early 17th century. In India, places like Leh and Shimla experience noticeable atmospheric pressure variations due to their altitude.

Measurement of the Atmospheric Pressure

Since the composition and the density of air vary with the altitude, the pressure exerted by air also varies. The atmospheric pressure decreases with an increase in the altitude. It is due to this reason that the atmospheric pressure is measured at sea level where it is maximum.

The instrument used to measure the atmospheric pressure is called **barometer**. Two types of barometers are in use for this purpose which are discussed below.

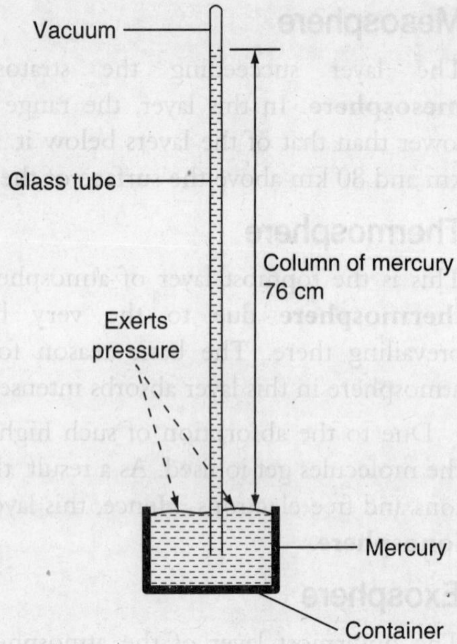

Figure 4.2 A mercury barometer

Mercury Barometer

This is the most common type of barometer used.

Principle: Mercury is a liquid which has high density (13.6 g/cc). Hence, it can rise as a short column when the pressure exactly balances the atmospheric pressure. Moreover, mercury does not stick to the walls of the glass tube due to weak adhesive forces between them.

Construction and Working: A graduated glass tube of about 840-mm length which is closed at one end and open at the other end is taken. This tube is filled completely with mercury and then inverted into a trough full of mercury. Depending on the external pressure, some mercury from glass tube comes out and stands at a certain height. This height is measured. Above this column, there is almost vacuum and it is called **torricellian vacuum**.

At normal atmospheric pressure at sea level, the height of the mercury column falls to about 760 mm of Hg. Hence, this is taken as the standard value of atmospheric pressure.

$$1 \text{ atm} = 760 \text{ mm of Hg} = 760 \text{ torr} = 101.3 \text{ kilopascals}$$

The pressure can be calculated by substituting the height of the mercury column in the formula $P = hdg$, where 'h' is the height of the mercury column, 'd' is the density of the mercury and 'g' is the acceleration due to gravity.

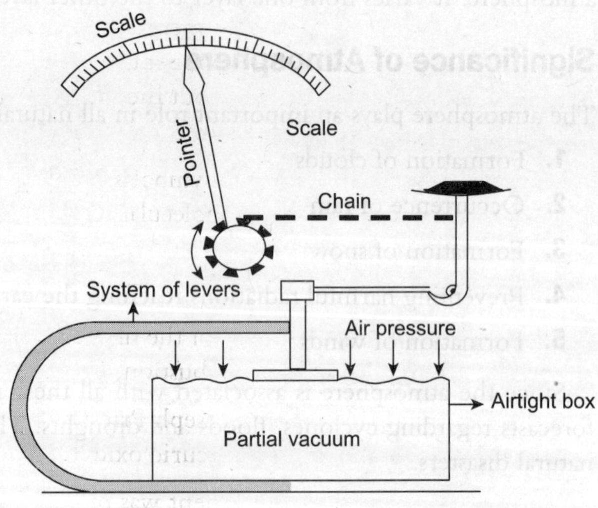

Figure 4.3 An aneroid barometer

Aneroid Barometer

This barometer does not contain any liquid. It is convenient to use because it is very light in weight and portable.

Principle: Balancing the atmospheric pressure by the elasticity of the metal.

Construction and Working: The aneroid barometer is basically operated by a metal cell that contains very small amount of air or a series of such cells joined together. One side is fixed to the base of the instrument while the other side is connected with a system of levers and pulleys. These levers and pulleys are connected to a pointer that moves over a scale fixed at the front side of the instrument.

Any change in pressure alters the thickness of the cells.

EXAMPLE 4.1 Why do mountaineers often face breathing difficulties at higher altitudes?

SOLUTION

Mountaineers often face breathing difficulties at higher altitudes due to the decreased air density and lower oxygen concentration. As altitude increases, the number of air molecules per unit volume decreases, leading to reduced atmospheric pressure. Consequently, the amount of available oxygen in each breath is reduced. The human body requires a certain partial pressure of oxygen for efficient oxygenation of the blood, and this is harder to achieve in the thin air of high altitudes. As a result, climbers can experience symptoms of altitude sickness, which include shortness of breath, dizziness, and fatigue.

EXAMPLE 4.2 The atmosphere contains about 78% nitrogen and 21% oxygen. Why don't these two gases react with each other under normal conditions?

SOLUTION

Under standard atmospheric conditions, nitrogen (N_2) and oxygen (O_2) are both diatomic molecules held together by strong triple and double bonds respectively. To break these bonds and form new ones, a considerable amount of energy is needed. While nitrogen and oxygen can react to form nitrogen oxides, this reaction typically requires elevated temperatures, such as those found in lightning strikes or combustion processes in engines. In the absence of such high energy conditions, nitrogen and oxygen remain largely unreactive with each other in the atmosphere.

EXAMPLE 4.3 Why is the mesosphere considered the coldest layer of Earth's atmosphere?

SOLUTION

The mesosphere is located above the stratosphere and below the thermosphere. In the stratosphere, the ozone layer absorbs ultraviolet radiation from the Sun, leading to an increase in temperature. However, the mesosphere lacks such a radiation-absorbing layer. Additionally, the mesosphere is too high up to benefit from the heat being transferred from the Earth's surface by convection. As a result, there is very little to no heat source in the mesosphere, and it experiences radiative cooling, where the minimal heat present is lost to outer space. These factors combined make the mesosphere the coldest layer of Earth's atmosphere.

Oxygen

Oxygen is one of the major components of air. Nitrogen, the other major component is present in greater proportions in air. As nitrogen is an inactive component, most of the properties of air are attributed to the presence of oxygen in air. As oxygen is responsible for carrying out the vital processes of nature, such as, respiration and burning, oxygen is considered to be the supporter of life on earth.

Oxygen is a diatomic element. Its symbol is O and formula is O_2. Its atomic number is 8, and hence, the electronic configuration is 2, 6. Its atomic weight is 16 and molecular weight is 32. The valency of oxygen is 2. It has an allotropic form, i.e., ozone (O_3).

Historical Aspects

A Swedish chemist, Carl Scheele for the first time prepared oxygen by heating potassium nitrate and mercuric oxide. Since this gas was found to support combustion, he named it as '*fire air*' or 'Vital Life.'

Later on, an English chemist, Joseph Priestley prepared oxygen by focusing intense sun rays using a short-focus convex lens on a test tube containing mercuric oxide.

The fact that oxygen is an element was proved by Lavoisier. Assuming that oxygen is invariably present in all acids, he named it as '**oxygen**' which means '*acid former.*'

Occurrence

Oxygen is the most abundant element on earth's crust. It occurs both in free and in combined states.

1. **Free State:** Oxygen is present in a free state in the atmospheric air. It comprises about 21% by volume and about 23% by mass of the total air. Water in oceans and other water bodies also contain some amount of oxygen in dissolved state. Due to the presence of this dissolved oxygen in water, all aquatic species are able to survive in water.
2. **Combined State:** Water is the most important compound which contains oxygen in combined state. Plants and animals also contain 50%–70% of oxygen in the combined state. Further, 50% of oxygen is present in the form of silicates, carbonates, limestone and other ores.

Info Bytes!

Plants are our little oxygen factories. Through photosynthesis, they take in carbon dioxide and release oxygen. Talk about natural air purifiers.

Preparation

Table 4.4 General methods of preparation of oxygen

Methods	Equations	Observations
Heating of oxides On heating, mercuric and silver oxides decompose to form their respective metals and oxygen gas	(a) $2HgO \xrightarrow{\Delta} 2Hg + O_2$ (b) $2Ag_2O \xrightarrow{\Delta} 4Ag + O_2$	(a) Forms mirror-like surface near the cooler parts of the test tube (b) Silvery white globules are formed
Thermal decomposition of heavy oxides Heavy metal oxides decompose to give oxygen and lower oxides	(a) $2Pb_3O_4 \longrightarrow 6PbO + O_2$ (b) $2PbO_2 \longrightarrow 2PbO + O_2$	(a) Reddish brown residue turning yellow on cooling is called **litharge** (b) Chocolate-brown PbO_2 turns to yellow litharge
Thermal decomposition of nitrates Alkali metal nitrates on heating decompose to give metal nitrites and oxygen	(a) $2KNO_3 \longrightarrow 2KNO_2 + O_2$ (b) $2NaNO_3 \longrightarrow 2NaNO_2 + O_2$	

Laboratory Methods of Preparation

1. **From Hydrogen Peroxide:** Hydrogen peroxide undergoes catalytic decomposition in the presence of manganese dioxide to give water and oxygen at room temperature.

$$2H_2O_2 \xrightarrow{MnO_2} 2H_2O + O_2$$

Experiment: MnO_2 is taken in a flat-bottomed flask. A solution of H_2O_2 is added dropwise to MnO_2 in the flask through a thistle funnel.

Observation: Effervescence starts with the evolution of oxygen gas. The gas rekindles a glowing splinter.

Precautions:

(a) No heating is required

(b) MnO_2 used should be pure

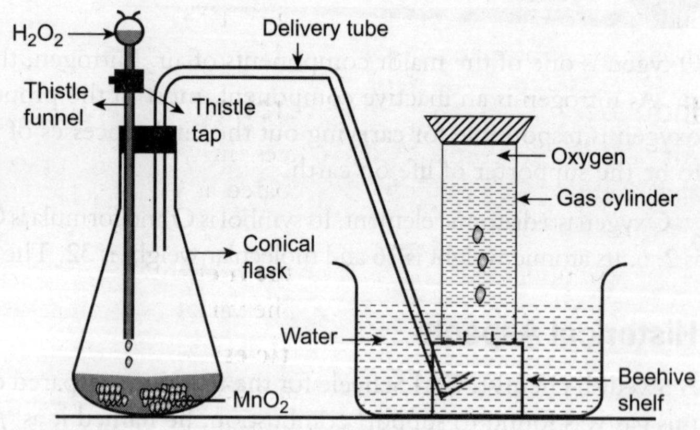

Figure 4.4 Laboratory preparation of oxygen from H_2O_2

2. **From Potassium Chlorate:** Potassium chlorate on heating strongly decomposes to give potassium chloride and oxygen. MnO_2 acts as a catalyst for this reaction.

$$2KClO_3 \xrightarrow[MnO_2]{\Delta} 2KCl + 3O_2$$

Experiment: A mixture of potassium chlorate and MnO_2 in the ratio of 4:1 is taken in a hard glass test tube. The test tube is fixed to a stand in a slightly slanting position. The mixture is heated.

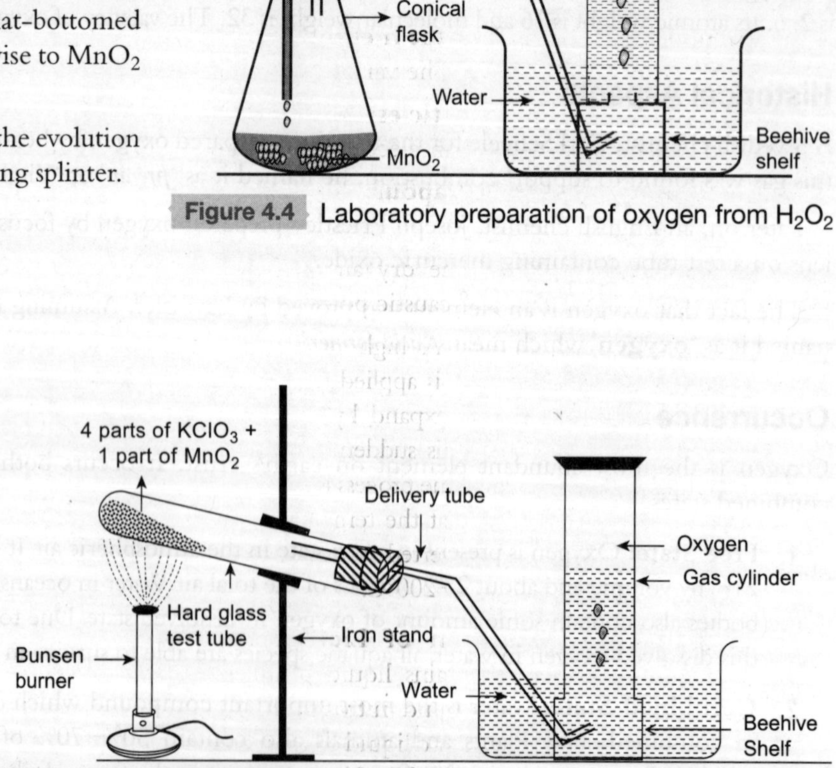

Figure 4.5 Preparation of oxygen from $KClO_3$

Observation: A colourless gas is evolved which rekindles the burning candle.

Precautions:

(a) The delivery tube should be removed from the trough before the burner is taken out after the experiment.

(b) MnO_2 used should be free of carbon.

3. From Potassium Permanganate: On heating, potassium permanganate decomposes to give potassium manganate, manganese dioxide and oxygen.

Experiment: $KMnO_4$ is taken into a hard glass test tube. It is then heated with a Bunsen burner.

$$2KMnO_4 \xrightarrow{\Delta} K_2MnO_4 + MnO_2 + O_2$$

Observation: A colourless gas which rekindles the glowing splinter is evolved.

Precaution: A cotton plug should be fixed at the mouth of the test tube.

Konnect

Role of MnO_2: MnO_2 reduces the melting point of potassium chlorate from 350°C to 327°C. The decomposition temperature is also brought down to 350°C from 370°C. It also acts as a positive catalyst for the reaction.

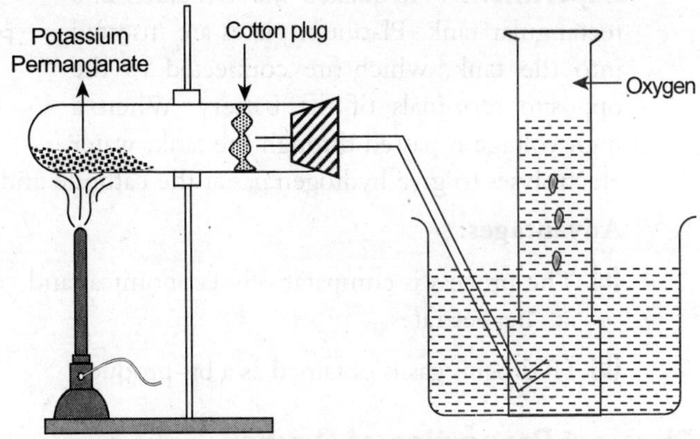

Figure 4.6 Laboratory preparation of oxygen

Method of Collection of Oxygen

In all the methods, the evolved gas is collected by the same method. A glass jar is inverted over the water tank in a trough and oxygen gas is collected in the glass jar by the downward displacement of water.

Industrial Methods of Preparation

Air and water being the resources in which oxygen is abundantly available, oxygen is prepared at a large scale from these natural resources.

1. Preparation of oxygen by the method of fractional distillation of liquid air: The various steps involved are given below:

(a) Removal of Dust Particles: Air should be first free from dust particles. This is done by passing air either through filters or through electric precipitators.

(b) Removal of Water Vapour: The air free of dust particles is passed through conc. H_2SO_4, or anhydrous calcium chloride.

(c) Removal of CO_2: The dry air is passed through caustic soda or caustic potash.

(d) Liquefaction of Air: A high pressure of 100 atm–200 atm range is applied to dry air. Then air is allowed to expand by pumping it through a fine jet. This sudden expansion results in cooling. The same process is repeated a number of times so that the temperature is decreased and air is converted to liquid state. Liquid air is obtained at −200°C.

(e) Fractional Distillation of Liquid Air: Liquid air mainly contains liquid nitrogen and liquid oxygen. Liquid nitrogen has a boiling point of −95°C and liquid oxygen has a boiling point of −182.9 °C. These liquids can be separated by fractional distillation.

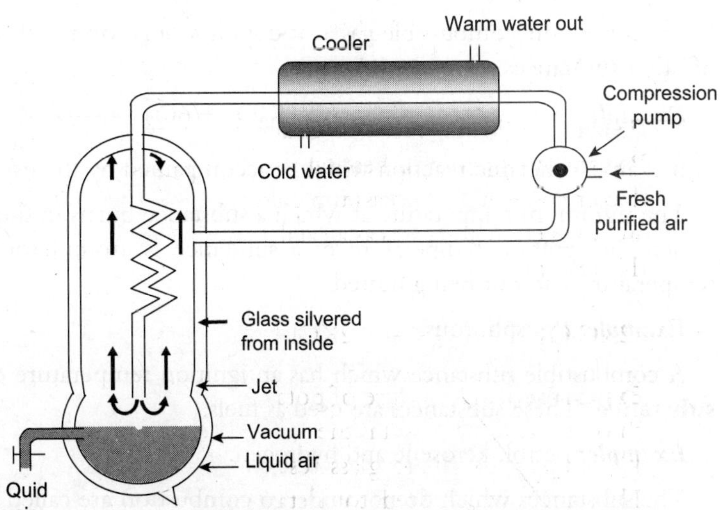

Figure 4.7 Liquefaction of air

As nitrogen has a lower boiling point, it evaporates first leaving behind liquid oxygen. Gentle heating of liquid oxygen gives oxygen gas.

2. Preparation of Oxygen by Electrolysis of Water: If a little amount of sulphuric acid is added to water, the water then is called **acidulated water**. When this is subjected to electrolysis, water decomposes to give hydrogen and oxygen. Hydrogen is liberated at the cathode and oxygen is liberated at the anode.

$$2H_2O \xrightarrow{\text{Electric current}} 2H_2(g) + O_2(g)$$

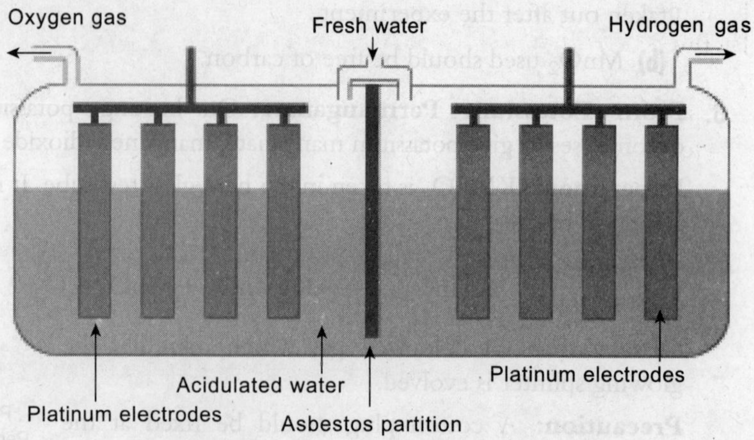

Figure 4.8 Industrial electrolysis of water

Experiment : Acidulated water is taken in a rectangular tank. Platinum plates are inserted into the tank, which are connected to the opposite terminals of the battery. When a high voltage is passed through the tank, water electrolyses to give hydrogen gas at the cathode and oxygen gas at the anode.

Advantages:

(a) The process is comparatively economical and can be used especially in places where the electricity is available at cheaper rates.

(b) Hydrogen gas is obtained as a by-product.

Physical Properties of Oxygen

- Oxygen is a colourless, odourless, tasteless and a non-poisonous gas.
- Its vapour density is 16.
- Boiling and freezing points of O_2 are −183°C and −218°C, respectively.
- Oxygen is slightly soluble in water.

Chemical Properties of Oxygen

Combustibility

Oxygen is a non-combustible gas as it does not burn on its own. It is a supporter of combustion as it allows combustion of other substances.

Example: $C_6H_{12}O_6 + 6O_2 \longrightarrow 6CO_2 + 6H_2O + \text{Energy}$

It is an exothermic reaction which is accompanied by the evolution of heat.

The minimum temperature at which a substance burns in the presence of oxygen is called its **ignition temperature**. When the ignition temperature of a substance is around room temperature, the substance burns in air at ordinary temperature without being heated.

Example: Phosphorous

A combustible substance which has an ignition temperature close to the room temperature is called an **inflammable substance**. These substances are used as fuels.

Example: petrol, kerosene and hydrogen.

The substances which do not undergo combustion are called **incombustible substances.**

Example: silica, calcium carbonate, etc.

Respiration

The process of respiration taking place in plants and animals is also a slow combustion reaction. During respiration, oxygen gas is inhaled which combines with haemoglobin of blood to form oxyhaemoglobin. This oxygen oxidizes the digested food (mostly present as glucose) to form carbon dioxide and water. During this process of combustion, energy is released. By this process, oxygen supports life on earth.

$$C_6H_{12}O_6 + 6O_2 \longrightarrow 6CO_2 + 6H_2O + \text{Energy}$$

Though respiration is similar to the combustion of organic compounds, these two processes differ in some respects.

Table 4.5 Differences between combustion and respiration

Combustion	Respiration
Fast process	Slow process
Takes place at high temperatures	Takes place at body temperature
Catalysts are not essential	Enzymes are essential
Energy is released in the form of heat and light	Energy is released in the form of heat only

Reaction with Metals

Oxygen reacts with metals to form metal oxides which are generally basic in nature. Though most of the metals form metal oxides, the metals differ in their reactivities with oxygen.

(a) Sodium and Potassium: Both react with oxygen vigorously and form oxides at room temperature.

$$4Na + O_2 \longrightarrow 2Na_2O$$

$$4K + O_2 \longrightarrow 2K_2O$$

(b) Magnesium and Calcium: Both react with oxygen on heating slightly to form corresponding oxides.

$$2Mg + O_2 \longrightarrow 2MgO$$

$$2Ca + O_2 \longrightarrow 2CaO$$

(c) Aluminium and Iron: They react with oxygen at room temperature forming an oxide coating over the metal surface. In the case of aluminium, it prevents further oxidation of the metal.

$$4Al + 3O_2 \longrightarrow 2Al_2O_3$$

$$4Fe + 3O_2 \longrightarrow 2Fe_2O_3$$

(d) At higher temperature, iron gives reddish brown powder with crackling noise due to the formation of ferric tetraoxide or ferrosoferric oxide.

$$4Fe + 2O_2 \longrightarrow Fe_3O_4$$

(e) Copper and Silver: On heating, copper reacts with oxygen to form black, powdery cupric oxide. Green sparks with crackling noise are also observed.

$$2Cu + O_2 \longrightarrow 2CuO$$

$$2Ag + O_2 \longrightarrow Ag_2O$$

(f) Gold and Platinum: These metals do not react with oxygen even at a high temperature.

Reactions with Non-metals

Oxygen also reacts with various non-metals to give corresponding oxides.

(a) Reaction with Hydrogen: Under normal conditions, oxygen does not react with hydrogen. Only when an electric spark is generated in a mixture of oxygen and hydrogen in 1 : 2 ratio, they react with a flash and an explosion to form water. Oxygen and hydrogen are also made to react by applying high pressure and passing through a pipe having a small hole. The mixture gets ignited and burns with hot blue flame. This flame is known as **oxyhydrogen flame**. This is used for welding purpose.

$$2H_2 + O_2 \longrightarrow 2H_2O$$

(b) Reaction with Nitrogen: Nitrogen being chemically less reactive does not react with oxygen under normal conditions. But when an electric spark is produced in a 1 : 1 mixture of nitrogen and oxygen, they react to form nitric oxide.

$$N_2 + O_2 \xrightleftharpoons{\text{Electric spark}} 2NO$$

(c) Reaction with Carbon: Red hot charcoal when burnt with oxygen produces CO_2 gas with the evolution of a large amount of heat.

$$C + O_2 \rightarrow CO_2 + \text{Heat}$$

Due to the evolution of large amount of heat in this reaction, charcoal, coal, coke, etc., are used as fuels.

(d) Reaction with Sulphur: Sulphur burns with oxygen to form sulphur dioxide gas. Along with SO_2 gas, trace amounts of sulphur trioxide are also produced. This mixture of oxides imparts brilliant blue colour to the flame.

$$S + O_2 \longrightarrow SO_2$$

$$2S + 3O_2 \longrightarrow 2SO_3$$

(only in traces)

(e) Reaction with Phosphorous: Phosphorous on burning with oxygen produces dense white fumes of phosphorous pentoxide.

$$4P + 5O_2 \longrightarrow 2P_2O_5$$

Reaction with Hydrocarbons

Hydrocarbons react with oxygen to form carbon dioxide and water. Different hydrocarbons react with oxygen at different temperatures. A large amount of heat is evolved during this reaction.

Due to the highly exothermic nature of the reaction, a mixture of hydrocarbons acts as a very good fuel, e.g., wood, petrol, diesel and LPG.

A candle made up of a mixture of lower hydrocarbons also burns in oxygen producing heat and light.

$$C_xH_y + O_2 \longrightarrow xCO_2 + \frac{y}{2}H_2O + \text{Energy}$$

The addition of oxygen to a metal or a non-metal is termed as oxidation. Some non-metal oxides also undergo oxidation to their higher oxides. As oxygen oxidizes most of the substances, it is a good oxidizing agent.

Oxidation of Non-metal Oxides

(a) Sulphur Dioxide : SO_2 on oxidation with V_2O_5 (vanadium pentoxide) or platinum gives SO_3. This reaction is made use of in the manufacturing of H_2SO_4. This reaction also takes place in the catalytic convertors of automobiles.

$$2SO_2 + O_2 \xrightarrow[\text{or Pt}]{V_2O_5} 2SO_3$$

(b) Carbon Monoxide: Carbon monoxide which is a major constituent of automobile exhaust gets converted to CO_2 which is less polluting in the catalytic convertors of automobile engines.

$$2CO + O_2 \longrightarrow 2CO_2$$

(c) Nitric Oxide: Nitric oxide reacts with oxygen to form nitrogen dioxide which is reddish brown in colour.

$$2NO + O_2 \longrightarrow 2NO_2$$

Oxidation of Other Compounds

(a) Oxidation of Ammonia: When a mixture of ammonia and oxygen in 4 : 5 ratio is passed over platinum gauze at 800°C, they react to form nitric oxide and steam.

$$4NH_3 + 5O_2 \xrightarrow[800^\circ C]{Pt} 4NO + 6H_2O$$

When ammonia is burnt with limited amount of oxygen, it burns with a blue flame with the evolution of nitrogen gas.

$$4NH_3 + 3O_2 \xrightarrow{\Delta} 2N_2 + 6H_2O$$

(b) Oxidation of Metallic Sulphides: Sulphides of some metals react with oxygen at higher temperature to form the corresponding metal oxides with the evolution of SO_2 gas.

$$2ZnS + 3O_2 \longrightarrow 2ZnO + 2SO_2$$

$$2FeS + 3O_2 \longrightarrow 2FeO + 2SO_2$$

$$2FeS_2 + 11O_2 \longrightarrow 2Fe_2O_3 + 8SO_2$$

$$2PbS + 3O_2 \longrightarrow 2PbO + 2SO_2$$

(c) Oxidation of Non-metallic Sulphides: Both hydrogen sulphide and carbon disulphide react with oxygen liberating SO_2 gas.

$$2H_2S + 3O_2 \longrightarrow 2H_2O + 2SO_2$$

$$CS_2 + 3O_2 \longrightarrow CO_2 + 2SO_2$$

Rusting of Iron

Corrosion of iron is generally termed as rusting of iron. It is a process in which iron is converted into the hydrated form of oxide in the presence of air and moisture.

Process

Atmospheric air contains oxygen and water vapour. When iron comes into contact with this atmospheric air, it slowly reacts with oxygen to form ferric oxide. This ferric oxide on further reaction with water vapour forms hydrated ferric oxide. This is called **rust**.

$$4Fe(s) + 3O_2(g) \longrightarrow 2Fe_2O_3(s)$$

$$Fe_2O_3(s) + H_2O(l) \longrightarrow Fe_2O_3.xH_2O(s)$$

(x = number of water molecules which is variable)

Effects

Rust formed is in the form of flakes which crumbles from the surface of the metal. In addition to corroding the metal, rusting also weakens the iron structures.

Prevention

1. **Painting:** The metal surface when coated with some other material prevents the exposure of the metal to the moist air. Thus, rusting is prevented. Since iron is used for making different structures used for different purposes, it is also necessary to coat the surfaces with different materials depending on their nature.

   (a) Doors, windows, cars, buses, vehicles, etc., are coated with red lead oxide paint. This coating prevents iron from rusting. In addition to protecting the metal from rusting, coating in these cases should also enhance the appearance of the structure. For this purpose, the enamel paint is coated on the surface of the red lead oxide paint.

(b) Ships, bridges, electric poles, etc., are coated with tar or red lead oxide paint. Though this is a costly process, this effectively prevents rusting. As these structures are in contact with water always, an effective method of protecting the metal from corrosion is absolutely essential.

(c) Cooking stoves, ovens, refrigerators, washbasins, utensils, etc., are coated on the metal surface at a high temperature. This process is called **enamelling**. This coating is resistant to high temperature. It also gives good appearance to the articles.

(d) *Machine parts/engine parts:* A protective layer on these parts is of no use since these parts keep moving which results in the weathering of the coating. Hence, these parts are coated with a layer of oil or grease. In addition to preventing rusting, this also acts as a lubricant for machines.

(e) Furniture and fixtures are coated with a thin layer of plastic.

2. **Galvanization**: Iron sheets are dipped in molten zinc and passed through heavy rollers. This iron coated with zinc metal is called **galvanized iron** and the process as **galvanization**. For example, tin roofs, buckets, tubs, iron trunks and suitcases.
3. **Tinning**: Forming a layer of tin over the iron surface is called **tinning.** This process is similar to galvanization.
   Example: Containers for edible materials, like, oils, fruit juices, vegetables, meat, etc.
4. **Electroplating**: The process of coating the iron metal by another metal by means of electrolysis is called **electroplating**. The metals used for this purpose are nickel and chromium. Though it is an expensive process, coating is long lasting and effective. For example, bicycle handles, rims, car bumpers, etc.
5. **Alloying**: The process of mixing of other metals with iron to make a homogeneous mixture is called **alloying**. The most commonly used alloy of iron is stainless steel, which contains 12%–20% chromium and 0.07%–0.1% carbon. By making this stainless steel alloy, iron metal is protected from corrosion.
   Example: Surgical instruments, utensils, tools and cutlery.

Detection of Oxygen

The following tests can be performed to detect the evolution of oxygen gas:

1. Rekindles a glowing splinter
2. Neutral to litmus
3. Colourless nitric oxide changes to reddish brown NO_2 gas
4. Turns alkaline pyrogallol to dark brown

Uses of Oxygen

1. Respiration of living organisms
2. Combustion or burning of fuels
3. Manufacture of H_2SO_4 and HNO_3 in industry
4. **Explosive:** For blasting big rocks in mines, a mixture of coal, petroleum jelly and liquid oxygen is used in the form of a cartridge.
5. **Metal Extraction:** Used in a blast furnace for the extraction of iron.
6. **Welding:** A mixture of oxygen and hydrogen on burning gives an oxyhydrogen flame which is at a temperature of 2800°C. In place of hydrogen, when acetylene is used, it becomes oxyacetylene flame which gives a still higher temperature of 3300°C. Both are used for welding purposes.
7. **Stimulant for Breathing:** A mixture of 95% oxygen and 5% CO_2 is called **carbogen**. It is used for aiding breathing in patients with breathing problems.
8. **As an Anaesthetic:** A mixture of N_2O and oxygen is used as an anaesthetic during surgical operations.

9. **Rocket Fuel:** Liquid oxygen is used as a rocket fuel.

10. **Artificial Respiration:** Oxygen cylinders are carried by mountaineers, astronauts, miners, divers, submariners, aviators, firemen, etc.

EXAMPLE 4.4 CO_2 is collected by upward displacement of air and O_2 is collected by downward displacement of water. Justify.

SOLUTION

Oxygen is collected by downward displacement of water and CO_2 is collected by upward displacement of air. This is due to more soluble nature of CO_2 in water forming carbonic acid whereas O_2 is slightly soluble in water. Since the difference in densities of O_2 and air is very less, O_2 cannot be effectively collected by upward or downward displacement of air.

EXAMPLE 4.5 State two reactions between non-metallic oxides and oxygen which take place in catalytic converter.

SOLUTION

SO_2 on oxidation in presence of V_2O_5 or platinum gives SO_3. This reaction takes place in the catalytic converter of automobiles.

$$2SO_2 + O_2 \xrightarrow[\text{or Pt}]{V_2O_2} 2SO_3$$

Carbon monoxide which is a major constituent of automobile exhaust gets converted to CO_2 in the catalytic converter of automobile engines.

$$2CO + O_2 \longrightarrow 2CO_2$$

EXAMPLE 4.6 A cotton plug is kept at the mouth of test tube during the preparation of oxygen by $KMnO_4$. Why?

SOLUTION

In the preparation of oxygen from $KMnO_4$ a cotton plug is kept near the mouth of test tube. It is to prevent the spillage of $KMnO_4$ into the gas jar in which the oxygen gas is being collected.

EXAMPLE 4.7 What is the advantage of preparation of O_2 by H_2O_2 over its preparation by $KClO_3$ and $KMnO_4$?

SOLUTION

The advantage of preparation of oxygen from H_2O_2 over its preparation from $KClO_3$ and $KMnO_4$ is that no heating is required and the reaction takes place at room temperature only.

EXAMPLE 4.8 What are the advantages of preparation of O_2 by electrolysis over fractional distillation of air?

SOLUTION

The advantage of preparation of oxygen by electrolysis of water over its preparation by fractional distillation of air is that industrially the process of electrolysis gives pure oxygen. Also, hydrogen gas is obtained as a by-product in this process.

Air Pollution

In addition to the various components (both major and minor) present in it, air also contains some other gases produced by the human activity. These gases are not only useless but also cause damage to the environment. Due to the presence of these gases, the composition of air in the atmosphere changes. The variation in the composition of air in the atmosphere due to the release of these gases is called **air pollution**.

Major Factors Affecting the Composition of Air

1. The area of forests in the region
2. The industries present in the area
3. Density of population
4. Urbanization.

Info Bytes!

Natural Air Purifiers—Indoor plants like Spider Plant, Peace Lily, and Boston Fern help improve air quality.

Hazards of Air Pollution and Their Prevention

1. **Acid Rain:** Rain water is actually the purest form of water. However, the presence of pollutants, such as, oxides of nitrogen and sulphur in the air impart acidity to the rain water. The sources of these gases are the eruption of

Table 4.6 Various pollutants responsible for air pollution

Pollutants	Sources	Processes	Effects on environment
Carbon monoxide	Automobiles	Incomplete combustion of fuels	Respiratory problems (reduction in intake of oxygen)
Sulphur dioxide	(i) Automobiles (ii) Industries (iii) Thermal power plants	(i) Incomplete combustion of fuels (ii) Metals' extraction (iii) Paper making	(i) Main cause of acid rain (ii) Respiratory disorders
Nitrogen oxides	(i) Automobiles (ii) Industries	Incomplete combustion of fuels	(i) Formation of smog (ii) Causes acid rain
Carbon dioxide	(i) Automobiles (ii) High density of population (iii) Decrease in forest area	Combustion of fuels and deforestation	Global warming
Ozone	Industries		Global warming
CFCs (chlorofluorocarbons)	(i) In air conditioners as organic chemicals (ii) Refrigeration systems		Depletion of ozone layer
Metals	(i) Automobiles (Pb) (ii) Thermal power plants (Pb, Hg, As, Co, Cu)	(i) Present in petrol as anti-knock (ii) Chemical reactions	(i) Nervous disorders (ii) Problems of digestion (iii) Cancer
Hydrocarbons	(i) Automobiles (ii) Degradation of organic wastes	Exhaust gas	Carcinogenic

Pollutants	Sources	Processes	Effects on environment
Fly ash	(i) Thermal power plants	Combustion of coal	(i) Metal oxides and toxic metals of fly ash cause health problems (ii) Silica causes bronchitis and lung cancer (iii) Contamination of ground water and clogging of drainage
Suspended particulate matter (SPM)	(i) Automobiles (ii) Industries	Exhaust gas	(i) Lung and respiratory disorders (ii) Formation of smog

volcanoes and the burning of fossil fuels, factory chimneys, etc. These gases dissolve in rain water forming nitric acid and sulphuric acid.

$$SO_3 + H_2O \longrightarrow H_2SO_4$$

$$2NO_2 + H_2O \longrightarrow HNO_3 + HNO_2$$

Acid rain reduces the fertility of soil, and thus, damages vegetation. It also pollutes water bodies, thus, affecting animal and aquatic life. Acid rain also results in the corrosion of buildings, statues and archaeological monuments.

Acid rains are not confined only to industrial areas. The regions free of industrial pollution may also be affected by acid rains due to the movement of the rain clouds from one region to the other region.

Prevention: The casual agents for acid rain being the oxides of sulphur and nitrogen are difficult to be controlled. But, avoiding the usage of fossil fuels, the use of the non-conventional sources of energy and safe disposal of industrial wastes to some extent can reduce the levels of these pollutants, thus, preventing the ill-effects of acid rains.

2. **Greenhouse Effect and Global Warming:** Land and ocean absorb solar energy to warm the earth's atmosphere. In turn, they release infrared radiation or heat into the atmosphere. The blanket of gases covering the earth's surface traps this radiation. Thus, the absorption of heat maintains the temperature of the earth's surface which is absolutely essential to support life on earth. This natural process is called **greenhouse effect.**

This natural phenomenon of greenhouse effect is caused mostly by CO_2 and water vapour in the atmosphere. Hence, these gases are called **greenhouse gases**.

However, increase in the levels of CO_2 and the presence of some other gases, such as, CH_4, ozone, etc., in the atmosphere result in a gradual rise in the temperature of earth's surface. This increasing greenhouse effect occurring due to the polluted gases in the atmosphere is called **global warming**. These gases which cause global warming are called **greenhouse gases**.

Melting of ice caps and glaciers, excessive evaporation of sea and ocean waters, increase in frequency of floods, soil erosion, unseasonal rains, health hazards for human beings and animals as a consequence of increased temperature on the earth are some harmful effects of global warming.

Reduction of Global Warming: Reduction in the use of fossil fuels, controlling deforestation and restricting the use of chlorofluorocarbons (CFCs) are some measures to be taken against increasing greenhouse effect. Growing more and more plants is obviously the most essential requirement for controlling global warming.

3. **Ozone Depletion:** Ozone when present in the troposphere causes greenhouse effect and contributes to pollution. But, in stratosphere, ozone has a very useful role to play. It absorbs ultraviolet radiations coming from the sun and prevents them from reaching the earth's atmosphere. Ultraviolet radiations are biologically harmful. The ozone layer acts as a screen for these radiations. This decrease in the level of ozone in the stratosphere by the pollutant gases is known as ozone depletion.

Some pollutants, such as, chlorofluorocarbons are chemically inactive and do not dissolve in rain water. Hence, they reach the stratosphere over a period of time. There they react with ozone and cause depletion of ozone in that region. Therefore, it cannot perfectly screen the UV radiations. Once this radiation reaches the earth's surface, it causes many undesirable effects, like, skin cancer, cataract, damage of plants and crops, etc.

Prevention: The most effective way of protecting the ozone layer is developing alternatives for CFCs in the refrigerating systems and aerosols.

Acid rains, global warming and ozone depletion are the major hazards to environment. In addition to these, the other pollutants, such as, carbon monoxide, fly ash, suspended particulate matter and toxic metals also cause considerable damage to man and environment. Some general methods have to be followed for curbing the air pollution in all respects.

Instead of finding out ways and means for the safe disposal of waste products, now focus has been shifted to designing of industrial equipment, like, scrubbers and precipitators, and synthesis of chemicals which are environment friendly. This involves the usage of raw materials and solvents which do not cause release of any harmful products. Researches are going on for the development of alternative chemical reactions which do not give an undesirable product. This is in fact a new area of chemistry known as green chemistry which has come to the forefront in the recent years.

Arresting the growth of population, judicious use of natural resources, recycling of products, such as, paper and restricting the usage of plastic bags are some easier control measures which can be of great help in controlling air pollution.

Above all, arresting deforestation and increase in greenery in our surroundings can go a long way in curbing the pollution. Following stringent norms and the maintenance of industrial units and avoiding accidents in industries also can contribute to a large extent for the control of air pollution.

EXAMPLE 4.9 Explain the working principle of scrubber.

SOLUTION

Scrubbers are used to remove acidic oxides, like oxides of sulphur and nitrogen. Lime water is spread in scrubber through which acidic oxides of sulphur and nitrogen are precipitated.

EXAMPLE 4.10 What is meant by fly ash? Give the sources of fly ash and its effect on the environment and human beings.

SOLUTION

Fly ash is the residue produced during the combustion of coal. Thermal power plants are the major sources of fly ash. Effects of fly ash on environment and on human beings are given below.

(i) Metal oxides and toxic metals present in fly ash cause health problems.

(ii) Silica causes bronchitis and lung cancer.

(iii) Fly ash is also responsible for contamination of ground water and clogging of drainage.

POINTS TO REMEMBER

- ✔ The layer of air that surrounds the Earth up to an altitude of 300 km is called atmosphere.
- ✔ Above this altitude, the region is absolutely free of air. This region above the atmosphere is called space.
- ✔ The layer of atmosphere which is in contact with the earth's surface is called troposphere.
- ✔ The layer of atmosphere above the troposphere is called stratosphere.
- ✔ The layer succeeding the stratosphere is called mesosphere.
- ✔ This is the topmost layer of atmosphere and it is called thermosphere due to the very high temperatures prevailing there.
- ✔ The atmosphere in any layer is composed of air, which exerts a downward pressure, and this downward pressure exerted by air due to its weight on the surroundings is called atmospheric pressure.
- ✔ Pressure is defined as the force exerted per unit area, it is expressed in N m^{-2} which is called pascal. Hence, the SI unit of pressure is pascal (Pa) or kilopascal.
- ✔ The instrument used to measure the atmospheric pressure is called barometer.
- ✔ The minimum temperature at which a substance burns in the presence of oxygen is called its ignition temperature.
- ✔ A combustible substance which has an ignition temperature close to the room temperature is called an inflammable substance.
- ✔ The substances which do not undergo combustion are called incombustible substances.
- ✔ This iron coated with zinc metal is called galvanized iron and the process as galvanization.
- ✔ Forming a layer of tin over the iron surface is called tinning.
- ✔ The process of mixing of other metals with iron to make a homogeneous mixture is called alloying.
- ✔ A mixture of 95% oxygen and 5% CO_2 is called carbogen
- ✔ The variation in the composition of air in the atmosphere due to the release of these gases is called air pollution.
- ✔ The absorption of heat maintains the temperature of the earth's surface which is absolutely essential to support life on earth. This natural process is called greenhouse effect.
- ✔ This natural phenomenon of greenhouse effect is caused mostly by CO_2 and water vapour in the atmosphere. Hence, these gases are called greenhouse gases.
- ✔ The increasing greenhouse effect occurring due to the polluted gases in the atmosphere is called global warming.

PRACTICE QUESTIONS CLASSROOM WING

Very Short Answer Type Questions

Directions for question from 1 to 4:
Fill in the blanks

1. The innermost zone of a candle flame is ________.
2. Respiration is a ________ combustion.
3. Coating of tin over iron is called ________.
4. Among all the layers of the atmosphere, the layer with the highest temperature is ______.

Directions for question from 5 to 24:
Answer the following questions.

5. In which layer of the atmosphere, the temperature increase with the increase in altitude?
6. For making surgical instruments, which process can be adopted for the prevention of corrosion of iron?
7. Which layer of the atmosphere exists in a plasma state (ionic state)?
8. Write the correct product/products: $H_2S + O_2 \rightarrow$
9. What is the layer of the atmosphere present just above the earth's surface?
10. Why is mercury taken in a barometer?
11. What is the SI unit for atmospheric pressure? Define it.
12. At a certain altitude, the atmospheric pressure is 0.05 atm. What would be the length of the mercury column in the barometer?
13. How is oxygen gas collected?
14. What happens when iron is subjected to strong heating with oxygen?
15. Name the metals which react with oxygen at room temperature.
16. Why is the atmospheric pressure measured at sea level?
17. Give the composition of nitrogen and oxygen by volume in air.
18. What is the main advantage of the manufacturing of oxygen gas by the electrolysis of water?
19. Define ignition temperature.
20. Define atmosphere.
21. Under what conditions, oxygen and hydrogen react with each other?
22. How does oxygen exist in the combined state in nature?
23. What happens when mercuric oxide is subjected to heating?
24. Name the layers of the atmosphere.

Short Answer Type Questions

25. Identify the following products of oxidation of non-metals in the order of their description given below.

    (A) P_2O_5 (B) NO_2 (C) CO_2 (D) NO

    Description:

    (i) The gas produces a brown coloured gas on oxidation.

    (ii) The gas used in fire extinguishers.

    (iii) A brown coloured gas.

    (iv) A dense white fume.

26. For manufacturing the containers for storing edible materials like oils, fruit juices, etc., which method can be adopted for the prevention of corrosion of iron?
27. Write the products formed when a mixture of NH_3 and O_2 in a 4:5 ratio is passed over platinum gauze at 800°C.
28. Give the differences between combustion and respiration.
29. Name some measures to control air pollution.
30. Why are acid rains not confined to only industrial areas?
31. Give some uses of oxygen.
32. Give any four characteristics of air as a mixture.
33. Which metals react with oxygen at room temperature? Give equations.

34. (a) What is meant by fly ash? Give the sources of fly ash and its effect on the environment.

(b) Aeroplanes prefer to fly in the stratosphere instead of troposphere. Give reason.

35. What is the role of atmosphere in nature?

36. How do chlorofluorocarbons cause air pollution?

37. Give the effect of acid rains.

38. How can you detect oxygen gas?

39. What are the sources of carbon monoxide and sulphur dioxide in air?

Essay Answer Type Questions

40. Explain the construction and working of the following:
   (i) Mercury barometer
   (ii) Aneroid barometer

41. Give equations for the decomposition of potassium permanganate and hydrogen peroxide. In what way do the two processes differ from each other?

42. (a) What is meant by rusting? What are its effects? Explain different methods adopted for the prevention of rusting?

(b) An experiment is carried out in laboratory. During the process, very little changes in the pressure of a gaseous substance take place and these changes are required to be measured at room temperature. Between mercury and coloured water, which one is the preferred barometric liquid in this situation? Give reason in support of your answer.

43. What are the effects of oxides of sulphur and nitrogen on the atmosphere?

44. How is oxygen gas prepared from potassium chlorate? What is the role of MnO_2 in this process?

PRACTICE QUESTIONS COMPETITION WING

Level 1: Apply Your Concepts

Directions for questions from 1 to 12:
State whether the following statements are true or false.

1. Photosynthesis does not consume O_2.
2. An increase in the levels of CO_2 in the atmosphere increases the temperature of the earth.
3. Combustion does not produce O_2.
4. Al is a metal, which can protect itself from further oxidation.
5. Carbon particles burn in the outermost zone of the flame of a candle.
6. Fe can form a mixed oxide on reaction with O_2.
7. Oxygen gas is collected by the downward displacement of air.
8. Atmospheric Pressure is a downward pressure exerted by air.
9. Thermometer is used to measure atmospheric pressure.
10. Nitrogen is used in respiration.
11. Pascal is the SI unit of atmospheric pressure.
12. Carbon dioxide is produced during combustion of fuels.

Directions for questions from 13 to 19:
Fill in the blanks.

13. The minimum temperature at which a substance burns in air is called ________.
14. The catalyst in the decomposition of hydrogen peroxide is ________.
15. Dust particles from air are removed by passing air through ________ or ________.
16. When ammonia gas is burnt in excess of oxygen at high temperature, the products formed are ________.
17. The vacuum present above the column in mercury barometer is called ________.
18. FeS_2 on burning in oxygen gives ________.
19. Thermosphere is associated with high temperature due to the absorption of ________.

Direction for question 20:
Match the entries in Column A with the appropriate ones in Column B.

20. Match the entries of Column A with those of Column B.

Column A (Compounds Used for the Formation of O_2)	Column B (Related Features of the Reaction Involved)
(i) H_2O_2	a. MnO_2 reduces the melting point as well as decomposition temperature of the reactant.
(ii) $KMnO_4$	b. Metallic nitrite is the solid product.
(iii) $KClO_3$	c. No heating is required.
(iv) $NaNO_3$	d. MnO_2 is one of the solid products.

Directions for questions from 21 to 50:
For each of the questions, four choices have been provided. Select the correct alternative.

21. **Assertion (A):** Air supports combustion.
Reason (R): Air is a mixture of different gases.
(a) Both A and R are true and R is the correct explanation of A.
(b) Both A and R are true, but R is not the correct explanation of A.
(c) A is true and R is false.
(d) A is false and R is true.

22. **Assertion (A):** Oxygen is used for the combustion of fuel.
Reason (R): Combustion is an exothermic reaction.
(a) Both A and R are true and R is the correct explanation of A.
(b) Both A and R are true, but R is not the correct explanation of A.
(c) A is true and R is false.
(d) A is false and R is true.

23. **Assertion (A):** Oxyacetylene flame is used for welding purposes.
Reason (R): Combustion of acetylene is an example of rapid combustion.
(a) Both A and R are true and R is the correct explanation of A.
(b) Both A and R are true, but R is not the correct explanation of A.
(c) A is true and R is false.
(d) A is false and R is true.

24. **Assertion (A):** When air is passed through lime water, it turns milky.
Reason (R): Constituents of a mixture retain their properties.
(a) Both A and R are true and R is the correct explanation of A.
(b) Both A and R are true, but R is not the correct explanation of A.
(c) A is true and R is false.
(d) A is false and R is true.

25. Global warming is mainly due to:
(a) reradiation of UV rays by CO_2 and H_2O
(b) reradiation of IR rays by CO_2 and H_2O
(c) reradiation of IR rays by O_2 and N_2
(d) reradiation of UV rays by O_2 and N_2

26. Which of the following minerals does not contain oxygen?
(a) Silicates (b) Carbonates
(c) Pyrites (d) None of these

27. $X + O_2 \longrightarrow Y$; $Y + H_2O \longrightarrow Z$; Z turns red litmus to blue, then X may be:
(a) Ca (b) S
(c) C (d) P

28. Tropospheric atmosphere is turbulent. Which of the following reasons can be attributed to this?
(a) convectional current of air rises up due to high temperature in lower layers of the earth
(b) temperature changes result in change in air pressure
(c) more effect of centrifugal force is more in this layer
(d) none of these

29. The layer of atmosphere that is just above the earth's surface is called ________.
(a) thermosphere (b) troposphere
(c) stratosphere (d) mesosphere

30. Which of the following pairs of oxides can give out oxygen on heating?
(a) MgO, PbO_2 (b) Na_2O, CaO
(c) K_2O, HgO (d) Ag_2O, Pb_3O_4

31. Which of the following are used in air conditioning and refrigeration systems?
(a) CO (b) CO_2
(c) CFCs (d) O_3

32. If a balloon filled with air is sent to moon, what would happen?
(a) The balloon expands because the atmospheric pressure of the moon is slightly lower than that of the earth.
(b) The balloon bursts because the atmospheric pressure of the moon is much lower than that of the earth.
(c) The balloon contracts because the atmospheric pressure of the moon is much lower than that of the earth.
(d) No change is observed because change of atmospheric pressure has no effect on the balloon.

33. A gas which is combustible and can support combustion is:
(a) oxygen (b) nitrous oxide
(c) nitric oxide (d) carbon monoxide

34. Which among the following has the lowest boiling point?
(a) O_2 (b) N_2
(c) F_2 (d) Ne

35. Passengers travelling in an aeroplane are advised not to carry fountain pens because at higher altitudes
(a) ink vaporises due to high external pressure
(b) solidification of ink takes places due to very low external pressure
(c) pressure within the tube is more than the external pressure and causes leakage of ink
(d) pressure within the tube is lesser than the external pressure and causes leakage of ink

36. With increase in altitude the temperature in the stratosphere
(a) first remains almost constant and then increases
(b) decreases
(c) remains same
(d) first decreases and then increases

37. Which of the following can be considered as spontaneous combustion?
(a) Burning of LPG
(b) Burning of magnesium ribbon
(c) Burning of camphor
(d) Burning of white phosphorus

38. Which of the following metals gives reddish powder on reaction with O_2 at higher temperature?
(a) Fe (b) Pb
(c) Zn (d) Sn

39. Which of the following reactions is associated with the formation of shining white globules?
(a) $2HgO \xrightarrow{\Delta} 2Hg + O_2$
(b) $2Ag_2O \xrightarrow{\Delta} 4Ag + O_2$
(c) $2Pb_3O_4 \xrightarrow{\Delta} 6PbO + 4O_2$
(d) $2NaNO_3 \xrightarrow{\Delta} 2NaNO_2 + O_2$

40. The ratio of $KClO_3$ and MnO_2 taken for the preparation of oxygen is
(a) 4 : 1 (b) 3 : 1
(c) 2 : 1 (d) 2 : 5

41. When ammonia is burnt in a limited supply of oxygen, which gas is evolved?
(a) NO (b) N_2O
(c) N_2 (d) NO_2

42. Which of the following compounds produces oxide on heating?
(a) PbO_2 (b) KNO_3
(c) Ag_2O (d) $NaNO_3$

43. Arrange the products of the following reactions in the increasing order of the number of oxygen atoms associated with one non-metallic atom.
(a) burning of phosphorus in an adequate supply of oxygen to produce an oxide of phosphorus
(b) the complete combustion of coke with the supply of sufficient oxygen
(c) an electric spark is provided to a 1 : 1 mixture of nitrogen and oxygen
(d) burning of sulphur dioxide gas in oxygen
(a) 3 4 1 2 (b) 3 2 1 4
(c) 2 3 1 4 (d) 3 2 4 1

44. Arrange the following steps involved in the preparation of oxygen from $KClO_3$ in a proper order.
(1) Content of the test tube is heated
(2) A mixture of finely ground $KClO_3$ and MnO_2 is taken in a test tube.
(3) The open end of the test tube is plugged with cotton.
(4) Delivery tube is taken out
(5) The test tube is fixed in a slanting position.
(6) Bunsen burner is put off.
(7) Oxygen is collected by downward displacement of water.
(a) 2 3 4 1 5 6 7 (b) 5 6 3 2 4 1 7
(c) 1 2 3 4 6 7 5 (d) 2 3 5 1 7 4 6

Level 2: Review Your Concepts

45. The height of the mercury column in the barometer is 19 cm at a certain place. Calculate the pressure in Pascal in that place. (1 atm = 101.3 kilopascals)

46. Why are tin coated iron cans used for cool drinks but not galvanized iron cans? Explain.

47. LPG stove can be lighted by using an automatic gas lighter. Is it possible to light kerosene stove by using the same?

48. The combustion of sulphur and phosphorous is possible even in the presence of nitrous oxide and nitric oxide at high temperatures. Justify

49. Is it possible to drink a soft drink by using a straw on the moon? Give reasons in support of your answer.

50. How do catalytic converters reduce air pollution?

51. A student was asked to prepare oxygen from $KClO_3$ in a laboratory. After the experiment was over, he put the burner off immediately. What do you think happened then?

52. (a) Water is not suitable to extinguish fire caused by petrol. Explain.
(b) CNG is considered to be the cleanest automobile fuel. Give reason.

53. Fishes and many other aquatic species live in river water. When they are kept in aquarium, we need to change the water very often. Give reasons.

54. Why don't we use soda acid fire extinguishers to extinguish metal fires?

55. Explain the principle of the working of smoke precipitators.

56. Explain the principle involved in the liquefaction of air.

57. Though the dust particles cause air pollution, the presence of dust particles help in sustenance of life. Explain.

58. In a chemistry laboratory, a laboratory assistant by mistake placed one currency note with a denomination of 100 on the desk and some amount of alcohol fell on it. The currency note was completely wet with alcohol. In order to dry it he immediately brought a burning match stick and exposed the currency note to its flame. Immediately the currency caught fire. But after few seconds, fire was put off by him and the note remained intact. Explain.

59. Two students A and B were asked to carry out one experiment. The smoke released due to the burning of a candle should be passed through lime water and anhydrous copper sulphate to prove the release of CO_2 and H_2O, respectively, due to the burning of the candle. A first passed the gases through lime water and then through copper sulphate, whereas B did it the other way round. The teacher commented that the set up used by A was wrong. What could be the reason for it?

60. When lime water is exposed to air for a long time, very thin white coating is found floating on the surface. Give reasons.

61. MnO_2 used as a catalyst in the preparation of oxygen from $KClO_3$ should be completely free of carbon. Justify.

62. Is it possible to prepare oxygen and hydrogen by the electrolysis of pure water? Give reasons in support of your answer. How are hydrogen and oxygen prepared in industry by the electrolysis of water?

63. Rain water is found to contain more percentage of oxygen than ordinary water. Explain.

64. Why is the carbon monoxide of automobile exhaust converted to carbon dioxide in the catalytic converters though both carbon monoxide and carbon dioxide add to air pollution?

65. (a) Why is LPG a better fuel than coal?

(b) Catalytic converters are introduced in exhaust systems of automobiles in order to curb air pollution. Illustrate the statement.

66. Rimjhim was dreaming in the morning that she went to a planet Pandora and in the atmosphere of Pandora there is no water vapour. Suddenly she woke up and started thinking what would happen if earth's atmosphere loses water vapour completely. Rimjhim was really worried. Can you find out the reason for Rimjhim's worry?

67. Why is the atmospheric pressure measured at sea level? Why is the atmospheric pressure not felt by us?

Level 3: Assess Your Concepts

68. 'Though oxygen is the supporter of life on earth, the presence of nitrogen in the atmosphere also contributes equally to the life processes on earth.' Justify the statement.

69. Why the position of freezer in the refrigerator is generally at the top? Explain.

70. How does sky appear from the moon?

71. Two liquids A and B were taken in two different barometers, and the density of A is greater than that of B. Which liquid is preferable to be used as barometric liquid if the variation in pressure is every minute and why?

72. What would happen if people travel in a non-pressurised aeroplane?

73. Electric bulbs are filled with argon gas but not air. Explain.

74. (a) The body temperature of a healthy person is around 98.4°F. Justify.

(b) If we keep some iron flakes in freshly prepared distilled water taken in a test tube and pour some amount of oil over it, will they get rusted? Give reason to support your comment.

75. UV rays find application in the purification of water, although it is harmful to human beings. Explain.

76. Deep sea divers carry oxygen diluted by helium in cylinders instead of air. Give reasons.

77. The temperature of the troposphere decreases with increase in altitude. Is the same true for the stratosphere? Justify.

PRACTICE QUESTIONS JEE-NEET SPECIAL WING

Multiple-Answer Type Questions

Directions for questions 1 to 5:
Select one or more correct alternative(s) from the given choices.

1. Identify the wrongly matched sets among the following.

	Pollutant	Source
(a)	CO	Complete combustion of petrol
(b)	CFCs	Automobile exhaust
(c)	Pb	Antiknock in petrol
(d)	NO_2	Refrigeration systems

2. Oxygen gas can be prepared by different methods. 160 g of pure oxygen is collected by the decomposition of various compounds under suitable conditions. Identify the correct sets which give this amount of oxygen by heating till the completion of reaction.
   (a) 408 g potassium chlorate
   (b) 340 g hydrogen peroxide
   (c) 1.58 kg potassium permanganate
   (d) 1 kg potassium nitrate

3. The density of a liquid used in barometer is *x g/cc*. The height of the liquid column at the ambient pressure is noted down as '*h*' cm. Which among the following liquids when taken in a barometer show a height of the column greater than 'h' cm at the same ambient pressure?

	Liquid	Density
(a)	P	3*x*/2
(b)	Q	2*x*/3
(c)	R	5*x*/3
(d)	S	3*x*/5

   (a) P (b) Q
   (c) R (d) S

4. A certain amount of ammonia on reaction with required amount of oxygen in the presence of platinum catalyst at 800°C gives a gaseous substance X which on prolonged exposure to oxygen turns to reddish brown colour. Identify the ratio of ammonia and oxygen required to be taken for the above activity respectively.
   (a) 2; 1.5 (b) 3; 3.5
   (c) 3 ; 4 (d) 5;6.5

5. Litharge is formed as one of the products in a reaction. Identify the statements which comply with the reaction concerned.
   (a) The raw material taken is called red lead
   (b) Lead dioxide is subjected to strong heating.
   (c) Lead shows the valency of 2 in the raw material taken for heating.
   (d) Litharge is one of the allotropic forms of lead

Comprehension-Based Questions

Directions for questions 6 to 11:
Read the content given in the following passage and answer the questions given below.

The following figure represents the hypothetical diagram of the various layers of atmosphere surrounding the earth.

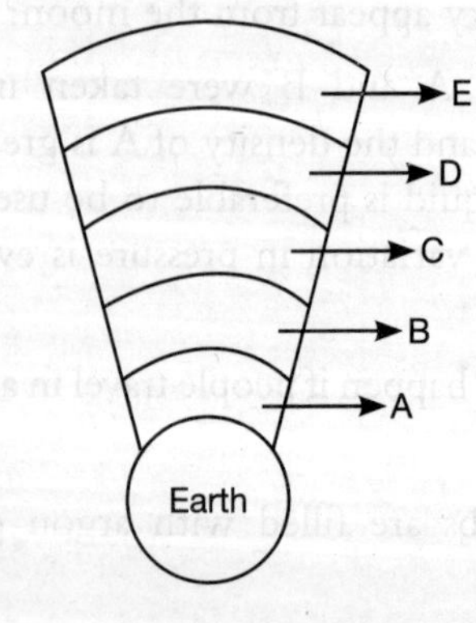

6. Name the layer of atmosphere which overlaps with the outer space.
   (a) Mesosphere (b) Exosphere
   (c) Thermosphere (d) Ionosphere

7. From the given diagram of the layers of atmosphere, Identify the layer in which the meteorites get burnt up.
   (a) D (b) C
   (c) B (d) A

8. In one layer of atmosphere, the temperature increases with the altitude and in the other layer, the temperature decreases with the altitude. Identify the set of layers.
   (a) A; B (b) C; D
   (c) C; B (d) B; A

9. **Assertion (A):** An astronaut's blood boils in the layer C if the person is without a protective covering.

   Reason (R): Layer B is associated with the absorption of UV radiation.
   (a) Both A and R are correct and R is the correct explanation of A
   (b) Both A and R are correct and R is not the correct explanation of A
   (c) A is correct and R is wrong
   (d) R is correct and A is wrong

10. Chlorofluorocarbons reach a layer of atmosphere and cause damage to the composition of that layer. Identify the layer of atmosphere and the substance that gets depleted.
    (a) A, ozone (b) B, oxygen
    (c) A, oxygen (d) B, ozone

11. Match the entries in column I with those in column II

Column I	Column II
A	(i) Aurora lights formation
B	(ii) Satellite station
C	(iii) Snow fall
D	(iv) Burning of meteorites
E	(v) Aeroplane flight

Directions for questions 12 to 16:

Read the content given in the following passage and answer the questions given below.

Many substances undergo reaction with oxygen. This reaction is known as burning or combustion. The combustion is of different types. Spontaneous combustion is the process where the material does not require any external energy for getting ignited and undergo combustion. Explosive combustion requires external energy for ignition. Once ignited, the substances undergo combustion at a very rapid rate and hence results in explosion. The most important type of combustion is rapid combustion. This requires external energy for combustion and the energy is released at a moderate rate. Therefore, this type of combustion finds wide range of applications in our day to day life as well as industry. The materials which undergo rapid combustion to produce a large amount of usable energy are called fuels. They can be in solid or liquid or gaseous state. The efficiency of a fuel is determined by its calorific value. Calorific value of a fuel is the amount of heat released when a unit mass of the fuel is subjected to complete combustion. It is usually measured in kJ/Kg . The amount of external energy required for initiating the combustion varies from one fuel to the other. The temperature to which a substance needs to be heated to undergo combustion is known as ignition temperature. The substances which possess ignition temperature close to the room temperature undergo spontaneous combustion.

12. `LPG is considered as the most ideal fuel among all the domestic fuels. Identify the probable reason.
    (a) It does not leave any residue at the end
    (b) It has high calorific value
    (c) It has lower ignition temperature than the other fuels.
    (d) All of the above

13. **Assertion (A):** Little amount of kerosene is added to the wood for easier combustion.

    Reason (R): Kerosene has a higher calorific value than wood.
    (a) Both A and R are correct and R is the correct explanation of A
    (b) Both A and R are correct and R is not the correct explanation of A
    (c) A is correct and R is wrong
    (d) R is correct and A is wrong

14. Which among the following materials can not be stored in a dry bottle.
    (a) Sodium (b) Magnesium
    (c) Phosphorus (d) All of these

15. Replacing petrol as automobile fuel with which among the following substances poses the most difficult challenges practically?
    (a) Hydrogen (b) LPG
    (c) Biodiesel (d) CNG

16. Among the following, which substance is least flammable and hence is safest for use as fuel?

	Material	Ignition temperature	Physical state
(a)	A	250°C	Liquid
(b)	B	405°C	Gas
(c)	C	220°C	Liquid
(d)	D	540°C	Gas

ANSWER KEYS

Crossword

Across

2. Catalyst
4. Alloy
6. Mesosphere
8. Galvanization
11. Non luminous zone
13. Global warming
16. Carbon dioxide
17. Troposphere
18. Lavoisier
19. Stratosphere
20. Franctional distillation

Down

1. Carbogen
3. Pollutants
5. Chlorofluoro carbons
7. Ultraviolet
9. Green house effect
10. Combustion
12. Ozone depletion
14. Thermosphere
15. Barometer

Classroom Wing

Very Short Answer Type Questions

1. coldest zone
2. Slow
3. tinning
4. thermosphere

Competition Wing

Level 1: Apply Your Concepts

1. True
2. True
3. True
4. True
5. True
6. True
7. False
8. True
9. False
10. False
11. True
12. True
13. Ignition temperature
14. MnO_2
15. precipitators, filters
16. NO, H_2O
17. Torricellian vacuum
18. FeO, SO_2
19. Intense solar radiation
20. (i) → (C); (ii) → (D); (iii) → (A); (iv) → (B)
21. (a)
22. (a)
23. (b)
24. (c)
25. (b)
26. (c)
27. (a)
28. (a)
29. (b)
30. (d)
31. (c)
32. (b)
33. (b)
34. (d)
35. (c)
36. (a)
37. (d)
38. (a)
39. (a)
40. (a)
41. (c)
42. (a)
43. (b)
44. (d)

JEE Special Wing

Multiple-Answer Type Questions

1. (a; b; d)
2. (a; b)
3. (b; d)
4. (c; d)
5. (a; b)

Comprehension-Based Questions

6. (b)
7. (b)
8. (d)
9. (a)
10. (d)
11. (a) ↔ (iii), (b) ↔ (v), (c) ↔ (iv), (d) ↔ (i), (e) ↔ (ii)
12. (d)
13. (b)
14. (c)
15. (a)
16. (d)

Hints and Explanations

CLASSROOM WING

Very Short Answer Type Questions

1. The innermost zone of a candle flame is the coldest zone.
2. Respiration is a slow combustion.
3. tinning
4. thermosphere
5. In the stratosphere, the temperature increases due to the increase in altitude.
6. Surgical instruments are manufactured from stainless steel which is an alloy of iron.
7. Thermosphere exists in a plasma state.
8. $H_2S + O_2 \rightarrow H_2O + SO_2$
9. troposphere
10. weak adhesive forces and high density
11. Pascal. One Newton of force acting per square metre of surface area
12. 1 atm → 76 cm
    0.05 atm
    $= 76 \times 0.05$ cm $= 3.8$ cm
13. downward displacement of water
14. ferrosoferric oxide is formed
15. sodium and potassium
16. atmosphere pressure is maximum
17. 78, 21
18. comparatively low cost and H_2 gas is obtained as a by-product
19. minimum temperature at which a substance burns
20. The layer of air that surrounds the earth up to an altitude of 300 km is called the atmosphere.
21. electric spark
22. water
23. Formation of mirror-like surface
24. troposphere, stratosphere, mesosphere and thermosphere

Short Answer Type Questions

25. (i) description belongs to (D) NO
    (ii) description belongs to → (C) CO_2
    (iii) description belongs to → (B) NO_2
    (iv) description belongs to (A) P_2O_5
26. Tinning can be adopted for the prevention of corrosion of iron. Tin-coated iron containers are used for storage of edible foodstuffs.
27. When a mixture of NH_3 and O_2 in 4:5 ratio is passed over platinum gauze at 800°C, NO and H_2O are formed.
28. Combustion is a fast process, takes place at high temperatures, does not require catalyst, and release energy in the form of heat and light.

    Respiration is a slow process, takes place at body temperature, requires catalyst, and release energy in the form of heat only.
29. (i) plants
    (ii) environment friendly chemicals
    (iii) disposal of waste products
30. Acid rains are not confined only to industrial areas. The regions free of industrial pollution may also be affected by acid rains due to the movement of the rain clouds from one region to the other region.
31. (i) combustion
    (ii) metal extraction
    (iii) welding
    (iv) rocket fuel
    (v) industry
32. (i) Variable composition of air in different places on earth.
    (ii) No heat change is involved in the mixing up of gases in air.
    (iii) No definite boiling point for liquid air.
    (iv) Separation of air into various components can be done by physical methods.
33. Metals in the reactivity series react with oxygen.
34. (a) Ash produced in small dark flecks by the burning of powdered coal or other materials and carried into

the air is called fly ash. The main source of fly-ash is coal combustion. Metal oxides and toxic metals of fly ash cause health problems. Silica causes bronchitis and lung cancer.

(b) In stratosphere temperature range does not alter up to a height of about 25 km. Above this the temperature gradually increases up to a range of 0°C to 10°C. Hence, there is no convection current of air in stratosphere. Since the air is not turbulent, aeroplane prefers to fly in the stratosphere,

35. (i) clouds
(ii) rain
(iii) snow
(iv) winds
(v) harmful radiations

36. (i) inert nature of CFCs
(ii) effect of UV rays on CFCs
(iii) reactivity of CFCs
(iv) action of CFCs on ozone

37. (i) chemicals in acid rain
(ii) reaction of these chemicals with buildings

38. (i) glowing splinter
(ii) litmus
(iii) alkaline pyrogallol

39. (i) Automobiles
(ii) Industries
(iii) Thermal power plants

Essay Answer Type Questions

40. Mercury barometer: A graduated glass tube of about 840-mm length which is closed at one end and open at the other end is taken. This tube is filled completely with mercury and then inverted into a trough full of mercury. Depending on the external pressure, some mercury from glass tube comes out and stands at a certain height. This height is measured. Above this column, there is almost vacuum and it is called torricellian vacuum. At normal atmospheric pressure at sea level, the height of the mercury column falls to about 760 mm of Hg. Hence, this is taken as the standard value of atmospheric pressure.The pressure can be calculated by substituting the height of the mercury column in the formula $P = hdg$, where 'h' is the height of the mercury column, 'd' is the density of the mercury and 'g' is the acceleration due to gravity.

Aneroid barometer: The aneroid barometer is basically operated by a metal cell that contains very small amount of air or a series of such cells joined together. One side is fixed to the base of the instrument while the other side is connected with a system of levers and pulleys. These levers and pulleys are connected to a pointer that moves over a scale fixed at the front side of the instrument. Any change in pressure alters the thickness of the cells.

41. (i) catalyst used
(ii) products obtained

42. (a) (i) corrosion of iron in the presence of oxygen and moisture
(ii) the formation of flakes and the weakening of iron structures
(iii) coating with different paints, galvanization, tinning, electroplating, alloying

(b) Coloured water is the preferred barometric liquid since the change in the length of water column is more than that of mercury due to a small change in pressure. The change in length of the mercury column is insignificant and cannot be visualized because its density is much higher than that of water.

43. (i) dissolution of oxides
(ii) effect on soil
(iii) effect on buildings

44. (i) decomposition reaction
(ii) change in reaction temperature

Competition Wing

Level 1: Apply Your Concepts

1. **True.** Photosynthesis does not consume O_2.

3. **True.** Combustion consumes but does not produce O_2.

4. **True.** A protective layer of Al_2O_3 is formed on Al upon reaction with O_2.

5. Carbon particle burns with a yellow flame in the middle zone of the candle flame

6. **True.** Fe forms a mixed oxide, i.e., Fe_3O_4 ($FeO + Fe_2O_3$) on reaction with O_2.

20. $H_2O_2 \rightarrow$ Heating is not required.

$$3KMnO_4 \xrightarrow[MnO_2]{\Delta} MnO_2 + O_2 + K_2MnO_4$$

$$KClO_3 \xrightarrow{\Delta} 2KCl + 3O_2$$

MnO_2 reduces the melting point as well as the decomposition temperature of $KClO_3$.

$$2NaNO_3 \xrightarrow{\Delta} 2NaNO_2 + O_2$$

21. Since air is a mixture of different gases and one of the components of air is oxygen, air supports combustion.

Hence, the correct option is (a).

22. Since combustion is an exothermic reaction, oxygen is used for the combustion of fuel because it is a good supporter of combustion.

Hence, the correct option is (b).

23. Combustion is an exothermic reaction and rapid combustion produces a lot of heat. Hence oxyacetylene flame is used for welding purposes.

Hence, the correct option is (a).

24. When air is passed through lime water, it turns milky because CO_2 is present in the air and it retains its properties.

Hence, the correct option is (a).

36. With the increase in altitude the temperature in the stratosphere first remains constant and then increases.

Hence, the correct answer is (a).

37. Spontaneous combustion is the burning of a substance at room temperature. White phosphorus burns at the room temperature.

Hence, the correct answer is (d).

38. At higher temperature, oxygen on reaction with iron gives a reddish brown powder with crackling noise due to the formation of ferric tetroxide or ferroso ferric oxide.

$$3Fe + 2O_2 \rightarrow Fe_3O_4$$

reddish brown powder

Hence, the correct answer is (a).

39. Silver (i) oxide on heating forms silvery white globules:

$$2Ag_2O \rightarrow 4Ag + O_2$$

Hence, the correct answer is (a).

40. 4 parts of $KClO_3$ and 1 part of MnO_2 on heating gives oxygen gas.

Hence, the correct answer is (a).

41. When ammonia is burnt with limited amount of oxygen, it burns with a blue flame with the evolution of nitrogen gas.

$$4NH_3 + 3O_2 \xrightarrow{\Delta} 2N_2 + 6H_2O$$

Hence, the correct answer is (c).

42. $2PbO_2 \rightarrow 2PbO + O_2$

$2KNO_3 \rightarrow 2KNO_2 + O_2$

$2Ag_2O \rightarrow 4Ag + O_2$

$2NaNO_3 \rightarrow 2NaNO_2 + O_2$

Hence, the correct answer is (a).

43. (3) Burning of phosphorus gives P_2O_5.

(2) Complete combustion gives CO_2

(1) When an electric spark is provided to a 1 : 1 mixture of N_2 and O_2, NO is produced.

(4) Burning of SO_2 gives SO_3.

∴ The correct sequence is 3 2 1 4.

Hence, the correct answer is (b).

44. (2) A mixture of finely ground $KClO_3$ and MnO_2 is taken in a test tube.

(3) The open end of the test tube is plugged with cotton.

(5) The test tube is fixed in a slanting position.

(1) Content of the test tube is heated.

(7) Oxygen is collected by downward displacement of water.

(4) Delivery tube is taken out.

(6) Bunsen burner is put off.

Hence, the correct answer is (d).

Level 2: Review Your Concepts

45. 76 cm of Hg → 101292 Pascal

∴ 19 cm Hg → ?

$= \frac{1,01,292 \times 19}{76}$ Pascal = 25,323 Pascal

46. (i) comparison of reactivities of iron, tin with the component (metal) used for galvanization

(ii) changes that take place in the food kept in the galvanized container

(iii) effect of the reactivity of tin on the food content

47. (i) ignition temperature

(ii) conditions at which a fuel can be burnt

(iii) comparison of these conditions to LPG and kerosene

(iv) Temperature produced by automatic gas lighter and the substance used to light kerosene stove

48. (i) changes that take place in N_2O and NO at high temperatures

(ii) products obtained from the oxides of nitrogen at high temperature

(iii) requisite for combustion

49. (i) conditions for fluid to rise up in straw

(ii) principle used in sucking a liquid through a straw

(iii) conditions existing on moon

(iv) effect of these conditions

50. (i) Metal used in catalytic converter

(ii) property of the metal used in catalytic converter

(iii) places where catalytic converter finds application

(iv) composition of petroleum products used in automobiles

(v) pollutants present in the automobile exhaust gases

(vi) influence of the metal present in the catalytic converter on the exhaust gases

51. (i) collection of oxygen

(ii) experimental set up

(iii) changes that take place after the burner is put off

(iv) effect of these changes

52. (a) (i) difference in the physical property of water and petrol

(ii) role of water for extinguishing fire

(b) CNG produces CO_2 and H_2O on combustion since major component of CNG is CH_4 (methane), no other harmful pollutants are released. Its calorific value is very high and hence consumption of the fuel is also less. Therefore, CNG can be considered to be the cleanest fuel.

53. (i) respiration of fishes in water

(ii) components required for the survival of fishes and aquatic species

(iii) comparison of these amounts in river water and aquarium

54. (i) material used in soda and fire extinguisher

(ii) reaction that takes place in soda acid fire extinguisher

(iii) products obtained

(iv) reaction between one of the products with metal that causes fire

(v) products obtained in the above reaction

(vi) effect of one of the products on the atmosphere

55. (i) reactivity of gaseous species at electrodes

(ii) components present in smoke

(iii) voltage in smoke precipitators

(iv) change in components of smoke

56. (i) result of sudden expansion of gases

(ii) temperature required for air to liquefy

(iii) conditions to attain the liquefaction

(iv) forces between molecules

(v) effect of temperature on movement of molecules

57. (i) role of dust particles in formation of cloud

(ii) role of cloud formation in water cycle

(iii) role of water cycle in sustenance of life

58. Currency notes are made up of thick papers and the ignition temperature of this type of paper is higher than the ordinary paper. When the currency note is soaked in alcohol, which has low ignition temperature and high volatility, it vaporises and burns before the ignition temperature of the paper is reached. Hence, the currency note does not burn.

59. The products of the combustion of a candle (mixture of hydrocarbons) are CO_2 and water vapour. CO_2 can be detected by passing it through lime water which turns milky. H_2O can be detected by passing it through anhydrous $CuSO_4$ which turns blue. After passing it through anhydrous $CuSO_4$ first, H_2O is removed and only CO_2 will be passed through lime water. If the process is reversed, then CO_2 will be absorbed in lime water and water vapour gets condensed. Hence, colour of anhydrous $CuSO_4$ remains unchanged.

60. Air contains a low percentage of CO_2. Though CO_2 turns lime water milky, since the amount of CO_2 is less in the atmospheric air, it does not turn lime water milky. Only over a long period of exposure, a thin white film of $CaCO_3$ is formed due to the minor amounts of CO_2 in the atmospheric air.

61. MnO_2 usually contains coal as impurity. If such MnO_2 is used, carbon when heated with potassium chlorate leads to an explosion with the release of enormous amount of heat since it is a highly exothermic reaction.

62. Electrolysis of pure water cannot give oxygen and hydrogen since water is a poor conductor. To make it an electrolytic conductor, some amount of acid should be added to water which is called **acidulated water.** Electrolysis of acidulated water gives hydrogen and oxygen at the respective electrodes.

63. Rain is due to condensation of water droplets in the atmosphere. It does not contain any dissolved salts like ordinary water. Therefore, rain water can dissolve more amount of oxygen than ordinary water. Moreover, rain water is in contact with atmospheric air. Hence, it contains more percentage of oxygen.

64. Carbon monoxide is formed by the incomplete combustion of fuels. It is not a constituent of normal atmospheric air. It is a pollutant. When it is released, the inhalation of the air with carbon monoxide results in reduction in the oxygen intake. Hence, it is converted to CO_2 in the catalytic converters. Though CO_2 is released into the atmosphere, it does not cause much damage immediately. Only in the long run, an increase in the levels of CO_2 in the atmospheric air results in global warming. This can be prevented by growing more trees and decreasing the density of the population. Such measures are not possible for carbon monoxide pollution. Hence, CO_2 is a less harmful pollutant than CO.

65. (a) LPG is a mixture of lower hydrocarbons. It has very low ignition temperature and the heat evolved per unit mass of LPG called calorific value of the fuel is very high. Coal is an allotropic form of carbon and has very high ignition temperature. Its calorific value is very low. Apart from these two reasons, LPG undergoes complete combustion and does not produce any ash. Burning coal produces ash and causes acid rain due to the presence of nitrogen and sulphur in it.

(b) Due to incomplete combustion of the fuel used in the automobiles, CO is produced which is very harmful for health. In catalytic converter platinum is used which converts CO to CO_2 and oxides of nitrogen to N_2. Oxides of N_2 leads to acid rain. But N_2, being inert, does not have any effect on the environment.

66. Water vapour present in the atmosphere forms clouds that result in rains. Rainwater is the main source of drinking water and is used for irrigation. If there are no rains, drought prevails. Life in the desert regions is very difficult as water vapour in the atmosphere here is very low. Water vapour also controls the excessive evaporation of water from living cells.

67. Since the composition and the density of air varies with the altitude, the pressure exerted by air also varies. The atmospheric pressure decreases with an increase in the altitude. It is due to this reason that the atmospheric pressure is measured at sea level where it is maximum. At sea level, atmospheric pressure is almost equal to the weight of a 1 kg mass acting on every square centimetre. We do not feel the atmospheric pressure because the pressure inside the body is equal to the atmospheric pressure.

Level 3: Assess Your Concepts

68. (i) consequences of breathing air with 100% oxygen
(ii) effect on body on breathing 100% O_2
(iii) components of the air we breathe in (under normal conditions)
(iv) role of nitrogen

69. (i) movement of air due to the change of temperature
(ii) change in temperature of air near the freezer
(iii) effect of change in temperature on the density of air
(iv) cause for movement of air inside the refrigerator
(v) requirement of movement of air inside the refrigerator

(vi) influence of the position of the freezer on the movement of air

70. (i) particles present in the earth's atmosphere which are responsible for scattering of light

(ii) atmosphere in moon

(iii) reason for the specific colour (blue) of the sky when observed from the earth

(iv) influence of the atmosphere on the colour of the sky

71. (i) relation between density of liquid, pressure variation and height of the column

(ii) relation between the density of the barometric liquid and height of the column of the liquid

(iii) Effect on the height of the column of the liquid due to the change in external pressure

(iv) Comparison of the change in the heights of column of liquid A and that of B with a minute change in external pressure.

72. (i) pressure inside non-pressurised aeroplanes at higher altitudes

(ii) comparison of pressure inside and outside a human body at sea level

(iii) comparison of pressure in a human body and non-pressurised aeroplane.

(iv) effect of difference in pressure

73. Argon is used in filling the ordinary electric bulbs because it is inert. Air containing oxygen cannot be used because it causes oxidation of tungsten. Moreover nitrogen and oxygen present in air can react at the high voltage to give nitric oxide.

74. (a) Oxygen in the air is used for burning the fuel which gives energy in the form of heat. In the same way oxygen inhaled by us is used inside the tissues to break down the glucose and liberate energy in the form of heat. This liberated heat maintains the body temperature at 98.4°F.

(b) Rust is hydrated ferric oxide. Hence, rusting of iron requires the presence of O_2 and moisture/water. Freshly prepared distilled water is devoid of any dissolved gases If oil is poured over it, further dissolution of O_2 is not possible. Hence, rusting of the ion flakes does not take place.

75. UV rays convert O_2 to O_3. Ozone is used to purify drinking water as it produces nascent oxygen which kills the bacteria present in water.

76. In deep sea the pressure is more than the normal atmospheric pressure. Solubility of a gas increases with the increase in pressure. Normal air contains 20% oxygen. Due to increase in solubility in deep sea, only 4% oxygen is required. If N_2 is used to dilute O_2, it also dissolves in blood due to high pressure. When the diver comes up, the dissolved nitrogen escapes out in the form of bubbles which hinders the flow of blood. This causes painful sensation called **blend**. The solubility of helium is the least among all the gases. Hence, He is used for diluting O_2.

77. The layer of atmosphere which is close to the earth's surface is called troposphere. Hence, the temperature of troposphere is inversely proportional to the distance between surface of the earth and the different regions of the troposphere. Hence, temperature in this layer decreases with an increase in altitude. Interconversion of ozone and oxygen is more in the upper layer of stratosphere. During this process lot of heat energy is released, and hence, with increasing altitude temperature also increases in the stratosphere.

JEE-NEET Special Wing

Multiple-Answer Type Questions

1. Carbon monoxide is released into the atmosphere by the incomplete combustion of petrol and other fossil fuels. CFCs are released by refrigeration systems and such other sources. Automobile exhaust does not contain CFCs. NO_2 is not released by refrigeration systems. It is present in automobile exhaust.

2. $2KClO_3 \rightarrow 2KCl + 3O_2$
2×122.5 g $KClO_3 \rightarrow 3 \times 32$ g
$2H_2O_2 \rightarrow 2H_2O + O_2$
2×34 g $H_2O_2 \rightarrow 32$ g
$2KMnO_4 \rightarrow K_2MnO_4 + 2O_2$
2×158 g $KMnO_4 \rightarrow 2 \times 32$ g
$2KNO_3 \rightarrow 2KNO_3 + 3O_2$
2×101g $KNO_3 \rightarrow 3 \times 32$ g

3. The densities of the liquids lower than '*x*' g/cc should be taken as barometric liquids as they can rise the liquid column to a height greater than '*h*' cm. They are Q and S.

4. 'X' in the given reaction should be nitric oxide which on further reaction with nitrogen gives reddish brown vapours of nitrogen dioxide. Nitric oxide is obtained by the reaction of ammonia with oxygen.
The reaction can be given as
$$4NH_3 + 5O_2 \xrightarrow[800^0 C]{Pt} 4NO + 6H_2O$$
The mole ratio of ammonia and oxygen should be 4:5 or greater than this.

5. Trilead tetroxide (red lead) and lead dioxide on strong heating produce oxygen gas and a solid compound of lead oxide. The lead oxide is called litharge.
$2Pb_3O_4 \rightarrow 6PbO + O_2$
$2PbO_2 \rightarrow 6PbO + O_2$

Comprehension-Based Questions

6. Exosphere is the layer of atmosphere which extends into space.

7. The layer indicated by C is mesosphere in which meteorites burn.

8. Temperature decreases with altitude in troposphere and mesosphere. In stratosphere, the temperature increases with altitude. B is stratosphere while A is troposphere.

9. Due to the UV radiation absorbed by the ozone layer in the stratosphere, the radiation is very intense and the blood gets boiled if the astronaut enters into mesosphere without protective covering.

10. Its stratosphere indicated by B and the layer that gets affected by chlorofluorocarbons is ozone layer.

11.

	Column I		Column II
A	Troposphere	(iii)	Snow fall
B	Stratosphere	(v)	Flight travel
C	Mesosphere	(iv)	Burning of meteorites
D	Thermosphere	(i)	Arora formation
E	Exosphere	(ii)	Satellite station

12. All the reasons can be attributed to the status of LPG as the most ideal fuel.

13. The lower ignition temperature of kerosene renders the rapid initiation of ignition of wood which actually has a higher ignition temperature. This is the reason for sprinkling some kerosene on the wood before ignition. The higher calorific value of kerosene is not the reason for this act.

14. Phosphorus has a low ignition temperature around room temperature and hence undergoes spontaneous combustion. It is stored in water.

15. Hydrogen. The liquefaction and transportation of hydrogen requires to be done at very low temperatures (cryogenic conditions) which makes the fuel much expensive. Also the inflammable nature of hydrogen rises safety concerns. Hence, usage of this becomes a challenging task.

16. D is the least flammable fuel due to its higher ignition temperature and hence is the safest to use.

CHAPTER

5

Water, Solution, Solubility and Hydrogen

Remember

Before beginning this chapter, you should be able to:

- know the importance, different sources and forms of water.
- physical properties and uses of water.

Key Ideas

After completing this chapter, you should be able to:

- understand the physical properties of water and its role in day-to-day life and for industrial uses.
- study about the causes and consequences of water pollution.
- expalin the concept of solubility and the factors affecting it with special emphasis on solubility curves.
- learn the types of crystals and the process of crystallization.
- understand various phenomena associated with different salts.
- study the various methods of preparation, and properties of hydrogen, and applications and uses of hydrogen in various fields.

Scientific Crypt

A Tribute to Antoine Lavoisier (1743 – 1794)

Antoine Lavoisier was 18th century French scientist who revolutionized the study of chemistry through his systematic methods.

Lavoisier was born in France in 1743 in a family of lawyers and hence acquired a degree in law despite his keen interest in science. He was a remarkable man who contributed to the progress of chemistry in many ways by his systematic methods and keen insight into many areas of his field.

Lavoisier's experiments on combustion lead to the discovery of flammable air which he later called hydrogen meaning water former. Discovery of oxygen as supporter of combustion was also the result of Lavoisier's work. His major and notable contribution was the establishment of law of conservation of mass which is considered as major landmark in quantitative chemistry. He complied his discoveries in a book entitled Elementary Treatise of Chemistry which was considered as the first text book in modern chemistry. The book also included principles of naming chemical substances and early versions of chemical equations given by him. In short, Lavoisier was the scientist who set about developing a systematic and experimental approach to chemistry and his conviction that there was order in chemistry led to the development of various basic concepts and paved a way for the modern concepts. In view of such commendable contributions, to the field of chemistry, he is very often regarded as father of modern chemistry.

FUN TIME

CROSSWORD

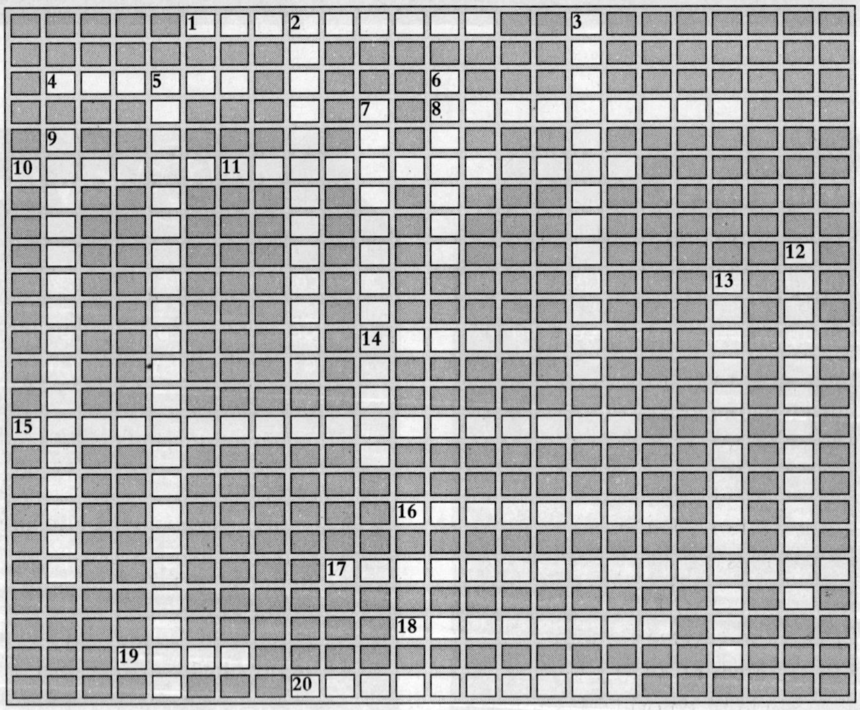

Across

1. Metal which catches fire and burns with lilac flame
4. Colour of zinc oxide in hot condition
8. Self protective metal
10. The property which makes hydrogen a good fuel
14. Shape of sodium chloride crystals
15. Ability of a solvent to break the forces of attraction between ions of the solute
16. Metal that is extracted by using hydrogen as reducing agent
17. The process of formation of crystalline solid from solution
18. Mixture of carbon monoxide and hydrogen
19. Metal which gives reversible reaction with steam
20. Phenomenon associated with the accumulation of hydrogen molecules on platinum surface

Down

2. Salt formed by loss of all water molecules from hydrated salt
3. Phenomenon of absorption of moisture by a salt associated with formation of solution
5. One of the constraints to use hydrogen as a fuel.
6. Metal makes the water milky and alkaline
7. Phenomenon of loss of water molecules on exposure to air
9. The property of water responsible for the use as coolant
11. Heat required to convert one gram of ice to water at 0°C
12. The reaction involved in the making of vanaspathi
13. Solution with two components

INTRODUCTION

Our planet Earth is bestowed with a wide variety of flora and fauna which makes Earth a unique planet in the entire universe. This existence of life on the Earth's surface can be attributed to various factors among which the abundant availability of water on the Earth is the most important one. Water plays the vital role in the biosphere due to it most common occurrence in liquid state, the easy interconversion of this substance into different physical states and its characteristic as a universal solvent and many other special features. Therefore, being a crucial compound for man's survival, water has become the most studied chemical substance.

Water

Let us study some important concepts regarding water.

Historical Aspects

Water in liquid form came into existence on the Earth about 43 billion years ago. Origin of life in this part of the universe also dates back to the same time since it is intimately linked with the origin of water. Water was believed to be an element in the ancient age. In 1781, Henry Cavendish was the first scientist to synthesize water from hydrogen and oxygen. This process of synthesis of water from its constituent elements led later scientists to recognize water as a compound.

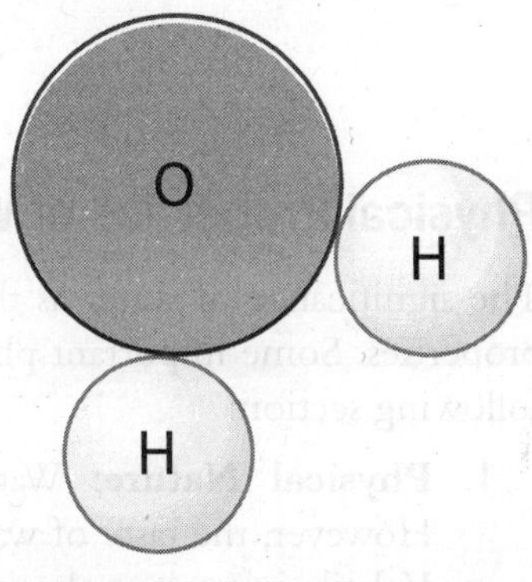

Figure 5.1 Diagrammatic representation of water molecule

Composition

A. I. Lavoisier was the first scientist to experimentally show that water is a compound with hydrogen and oxygen as its constituents. It has been established that one molecule of water contains two atoms of hydrogen and one atom of oxygen.

Occurrence

The distribution of water over the Earth's surface is not uniform throughout. Water is available in nature mostly in a free state and to a somewhat lesser extent in a combined state. Water exists in the free state in all the three physical states, namely, solid, liquid and gaseous states.

1. **Solid State**: Certain regions on the Earth, like, high peaks of mountains, polar regions in Antarctica and the Arctic circle contain water as snow or ice. In these places, water exists in a solid state due to the very low temperatures prevailing in these regions.
2. **Liquid State**: It is the most common state in which water exists. Most of the liquid water is found in oceans and seas. Apart from this, liquid water is also found in rivers, lakes, streams and other water bodies. Water available in the above sources is called **surface water**. Water present in oceans and seas contain appreciable proportions of dissolved salts, predominantly sodium chloride. The presence of these salts imparts salty taste to water and this water is, hence, called **saline water**.
   In addition to surface water, water is also available under the Earth's surface. This is called **underground water**. This water is stored due to the seepage of rainwater through the soil. The underground water may come out in the form of springs. This can be drawn out artificially by digging wells or with the help of tube wells.
3. **Gaseous State**: In gaseous state, water exists as water vapour in the atmospheric air. Clouds, fog, mist, etc., contain water vapour in condensed form.
   Water exists in a combined state in the form of body fluids in the body of living beings. Water is also present in the combined state in hydrated crystals, like, $CuSO_4.5H_2O$, $FeSO_4.7H_2O$, etc. Saline water of oceans and seas can also be considered as one form of combined state of water.

Info Bytes!

Despite being one of the most abundant substances on Earth, pure water, with its H_2O molecular structure, is actually quite rare to find in nature due to impurities.

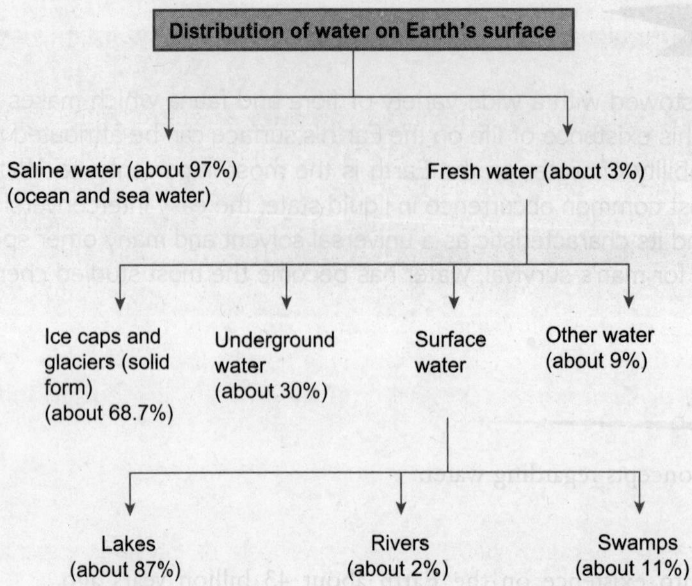

Figure 5.2 Distribution of water on earth's surface

Physical Properties of Water

The significance of water as the most important liquid is mainly due to its physical properties. Some important physical properties of water are discussed in detail in the following section:

1. **Physical Nature**: Water is an odourless, tasteless and transparent liquid. However, the taste of water is attributed to the presence of dissolved salts in it. Volatile impurities also impart some odour to water. Water is colourless in thin layers but it appears bluish in thick layers.
2. **Freezing Point**: The freezing point of water is 0°C under normal atmospheric pressure. The freezing point of water decreases with an increase in external pressure. Presence of soluble impurities decreases the freezing point of water.
3. **Boiling Point**: The boiling point of pure water is 100°C under normal atmospheric pressure. The boiling point of water gets elevated due to the presence of soluble impurities. Increase in external pressure increases the boiling point of water.
4. **Density**: The maximum density of water is 1 g/cc and is obtained at 4°C. The density of water increases with increase in temperature up to 4°C. Later, density of water decreases with increase in temperature beyond 4°C.
5. **Conductivity**: Pure water is a bad conductor of heat and electricity. The electrical conductivity of water is due to the presence of dissolved salts in water.
6. **Specific Heat**: The amount of heat energy required to raise the temperature of unit mass of a substance through 1°C or 1 K is called **specific heat capacity** of that substance.

   Specific heat capacity of pure water is 1 Calorie $g^{-1}°C^{-1}$ = 4.2 Joule $g^{-1}°C^{-1}$.
7. **Latent Heat of Fusion and Latent Heat of Vaporization**: The amount of heat required to be supplied to unit mass of ice for converting it to water without any change in the temperature is called **latent heat of fusion of ice.** Latent heat of fusion of ice = 80 Calories/g.

Konnect

Water shows an unusual behaviour between 0°C and 4°C. In this range of temperature, water expands on cooling instead of contracting. This phenomenon of unusual expansion of water between 0°C and 4°C is called **anomalous expansion.**

Info Bytes!

Water has the highest specific heat capacity among all the substances.

The amount of heat required to be supplied to unit mass of water for converting it to steam without any change in the temperature is called **latent heat of vaporization of water**. Latent heat of vaporization of water = 540 calories/g.

8. **Solvent Properties:** The significance of solutions in chemistry originates from the universal solvent property of water. Water can dissolve many substances in it due to its high dielectric constant. Dielectric constant is the property of a solvent to reduce the force of attraction between the ions (cations and anions) of inorganic compounds. It can also dissolve a large number of organic compounds, like, glucose, sugar, alcohol, etc. Due to the ability to dissolve a wide range of substances in it, water is called **universal solvent**.
   Day-to-day human activities, like, washing, cooking, cleaning, etc., and all life processes occurring in nature involve the formation of solutions with water. Therefore, the ability of water to form solutions is responsible for sustenance of life. On the other hand, the same characteristic forms the basic cause for adding pollutants to water. In whichever way it is considered, the ability of water to form solutions influences the survival of man on the Earth.

EXAMPLE 5.1 Two metallic spheres A and B are made of the same material and have the same volume. Sphere A is hollow, while sphere B is solid. If both spheres are heated using the same heat source and for the same duration, which one will attain a higher temperature first?

SOLUTION

Given that spheres A and B are made of the same material, they will have the same specific heat capacity. However, the mass of the solid sphere B is greater than the hollow sphere A because it contains more of the material.

Heat absorbed or given off is given by: $Q = m \times c \times \Delta T$

Where: Q is the heat absorbed or given off, m is the mass of the object, c is the specific heat capacity, and ΔT is the change in temperature.

Since both spheres receive the same amount of heat and have the same specific heat capacity, the sphere with the lesser mass (sphere A) will experience a greater change in temperature, according to the formula.

Chemical Properties of Water

1. **Chemical Nature:** Water, being a compound of hydrogen and oxygen, is considered an oxide of hydrogen. Since it does not respond to litmus test, it is a neutral oxide.
2. **Catalytic Property:** Water catalyzes some chemical reactions. Few of them are listed below:
   (a) The reaction between perfectly dry hydrogen and chlorine does not take place even in the presence of direct sunlight. The reaction is catalyzed by a few drops of water.

$$H_2 + Cl_2 \rightarrow HCl$$

   (b) Some other reactions like the reaction between hydrogen and oxygen, and the combustion of phosphorous also occur only in the presence of trace amounts of moisture.

$$2H_2 + O_2 \xrightarrow{\text{moisture}} 2H_2O$$

$$4P + 5O_2 \xrightarrow{\text{moisture}} 2P_2O_5$$

3. **Action of Water on Metals:** Water reacts with different metals in different ways. Some of them are tabulated below.

Table 5.1 Action of water on different metals

Metals	Reactions	Observations
Potassium	Potassium reacts with cold water. It even reacts with moisture (water vapour) $2K + 2H_2O \longrightarrow 2KOH + H_2$	(i) Potassium floats on water in the form of silvery grey globules (ii) Reaction is vigorous and exothermic (iii) It catches fire and burns with lilac flame (iv) Effervescence of hydrogen is observed and water becomes alkaline
Sodium	The reaction takes place in cold water $2Na + 2H_2O \longrightarrow 2NaOH + H_2$ It even reacts with moisture (water vapour)	(i) Sodium floats on water in the form of silvery globules (ii) Reaction is less exothermic and vigorous than that with potassium (iii) It catches fire and burns with a golden yellow flame (iv) Effervescence of hydrogen is observed and water becomes alkaline
Calcium	The reaction takes place in cold water $Ca + 2H_2O \longrightarrow Ca(OH)_2 + H_2$	(i) Calcium sinks in water and the water becomes milky and alkaline (ii) It does not catch fire (iii) Effervescence of hydrogen is observed
Magnesium	The reaction takes place with boiling water, but a moderate reaction takes place when burning magnesium reacts with steam $Mg + H_2O \longrightarrow MgO + H_2$	(i) It burns brilliantly with white light (ii) White ash of MgO is produced (iii) Liberation of hydrogen takes place
Zinc	The reaction takes place when steam is passed over red hot zinc $Zn + \underset{\text{(steam)}}{H_2O} \longrightarrow ZnO + H_2$	(i) Yellow-coloured ZnO is produced. On cooling, yellow-coloured ZnO becomes white in colour (ii) Liberation of hydrogen takes place
Aluminium	Aluminium also reacts with steam $2Al + \underset{\text{(steam)}}{3H_2O} \longrightarrow Al_2O_3 + 3H_2$	(i) A coating of Al_2O_3 is formed over the metal which protects the metal from further reaction (ii) Liberation of hydrogen is observed
Iron	When steam is passed over red hot iron, the reaction takes place $3Fe + \underset{\text{(steam)}}{4H_2O} \longrightarrow Fe_3O_4 + 4H_2$	(i) Brown-coloured ferrosoferric oxide is formed and hydrogen is liberated (ii) Reaction is reversible when it takes place in a closed container

4. **Action of Water on Non-metals**
   - **Reaction with Carbon**: When superheated steam is passed over red hot coke, a mixture of carbon monoxide and hydrogen, called **water gas**, is produced. It is a good fuel and a reducing agent.

$$C + H_2O \longrightarrow CO + H_2 \text{ (water gas)}$$

   - **Reaction with Chlorine**: When chlorine gas is passed through water, hydrochloric acid and hypochlorous acid are produced.

$$Cl_2 + H_2O \longrightarrow HCl + HOCl$$

5. **Reaction with Metallic Oxides:** Metallic oxides react with water to form respective bases.

Examples:

$$K_2O + H_2O \longrightarrow 2KOH$$

$$Na_2O + H_2O \longrightarrow 2NaOH$$

$$CaO + H_2O \longrightarrow Ca(OH)_2$$

6. **Reaction with Non-metallic Oxides:** Non-metallic oxides react with water to form respective acids.

Examples:

$$SO_2 + H_2O \longrightarrow H_2SO_3$$

$$P_2O_5 + 3H_2O \longrightarrow 2H_3PO_4$$

$$CO_2 + H_2O \longrightarrow H_2CO_3$$

Tests for Water

1. Water turns white-coloured anhydrous copper sulphate to blue-coloured copper sulphate ($CuSO_4.5H_2O$).
2. Blue-coloured anhydrous cobalt chloride turns pink on addition of water due to the formation of cobalt chloride hexahydrate ($CoCl_2.6H_2O$).

Uses of Water

Fresh water is widely used for our day-to-day domestic activities, for power generation, irrigation and many industrial activities.

1. About 8% of the water is used for domestic purposes, like, cooking, washing, cleaning, flushing, etc.
2. About 22% of fresh water is used in industries.
   (a) Water is used in chemical laboratories because of its solvent property. Many reactions are carried out in the laboratory in aqueous solutions. Many organic compounds do not dissolve in water, hence, water is used for solvent extraction process to separate organic and inorganic compounds. It is also used in the manufacturing of hydrogen, oxygen, acids, alkalis, salts, water gas, etc.
   (b) Pharmaceutical industries also use water extensively.
   (c) Water in the form of steam is used for the generation of electricity.
   (d) Water is used in cooling systems due to its high specific heat capacity.
3. About 70% of the fresh water is used for irrigation.
   (a) Water acts as a medium for the transportation of mineral nutrients through soil in plants.
   (b) Fertilizers and insecticides dissolve in water and they are sprayed on plants in the form of solutions in required concentrations.
4. Saline water is used as a major source for the production of common salt. It is also used for the production of magnesia (MgO) which is used in refractories.

Water Pollution

All these uses make water as the most essential chemical substance. The water we drink is required to be purified because it contains many insoluble impurities, bacteria, microorganisms which affects our health. Water of rivers and lakes are contaminated with unwanted and harmful substances. Polluted water changes the physical, chemical and biological characteristics which in turn affect the biosphere.

Causes of Water Pollution

1. Excess and non-judicious usage of fertilizers and pesticides.

2. Dumping of sewage products from homes and waste from factories in rivers or lakes.

3. Discharge of hot and cold water from industries affects the normal temperature of water and is harmful to aquatic organisms.

Konnect

The golden triangle of water purification in ancient India consisted of boiling, filtering through sand, and sunlight exposure. These methods were rudimentary but effective.

Effects of Water Pollution

1. Fertilizers and pesticides used in farming, mercury salts used in paper and other harmful substances from paint industries could be poisonous. It also helps in generating disease causing organisms like bacteria which cause cholera etc.,

2. Industrial and household waste reduces the dissolved oxygen content in water bodies thereby affecting aquatic life.

3. Sudden change in temperatures due to discharge of hot or cold water affects the breeding of aquatic plants and animals.

Prevention

1. Sewage should not be released directly into rivers or lakes. They should be properly treated in sewage treatment plants, before releasing into water bodies.

2. Harmful chemicals should not be dumped into water bodies. They should be transformed into less harmful or harmless substances.

3. Judicious and rational use of pesticides and fertilizers. Preferential usage of large amount of natural manure and natural pesticides such as neem oil in place of synthetic fertilizers and pesticides.

4. Using drip irrigation to avoid percolation of harmful chemicals through soil.

5. To minimise thermal water pollution, cooling and recycling the water in the plant itself has to be carried out. If not possible, then water should be cooled in cooling towers or by the sprinders before discharging it in the river.

Potable Water

Inspite of all the measures taken for purification of water, the water available is not fit for drinking. Therefore, it is subjected to purification in water works. By this method it is almost free of suspended particles and microorganisms. This is called **potable water.**

Water Purification System in Water Works

Water from reservoir is sent into sedimentation tank in which the suspended particles are allowed to settle down and removed. The water is then sent into filtration tank in which the fine particles of sand, gravel and soil are filtered off. The water free from insoluble impurities is sent into chlorination tower. In this, chlorine dissolves in water forming hypochlorous acid which releases nascent oxygen which kills bacteria and other micro organisms. Now, the water is fit for drinking and hence is supplied.

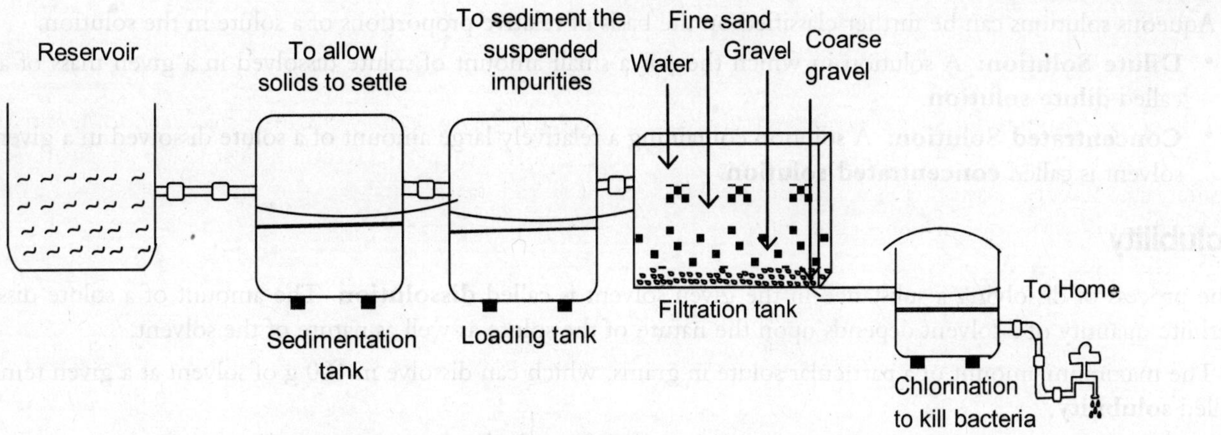

Figure 5.3 Water purification system in water works

Solution

A **solution** is a homogeneous mixture of two or more substances. The proportion of the constituents of the solution can be varied within certain limits. The solutions comprising the two components are called **binary solutions**.

That component of a solution which is in the same physical state (i.e., solid, liquid or gas) as the solution is called **solvent**, and the other component is called **solute**.

If both the components are in the same state, the component which is present in larger proportions is called **solvent** and the one which is present in minor proportions is called **solute**.

Classification of Solutions

Depending on the physical states of the solute and the solvent, solutions can be classified into various types.

Table 5.2 Classification of solutions

Solvent	Solute	Examples
Solid	Solid	Alloys like brass, bronze, etc
	Liquid	Hydrated crystalline salts
	Gas	Hydrogen gas adsorbed on platinum or palladium
Liquid	Solid	Common salt in water
	Liquid	Petrol in kerosene
	Gas	Aerated water or soft drinks
Gas	Gas	Air

When the solvent is a gas and the solute is a solid or a liquid, the resultant mixture becomes heterogeneous. All other solutions being homogeneous are called **true solutions**.

The other two types of mixtures being heterogeneous are called **suspensions**.

Examples: Fog, mist and dust particles in air.

The study of solutions is generally confined to the solutions of a solid solute in a liquid solvent. In most of the cases, water is taken as the solvent since it can dissolve a wide range of chemical compounds. Those solutions in which water is taken as the solvent are called **aqueous solutions**.

Apart from water, other liquids can also be taken as solvents. Examples of such solvents are alcohol, petrol, ether, benzene, etc. Those solutions in which a liquid other than water is taken as a solvent are called **non-aqueous solutions**.

Aqueous solutions can be further classified on the basis of relative proportions of a solute in the solution.

- **Dilute Solution:** A solution in which there is a small amount of solute dissolved in a given mass of a solvent is called **dilute solution.**
- **Concentrated Solution:** A solution containing a relatively large amount of a solute dissolved in a given mass of a solvent is called **concentrated solution.**

Solubility

The process of dissolving a substance in the given solvent is called **dissolution**. The amount of a solute dissolved in a definite quantity of a solvent depends upon the nature of the solute as well as nature of the solvent.

The maximum amount of a particular solute in grams, which can dissolve in 100 g of solvent at a given temperature is called **solubility**.

$$\text{Solubility} = \frac{\text{Mass of solute}}{\text{Mass of solvent}} \times 100$$

Example: Solubility of copper sulphate in water at 20°C is 20.7 g and solubility of potassium chloride in water at 20°C is 34 g.

A given solution may or may not contain the maximum amount of a solute in it. The further dissolving capacity of a given solution depends on the amount of the solute already present in the solution. On the basis of the capacity of the solution to dissolve certain amount of solute further, the solutions are classified into three types as discussed hereunder.

Saturated Solution

A solution which contains the maximum amount of the solute that can be dissolved in the solvent at a given temperature is called **saturated solution** at that particular temperature. This solution can no longer dissolve any more solute under the given conditions.

Unsaturated Solution

The solution containing lesser amount of the solute than the saturated solution at a given temperature is called an **unsaturated solution**. In an unsaturated solution, the solvent has the capacity of dissolving more amount of the solute at that particular temperature.

Supersaturated Solution

If a solution holds more solute than the saturated solution at a given temperature, it is called **supersaturated solution**. When more solute is made to dissolve in a saturated solution by raising its temperature and then cooling it slowly without causing any disturbances (like shaking), then the resultant solution holds more solute than the saturated solution.

Supersaturated solution is metastable and slight disturbances, like, shaking, stirring and scratching the wall of the container or adding a solute crystal to the solution make the additional amount of the solute to precipitate out, thereby resulting in the formation of the saturated solution again.

Factors Affecting Solubility

1. **Nature of the Solute**: Ionic compounds or polar compounds are more soluble in polar solvents like water. Non-polar compounds are more soluble in non-polar solvents like benzene.
2. **Nature of the Solvent**: The solvents which have high dielectric constants can dissolve polar and ionic compounds to a greater extent than the solvents with low dielectric constants.
   Example:
   NaCl is highly soluble in water.
   NaCl is sparingly soluble in benzene.
3. **Temperature**: For most of the substances, solubility increases with the increase in temperature. However, the solubility of some substances decreases with increase in temperature. In case of some substances, the temperature has no or little effect on the solubility.

Solubility Curves

The graphs which show variation of solubility with temperature are called **solubility curves.**

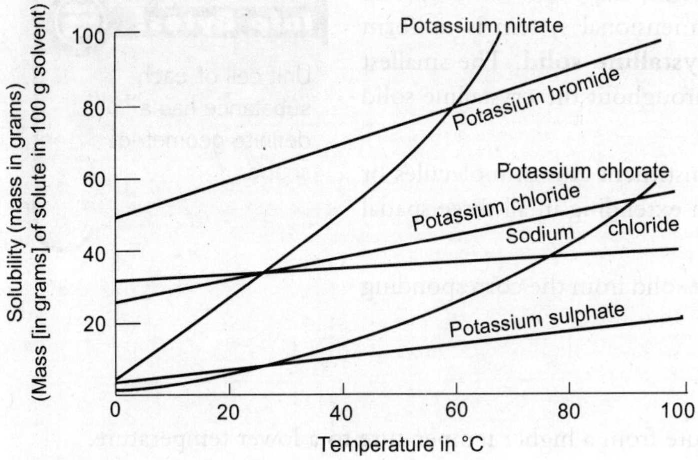

Figure 5.4 Variation of solubility of various solids with temperatures

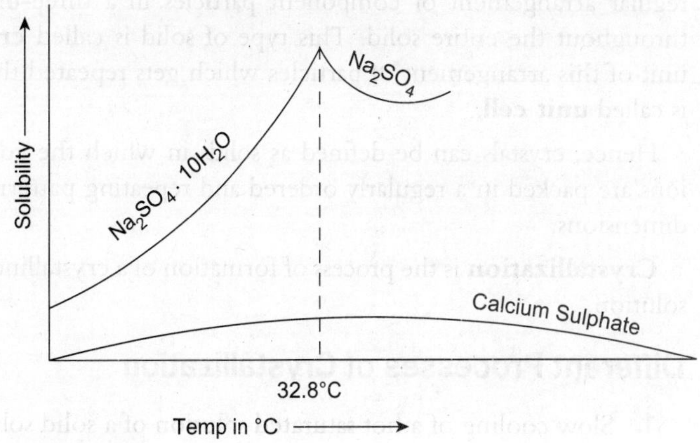

Figure 5.5 Solubility curve of $Na_2SO_4.10H_2O$ and $CaSO_4$

Importance of Solubility Curves

1. The solubility of a particular solute in a given solvent at a given temperature can be found out.
2. Solubilities of different solutes in a given solvent at a particular temperature can be compared.
3. It is possible to determine the amount of solute that can be precipitated by cooling the saturated solution of that solute to a certain temperature.
4. From the solubility curves, it is possible to know the preferential precipitation of different salts during the fractional crystallization process since the solution contains more than one salt dissolved in it.

Rate of Dissolution of a Solid in a Liquid

Though each solute has a certain fixed value of solubility, the rate at which a solute dissolves in a particular solvent depends on certain factors.

1. **Size of the Solute Particles**: The smaller the solute particles, the faster the rate of dissolution. This is because division into smaller particles increases the surface area of contact between the solute and solvent particles. Greater area of contact increases the rate of dissolution.
2. **Agitation of Solution**: Agitation or stirring improves the contact between the solute and solvent molecules. Consequently, the rate of dissolution increases.
3. **Temperature**: Rate of dissolution of most of the solids increases with the increase in temperature because the solubility of the solid increases with the increase in temperature. However, in case of some solids, the rate of dissolution increases with the increase in temperature up to a certain point and decreases beyond a certain point.
   Examples: $Na_2SO_4.10H_2O$ and $CaSO_4$

   Effect of Temperature: With the increase in temperature, the solubility of a gas in a particular liquid decreases.
4. **Effect of Pressure**: The effect of pressure on the solubility of a gas in a liquid is given by Henry's law, which states that at constant temperature, the increase in pressure on the surface of the liquid increases the solubility of the gas in the liquid.

Konnect

The solubilities of gases in liquids show a different trend with regard to the effect of temperature. In these solutions, the solubility is also influenced by the pressure.

Crystallization

When a saturated solid–liquid solution is cooled slowly, solid solute settles down with a highly regular arrangement of its constituent particles (atoms, molecules or ions). This regular arrangement of component particles in a three-dimensional system is uniform throughout the entire solid. This type of solid is called **crystalline solid**. The smallest unit of this arrangement of particles which gets repeated throughout the crystalline solid is called **unit cell**.

> **Info Bytes!**
> Unit cell of each substance has a definite geometric shape.

Hence, crystals can be defined as solids in which the constituent atoms, molecules or ions are packed in a regularly ordered and repeating pattern extending in all three spatial dimensions.

Crystallization is the process of formation of a crystalline solid from the corresponding solution.

Different Processes of Crystallization

1. Slow cooling of a hot saturated solution of a solid solute from a higher temperature to a lower temperature.
2. Evaporation of an unsaturated solution at moderate temperature.
3. Slow cooling of a molten solid.
4. Sublimation of the solid followed by condensation of the resultant vapours.

Types of Crystals

Each crystal consists of a set of three axes in a particular geometrical arrangement. There are seven unique crystal systems depending on the orientation of the particles along the three axes.

Table 5.3 Types of crystal systems

Types of crystal systems	Examples
Cubic	NaCl, CsCl
Hexagonal	Graphite, ZnO
Tetragonal	SnO_2, TiO_2
Rhombohedral	$CaCO_3$, HgS
Orthorhombic	Rhombic sulphur
Monoclinic	Monoclinic sulphur, $PbCrO_2$
Triclinic	$K_2Cr_2O_7$, $CuSO_4.5H_2O$

> **Konnect**
> Not all that glitters is gold. Sometimes it's just salt. Halite crystals, formed from salt, can often be mistaken for gemstones because of their cubic shape and shine.

Water of Crystallization

When a solid gets crystallized from its respective hot concentrated aqueous solution, a certain fixed number of water molecules also get attached to the solid crystals to form unit cells of the crystals.

The fixed number of water molecules which combine with a crystal and are necessary for the maintenance of crystalline properties, but capable of being lost either at normal temperature or at a higher temperature is called **water of crystallization**.

Examples of such solids (salts) are green vitriol ($FeSO_4.7H_2O$), blue vitriol ($CuSO_4.5H_2O$), washing soda ($Na_2CO_3.10H_2O$), etc.

Hydrated Salts and Anhydrous Salts

The salts which contain water of crystallization are called **hydrated salts**. When the hydrated salts completely lose their water molecules, then such salts are called **anhydrous salt**. When a hydrated salt gets dehydrated and forms anhydrous salt, the colour of the salt changes.

Example: $CuSO_4.5H_2O$ is blue in colour. It changes to white colour due to the loss of water molecules on heating.

Efflorescence and Deliquescence

There are some hydrated crystals which lose some of the water of crystallization or all the water of crystallization on exposure to air at normal temperature. This phenomenon is known as **efflorescence** and the hydrated crystals which lose water molecules are called **efflorescent substances**.

After the release of the water molecules, efflorescent substances lose their crystalline property and get transformed into a powdery mass.

Example: Glauber salt, $Na_2SO_4.10H_2O$ loses all of its water molecules on exposure to air at ordinary temperature.

Some crystalline salts absorb moisture on exposure to air and ultimately dissolve in it to form an aqueous solution. This phenomenon is called **deliquescence** and these crystalline salts are called **deliquescent substances**. These salts may or may not contain water of crystallization.

Example: Hydrated magnesium chloride ($MgCl_2.6H_2O$), hydrated calcium chloride ($CaCl_2$. $6H_2O$), etc.

Hygroscopic Substances and Desiccating Agents

There are certain substances which absorb moisture from air without changing their physical state. These substances are called **hygroscopic substances**. They may exist in solid or liquid state under normal temperature and pressure.

Example: calcium oxide (solid), concentrated sulphuric acid (liquid), etc.

After absorbing moisture, solid hygroscopic substances remain as solids and liquid substances remain as liquids.

Unlike deliquescent substances, these hygroscopic substances retain their physical states (solids or liquid) upon absorption of moisture. Hygroscopic substances which are used to remove water from the surroundings are called **desiccating agents**.

Example: Calcium oxide and anhydrous calcium chloride.

Water has unique physical properties due to which existence of life on the earth is possible. However, chemical properties of water also play a vital role in the progress of human civilization.

EXAMPLE 5.2 Anhydrous calcium chloride is often found to be damp when exposed to air. Why isn't it categorized as a deliquescent substance? Give reason.

SOLUTION

While anhydrous calcium chloride does absorb moisture from the atmosphere, it does not dissolve completely in the absorbed water under typical conditions to form a clear solution. For a substance to be classified as deliquescent, it must not only absorb moisture from the air but also dissolve in it to form a liquid solution. Since anhydrous calcium chloride does not fully meet this criterion, it is not considered a deliquescent substance.

Hydrogen

Hydrogen is the lightest among all elements. Atmospheric air is found to contain only trace amounts of hydrogen. Hydrogen gas was first prepared by the action of H_2SO_4 on iron. In 1762, Henry Cavendish for the first time established the elemental nature of hydrogen. He prepared this gas by the action of H_2SO_4 on zinc. Lavoisier named it hydrogen which means *water-former* (Hydro—water, gen—producing).

Occurrence

Availability of hydrogen gas in a free state is very rare. Though it is present in trace amounts in the atmosphere, hydrogen is present in sun's atmosphere up to 1.1%. Very minute quantities of hydrogen are present in volcanic gases.

Most of the hydrogen is present in a combined state in nature. Hydrogen is present in various carbon compounds in the form of proteins, nucleic acids, vitamins, hormones, enzymes, etc., in plants and animals. Most of the naturally occurring substances, such as, wood, cotton, paper pulp, rubber, etc., contain hydrogen. Water is the most important source of hydrogen as hydrogen is present up to 11.1% by weight in water.

Preparation of Hydrogen

Some general, laboratory and industrial preparation methods of hydrogen are discussed below.

General Methods of Preparation

Table 5.4 General methods of preparation of hydrogen

Methods	Equations	Observations
Action of active metals with water	$2Na + 2H_2O \longrightarrow 2NaOH + H_2$	Na and K $\longrightarrow$ Reaction is violent. They float on the surface of water Ca $\longrightarrow$ Brisk reaction and metal sinks in water
Action of steam on hot metals	$Mg + H_2O \longrightarrow MgO + H_2$	Reaction is fast for Mg and slow for Al, Zn and Fe
Action of dil acids on metals	$Zn + 2HCl \longrightarrow ZnCl_2 + H_2$	The reaction takes place at moderate speed with zinc.
Action of concentrated alkali on metals	$2NaOH + 2Al + 2H_2O \longrightarrow 2NaAlO_2 + 3H_2$	Reaction takes place only on boiling

Laboratory Method of Preparation

All the metals present above hydrogen in the reactivity series on reaction with dil HCl or dil. H_2SO_4 liberate hydrogen gas. Zinc metal is preferred for this reaction.

$$Zn + 2HCl \longrightarrow ZnCl_2 + H_2 \uparrow$$

$$Zn + H_2SO_4 \longrightarrow ZnSO_4 + H_2 \uparrow$$

Experiment I

Some granulated zinc pieces are taken in a flat-bottomed flask fitted with a two-holed air-tight cork. In the one hole, a thistle funnel is inserted and in the other hole, a long delivery tube is inserted. Dilute H_2SO_4 is allowed to fall into the flask dropwise through the thistle funnel.

Observation: Effervescence is observed in the initial stages of the reaction. Then a colourless and odourless gas is evolved.

Collection of Gas: Hydrogen is collected by the downward displacement of water.

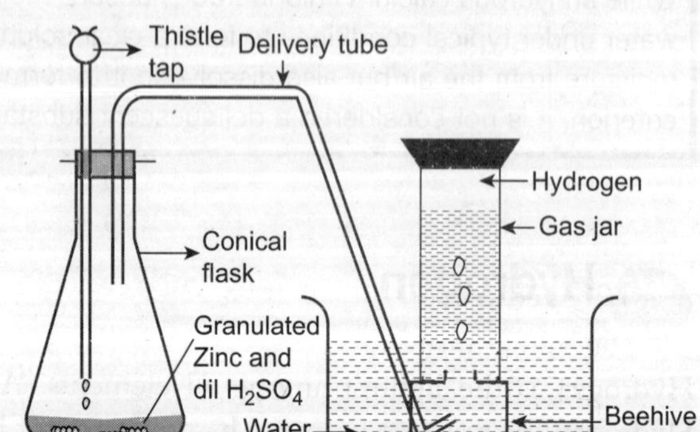

Figure 5.6 Laboratory preparation of Hydrogen

Purification of Hydrogen Gas: Since impure zinc is used for hydrogen gas preparation, the hydrogen gas collected is found to contain some impurities, such as, H_2S, SO_2, PH_3, AsH_3 and CO_2. These impurities are removed in stages.

Table 5.5 Impurities and process of their removal

Impurities	Processes of removal
AsH_3, PH_3	Silver nitrate solution
H_2S	Lead nitrate solution
CO_2, SO_2, NO_2	Caustic potash
H_2O (water vapour)	$CaCl_2$ or P_2O_5 (drying agent)

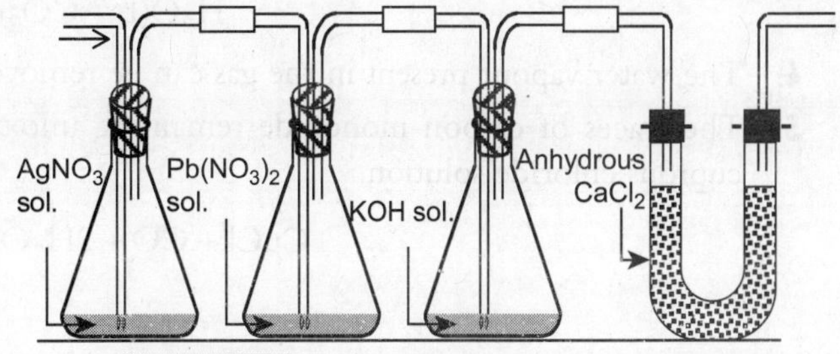

Figure 5.7 Purification of hydrogen gas

Collection of Purified Hydrogen Gas: To obtain pure and dry hydrogen, pure hydrogen gas is collected over mercury.

Precautions:

1. Entire apparatus should be kept air-tight.
2. Contact with flame should be avoided.
3. Collection of the gas should be done only after the expulsion of air.
4. The end of the thistle funnel should almost touch the bottom.

Though all active metals liberate hydrogen gas, zinc is the preferred metal and the other metals are not used for this preparation method.

Table 5.6 Metals not used for preparation of hydrogen

Metals	Reasons for not using
Sodium and potassium	Violent reaction with explosion
Calcium and magnesium	Expensive metals
Aluminium	Formation of protective coating of Al_2O_3 renders the metal passive
Iron	Reversible reaction
Lead	Formation of insoluble $PbCl_2$ or $PbSO_4$ stops the further reaction

Industrial Methods of Preparation

1. **Electrolysis of Water**: Electrolysis of acidulated water liberates oxygen at the cathode and hydrogen at the anode. In fact, this method is employed for the preparation of oxygen gas where hydrogen is obtained as a by-product.

$$2H_2O \longrightarrow 2H_2 + O_2$$

2. **Bosch Process:** Water gas is a mixture of carbon monoxide and hydrogen. Catalytic oxidation of carbon monoxide gives hydrogen gas. Water gas can be prepared by passing steam over red hot coke.

$$\underset{\text{Steam}}{C + H_2O} \longrightarrow \underset{\text{Water gas}}{CO + H_2}$$

$$CO + H_2 + H_2O \xrightarrow[450°C-500°C]{Fe_2O_3} CO_2 + 2H_2$$

Procedure:

(a) Superheated steam at 170°C when passed through white hot coke or charcoal gives a mixture of CO gas and hydrogen known as **water gas.**

(b) Water gas obtained is made to pass over Fe_2O_3 or Cr_2O_3 along with superheated steam at 500°C. Carbon monoxide gets oxidized to CO_2 leaving hydrogen gas.

3. The CO_2 gas is removed by compressing the gas at 30 atm pressure and passing it through water. Hydrogen being insoluble remains as such.

$$H_2O(l) + CO_2(g) \xrightarrow{300\ atm} H_2CO_3$$

4. The water vapour present in the gas can be removed by cooling the gas to –20°C.
5. The traces of carbon monoxide remaining unoxidized can be removed by passing the gas through ammonical cuprous chloride solution.

$$CuCl + CO + 2H_2O \longrightarrow \underset{\text{addition compound}}{CuCl.CO.2H_2O}$$

Bosch process can also be carried out for the preparation of hydrogen from natural gas. Natural gas contains methane as a major constituent. Methane on mixing with superheated steam at high temperature followed by compression to 30 atm pressure also gives water gas. This is subjected to Bosch process for getting pure hydrogen gas.

Physical Properties of Hydrogen

Table 5.7 Physical properties of hydrogen

Properties	Description
Colour	Colourless
Odour	No characteristic odour for pure hydrogen. But fishy odour of hydrogen gas is attributed to the presence of impurities
Solubility	Negligible
Density	Least density
Action on litmus	Neutral
Liquefaction	Difficult due to very low critical temperature and not possible at room temperature
Diffusion	Fast rate of diffusion

Adsorption or Occlusion: In addition to the normal physical properties, hydrogen shows a specific property called **adsorption** or **occlusion**. The accumulation of molecules of one compound over the surface of another substance is called **adsorption**. Hydrogen gas gets adsorbed on the surface of some metals, such as, palladium, platinum, nickel, etc.

Chemical Properties of Hydrogen

1. **Reaction with Air**: Hydrogen burns in air and reacts with oxygen forming water. A blue flame is also observed.

$$2H_2 + O_2 \longrightarrow 2H_2O$$

2. **Reaction with Non-metals**: Hydrogen reacts with most of the non-metals forming corresponding hydrides.

   (a) **Reaction with Chlorine**: Hydrogen reacts with chlorine in the presence of sunlight to give hydrogen chloride. This is a photochemical reaction as shown below:

$$H_2 + Cl_2 \xrightarrow{light} 2HCl$$

   (b) **Reaction with Nitrogen**: Nitrogen and hydrogen react in 1 : 3 ratio at high temperature and high pressure to form ammonia.

$$N_2 + 3H_2 \longrightarrow 2NH_3$$

   (c) **Reaction with Sulphur**: On reaction with molten sulphur, hydrogen gas gives hydrogen sulphide.

$$H_2 + S \longrightarrow H_2S$$

3. **Reactions with Metals**: Hydrogen reacts with highly electropositive metals to form metallic hydrides.
Examples:

$$2K + H_2 \xrightarrow{\Delta} 2KH$$

$$2Na + H_2 \xrightarrow{\Delta} 2NaH$$

$$Ca + H_2 \longrightarrow CaH_2$$

4. **Reactions with Metal Oxides**: Oxides of less reactive metals react with hydrogen to form the corresponding metal and water. This is due to the reduction of metallic oxide.
Examples:

$$\underset{\text{White}}{ZnO} + H_2 \longrightarrow \underset{\text{Bluish white}}{Zn} + H_2O$$

$$\underset{\text{Brown}}{2Fe_2O_3} + 6H_2 \longrightarrow \underset{\text{Grey}}{4Fe} + 6H_2O$$

$$\underset{\text{Yellow}}{PbO} + H_2 \longrightarrow \underset{\text{Grey}}{Pb} + H_2O$$

$$\underset{\text{Black}}{CuO} + H_2 \longrightarrow \underset{\text{Red}}{Cu} + H_2O$$

5. **Hydrogenation**: Catalytic addition of hydrogen to some carbon compounds is called hydrogenation.

$$\underset{\text{Ethylene}}{H_2C = CH_2} + H_2 \longrightarrow \underset{\text{Ethane}}{H_3C - CH_3}$$

This principle is used in the process of hydrogenation of oils or hardening of oils.

Hydrogenation of Oils: Vegetable oil which contains carbon and oxygen in greater percentage and contains less amount of hydrogen cannot be solidified easily due to less percentage of hydrogen.

Examples: Ground nut oil and sunflower oil.

Animal oils such as ghee which contain hydrogen in greater percentage get solidified easily under normal conditions. Vegetable oils also get solidified when hydrogen gas is passed through them at high pressure and high temperature in the presence of a nickel catalyst.

Examples: Palm oil, vanaspathi, soap, etc.

Uses of Hydrogen

1. **In the Synthesis of Industrial Chemicals.**
   (a) Manufacture of ammonia (Haber's process)

$$N_2 + 3H_2 \xrightarrow{Fe} 2NH_3$$

   (b) Manufacture of HCl

$$H_2 + Cl_2 \xrightarrow{\text{sunlight}} 2HCl$$

   (c) Manufacture of methyl alcohol

$$CO + H_2 + H_2 \xrightarrow[\text{Catalyst}]{\Delta} CH_3OH$$

   (d) Manufacture of Dalda/Vansapati and soap by hydrogenation of oils.
   (e) Manufacture of petrol/gasoline from coal.

> **Info Bytes!**
>
> Hydrogen is often termed as the fuel of the future. If you filled a balloon with hydrogen (not recommended), it would float up faster than with helium.

2. **Fuel**: Many fuel gases contain hydrogen as a major constituent. This is because of high heat of combustion of hydrogen.

   Examples: Water gas, coal gas, semi-water gas, etc.

   (a) Electrical cells called **fuel cells** are also designed which use hydrogen gas.

   (b) Liquid hydrogen is used as a rocket fuel.

3. **Oxyhydrogen Blow Torch**: A mixture of hydrogen and oxygen is burnt to give a high temperature of 2800°C. This is used for welding of metals and for melting platinum and quartz.

4. **Atomic Hydrogen Torch**: When an electric arc is generated in a stream of hydrogen between tungsten electrodes, the hydrogen molecules dissociate to give hydrogen atoms by absorbing large amount of energy. The atoms recombine to form hydrogen molecules by evolving the absorbed heat energy. As a result, high temperature is generated. This can be made use of in welding alloys.

5. **Metallurgy**: Hydrogen is used as a good reducing agent in the extraction of some metals from their oxides.

   Examples: Tungsten, molybdenum, etc.

$$WO_3 + 3H_2 \longrightarrow W + 3H_2O$$

EXAMPLE 5.3 Explain the principle of atomic hydrogen torch.

SOLUTION

When an electric arc is generated in a stream of hydrogen between tungsten electrodes, the hydrogen molecules dissociate to give hydrogen atoms. The atoms recombine to form hydrogen molecules by releasing heat energy. As a result, high temperature can be obtained. This can be made use of in welding alloys.

EXAMPLE 5.4 What makes the use of hydrogen as a fuel difficult? Give reasons in support of your answer.

SOLUTION

Though there are many advantages of hydrogen as an automobile fuel, there are a few drawbacks in this process.

(i) Liquefaction of hydrogen gas is very difficult since its critical temperature is very less. This makes liquid hydrogen very expensive.

(ii) Since hydrogen is highly inflammable, its storage and transportation are difficult.

POINTS TO REMEMBER

- ✔ Water available in the above sources is called surface water.
- ✔ The presence of these salts imparts salty taste to water and this water is, hence, called saline water.
- ✔ In addition to surface water, water is also available under the Earth's surface. This is called underground water.
- ✔ The amount of heat energy required to raise the temperature of unit mass of a substance through 1°C or 1 K is called specific heat capacity of that substance.
- ✔ The amount of heat required to be supplied to unit mass of ice for converting it to water without any change in the temperature is called latent heat of fusion of ice.
- ✔ The amount of heat required to be supplied to unit mass of water for converting it to steam without any change in the temperature is called latent heat of vaporization of water.
- ✔ A solution is a homogeneous mixture of two or more substances.
- ✔ The solutions comprising the two components are called binary solutions.
- ✔ The component which is present in larger proportions is called solvent and the one which is present in minor proportions is called solute.
- ✔ Those solutions in which water is taken as the solvent are called aqueous solutions.
- ✔ Those solutions in which a liquid other than water is taken as a solvent are called non-aqueous solutions.
- ✔ A solution in which there is a small amount of solute dissolved in a given mass of a solvent is called dilute solution.
- ✔ A solution containing a relatively large amount of a solute dissolved in a given mass of a solvent is called concentrated solution.
- ✔ The process of dissolving a substance in the given solvent is called dissolution.
- ✔ The maximum amount of a particular solute in grams, which can dissolve in 100 g of solvent at a given temperature is called solubility.
- ✔ A solution which contains the maximum amount of the solute that can be dissolved in the solvent at a given temperature is called saturated solution at that particular temperature.
- ✔ The solution containing lesser amount of the solute than the saturated solution at a given temperature is called an unsaturated solution.
- ✔ If a solution holds more solute than the saturated solution at a given temperature, it is called supersaturated solution.
- ✔ The graphs which show variation of solubility with temperature are called solubility curves.
- ✔ The smallest unit of this arrangement of particles which gets repeated throughout the crystalline solid is called unit cell.
- ✔ Crystallization is the process of formation of a crystalline solid from the corresponding solution.
- ✔ The fixed number of water molecules which combine with a crystal and are necessary for the maintenance of crystalline properties, but capable of being lost either at normal temperature or at a higher temperature is called water of crystallization.
- ✔ The salts which contain water of crystallization are called hydrated salts.
- ✔ When the hydrated salts completely lose their water molecules, then such salts are called anhydrous salt.
- ✔ The accumulation of molecules of one compound over the surface of another substance is called adsorption.

PRACTICE QUESTIONS CLASSROOM WING

Very Short Answer Type Questions

Direction for questions from 1 to 3:
Fill in the blanks

1. If a saturated hydrocarbon has 4 carbon atoms, then the formula of the hydrocarbon could be ________.
2. When phosphorus pentoxide reacts with water, the product is ______.
3. ______ can catalyze the reaction between dry chlorine and hydrogen.

Direction for questions from 4 to 25:
Answer the following questions.

4. Write the name of a harmful gas released in coal mines.
5. Which process is involved in the preparation of carbon black from methane?
6. A saturated hydrocarbon contains 14 hydrogen atoms. What could be the number of carbon atoms in it?
7. The name given to the heating of methane in the absence of air is ________.
8. Solubility of copper sulphate in water is 20.7 g at 20°C. What do you mean by this statement?
9. How does freezing point get affected due to the presence of impurities?
10. Name two metals which react with moisture.
11. How is hydrogen gas used in metallurgy? Give an example.
12. What is the value of specific heat capacity of water? How much heat energy is required to increase the temperature of 5 g of water to 1°C?
13. What is meant by hardening of oils? How is it done?
14. How is water gas formed?
15. What is the difference between latent heat of fusion and latent heat of vaporization? Discuss the difference taking water as an example.
16. What is unit cell of a crystal?
17. Will there be any change in the boiling point of water if we go to the top of a hill? Give reasons.
18. Complete the following table:

Solution	Solvent	Solute
(a) Sugar solution		
(b) Solution of alcohol and water (5% alcohol and 95% water)		
(c) Blue vitriol		
(d) Brass		
(e) Hydrogen adsorbed by platinum		

19. Name the acid formed by the reaction between SO_2 gas and water. Also write the reaction involved.
20. Why is granulated zinc used for the preparation of hydrogen gas?
21. Hydrated copper sulphate is not considered an efflorescent substance. Give a reason.
22. What happens when steam is passed over hot magnesium metal?
23. Differentiate between efflorescent and deliquescent substances.
24. What is meant by occlusion? Give one example.
25. State whether the solution is a mixture or a compound. Justify your answer.

Short Answer Type Questions

26. What is the principle involved in the usage of baking powder in cakes?
27. How is the little amount of CO_2 present dissolved in water utilized for photosynthesis by aquatic plants?
28. Two substances x and y are taken in two test tubes and heated. The gas coming out of only y when passed through lime water turns it milky. Identify x and y if the metals are out two of Zn, Mg, K and Na.

29. How is the little amount of CO_2 present dissolved in water utilized for pho-tosynthesis by aquatic plants?

30. Water obtained from which source contains more minerals and why?

31. What are the different factors on which solubility of a solid in a liquid depend? Explain with a reason.

32. In which way is water useful for generating electricity?

33. Establish water as a compound.

34. How can hydrogen be prepared from natural gas?

35. Why is pure water a bad conductor of electricity?

36. How do temperature and pressure affect the solubility of gases in water?

37. Why is distilled water not useful for drinking purpose though it is the purest form of water?

38. Give some examples of reactions where metal oxides react with hydrogen.

39. Differentiate solvent and solute with an example each when

(a) both are in the same physical state and

(b) the physical state of the solute and the solvent is different.

Essay Answer Type Questions

40. (a) Discuss in detail Bosch process of preparation of hydrogen gas.

(b) The survival of aquatic animals in cold countries can be attributed to the property of anomalous expansion of water. Justify.

41. Observe the following flow chart and identify 'X' and 'Y'.

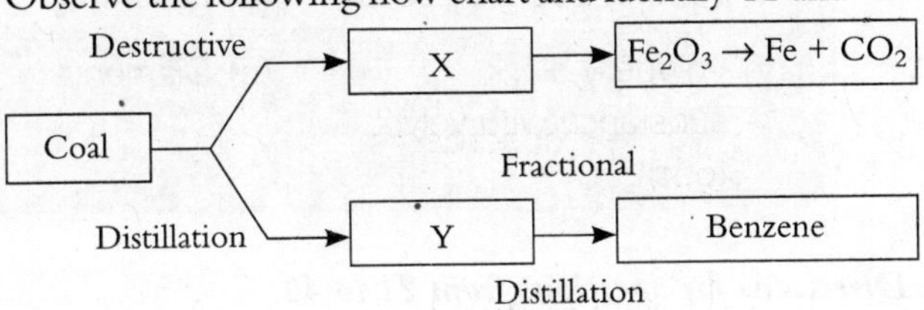

42. What are solubility curves? Explain different areas of applications of solubility curves.

43. Explain the general methods of preparation of hydrogen giving one example each. Among these, which method is preferred for laboratory preparation and why?

44. Write the effect of impurities and external pressure on the freezing and boiling points of water. Explain with examples.

PRACTICE QUESTIONS COMPETITION WING

Level 1: Apply Your Concepts

Directions for questions from 1 to 12:
State whether the following statements are true or false:

1. An ideal fuel has a high ignition temperature.
2. Butane, Phosgene and CO are harmful gases.
3. Heating of Na_2CO_3 does not produce CO_2.
4. Reaction of carbonic acid with NaOH does not involve the formation of a white precipitate.
5. The density of water is maximum at 4 K.
6. Blue-coloured $CuSO_4$ can act as a dehumidifying agent.
7. Alloys are homogeneous mixtures.
8. Ice floats on water.
9. Hydrated salts do not have water of crystallization.
10. Solubility can tell us the amount of solute that can be dissolved in the solvent.
11. Surface water is stored due to seepage of rainwater.
12. In alloy, constituent metals retain their physical properties.

Directions for questions from 13 to 19:
Fill in the blanks.

13. _____ substances when exposed to moisture dissolve in it.
14. Metallic oxides on reaction with water give _____.
15. ______ solution is more concentrated than a saturated solution.
16. Due to its high _____, water is called universal solvent.
17. The number of oxygen atoms present in five molecules of ferrosoferric oxide is ______.
18. The formula for Glauber's salt is ______.
19. Salts with water of crystallization are called ______ salts.

Directions for question 20:
Match the entries given in Column A with appropriate ones in Column B.

20. Match the statements of Column A with those of Column B.

Column A	Column B
(i) Layer lattice structure	(a) Gas carbon
(ii) Spherical cage molecules	(b) Lamp black
(iii) Rigid three-dimensional structure	(c) Graphite
(iv) Amorphous grey solid	(d) Fullerene
(v) Powdery black substance with velvet touch	(e) Diamond

Directions for questions from 21 to 40:
For each of the questions, four choices have been provided. Select the correct alternative.

21. **Assertion (A):** Diamond is a good thermal conductor.
    Reason (R): Diamond is a crystalline allotrope of carbon in which carbon ex-hibits tetravalency.
    (a) Both A and R are true and R is the correct explanation of A.
    (b) Both A and R are true, but R is not the correct explanation of A.
    (c) A is true and R is false.
    (d) A is false and R is true.
22. **Assertion (A):** Dry ice is used for cloud seeding.
    Reason (R): Dry ice sublimes.
    (a) Both A and R are true and R is the correct explanation of A.
    (b) Both A and R are true, but R is not the correct explanation of A.
    (c) A is true and R is false.
    (d) A is false and R is true.

23. **Assertion (A):** Graphite is a good electrical conductor.
Reason (R): Carbon exhibits a valency of three in graphite.
(a) Both A and R are true and R is the correct explanation of A.
(b) Both A and R are true, but R is not the correct explanation of A.
(c) A is true and R is false.
(d) A is false and R is true.

24. **Assertion (A):** A sealed bottle containing dry ice explodes after some time.
Reason (R): Dry ice produces very low temperatures.
(a) Both A and R are true and R is the correct explanation of A.
(b) Both A and R are true, but R is not the correct explanation of A.
(c) A is true and R is false.
(d) A is false and R is true

25. Which among the following elements does not float on water?
(a) Na (b) K
(c) Ca (d) Ca, K

26. 50 g of oil 'A' and 100 g of oil 'B' are taken in separate containers at same temperature and specific heat of oil 'B' is double that of oil 'A.' Both are heated in such a way that increase in temperature is also the same. Calculate the ratio of heat required to be supplied for increasing the temperature.
(a) 1 : 2 (b) 1 : 1
(c) 4 : 1 (d) 1 : 4

27. Anhydride of sulphurous acid is
(a) sulphur dioxide (b) sulphate ion
(c) sulphur trioxide (d) sulphite ion

28. Which of the following compounds is not associated with water molecules?
(a) blue vitriol (b) nitre
(c) washing soda (d) Epsom salt

29. When two substances A and B of same mass are heated under similar conditions, number of free surfaces has been found to reduce to zero from one. If A maintains constancy in the temperature for a longer time than B during heating, then
(a) latent heat of fusion of A is more than that of B
(b) latent heat of vaporization of A is more than that of B
(c) latent heat of fusion of B is more than that of A
(d) latent heat of vaporization of B is more than that of A

30. The specific heat capacity of water is
(a) more than petrol and kerosene
(b) less than oil and petrol
(c) less than kerosene
(d) less than honey and oil

31. In the given graph, identify the substance associated with the highest solubility at 10°C.
(a) A (b) B
(c) C (d) D

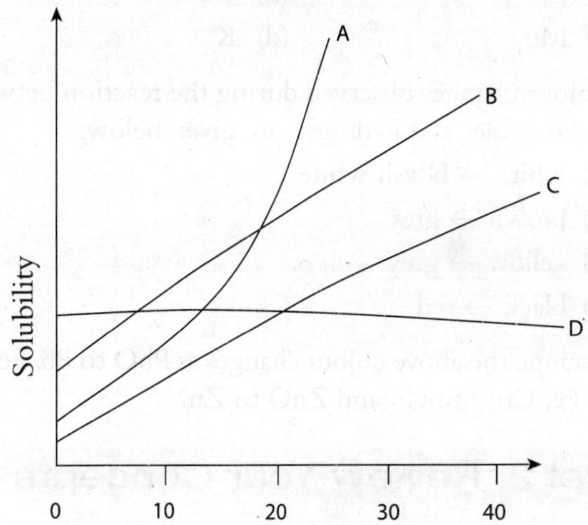

32. Reaction: Non-metal + H_2 A
A + PbO ⟶ Pb – Non-metal
If A formed in the above reaction has a rotten egg smell, identity the non-metal.
(a) N (b) P
(c) S (d) O

33. Identify the binary solution among the following:
(a) steel (b) bronze
(c) nichrome (d) gunmetal

34. Hydrogen acts as an oxidizing agent when it
(a) reacts with highly electropositive metals
(b) burns in the presence of O_2
(c) forms ammonia when it reacts with nitrogen
(d) passes through boiling sulphur and forms H_2S gas

35. Tyndal effect cannot be shown by
(a) smoke
(b) dust particles present in air
(c) fog
(d) iron powder in hydrochloric acid

36. Sodium catches fire and burns with a
(a) lilac flame (b) golden yellow flame
(c) blue flame (d) green flame

37. Which of the following metals on reaction with steam provides a coating over the metal and prevents further reaction?
(a) Al (b) Ca
(c) Mg (d) K

38. Colour changes observed during the reaction between metal oxides and hydrogen are given below:
(1) white → bluish white
(2) brown → grey
(3) yellow → grey
(4) black → red

Arrange the above colour changes as PbO to Pb, Fe_2O_3 to Fe, CuO to Cu and ZnO to Zn.
(a) 3 2 4 1 (b) 3 4 1 2
(c) 3 2 1 4 (d) 2 3 4 1

39. Amount of solutes A, B, C, D and E in 1500 g of water at 25°C, 50°C and 75°C in their saturated solutions are given below:

	25°C	50°C	75°C
A.	235 g	280 g	240 g
B.	180 g	190 g	220 g
C.	160 g	170 g	180 g
D.	175 g	220 g	200 g

Arrange the solutes in the increasing order of the amount of solutes that crystallizes out by cooling from 75°C to 25°C:
(a) ABDC (b) ACDB
(c) CABD (d) ACBD

40. Among the following oxides which one is converted to metal by treating with hydrogen?
(a) Al_2O_3 (b) ZnO
(c) CuO (d) BaO

Level 2: Review Your Concepts

41. A fire extinguisher has been used for putting off a petrol fire. It involves the principle of neutralization. Identify the type of extinguisher.

42. Which characteristics are the reason for the usage of graphite as a lubricant in machines?

43. Action of HCl on magnesium bicarbonate involves: precipitation or release of a gaseous product or both.

44. Amount of solutes A, B and C in 500 g of water at 30°C, 60°C, 100°C in their saturated solutions are given below:

	30°C	60°C	100°C
A.	140 g	135 g	131 g
B.	160 g	175 g	182 g
C.	152 g	170 g	161 g

When the hot saturated solutions of A, B and C are cooled slowly, identify the order in which they crystallize out of the solution. Give a reason in support of your answer.

45. 'Steam at 100°C causes more burns when exposed to skin than water at 100°C.' Justify.

46. Rain water and tap water are boiled in metallic containers A and B. The containers are emptied and then rain water samples are subjected to boiling in the same containers. In which case boiling gets delayed? Give a reason in support of your answer.

47. If a small crystal of a solute is added to unsaturated, saturated and supersaturated solutions, what observations do you find? Justify.

48. Why is pure water a bad conductor of electricity?

49. Why do the solubilities of most of the solids in water increase with an increase in temperature?

50. Explain why $CuSO_4.5H_2O$ can be dehydrated by reducing the external pressure at room temperature.

51. Explain why cobalt chloride acts as a humidity indicator.

52. The boiling point of a solution is more than that of the pure solvent. Justify.

53. With respect to the saturation of a solution, what type of solution is aerated water? Give reasons in support of answer.

54. What are the changes that take place in lead nitrate solution by passing impure hydrogen through it?

55. Why is water used widely in cooling systems?

56. $Na_2CO_3.10H_2O$ on exposure to air loses some water of crystallization and the rest on heating. How do you account for the above phenomenon?

57. What do you observe when CaO and $CaCl_2$ are exposed to moisture separately?

58. A china dish weighs 25 g when empty. When saturated solution of potassium chloride is poured into it at 40°C, the weight of the dish is 63 g. When the solution is evaporated to dryness, the china dish along with crystals weighs 40 g. Find the solubility of potassium chloride at 40°C.

59. The reaction of sodium and potassium with humid air is violent and explosive. However, when these metals are kept in an air-tight container having silica gel, no reaction has been observed. Give a reason.

60. A deliquescent substance does not become sticky in an air-tight container. Justify.

61. (a) Rain water does not leave any scales on boiling. Give a reason.

(b) Two containers A and B of same dimensions are filled with water of equal mass and same temperature. Few ice cubes made up of sea water are placed in A. Ice cubes of same mass and temperature, but made up of tap water, are placed in B. After same time before the melting of entire ice, the temperature of water in both the containers is measured. Compare the temperatures. Give appropriate reason.

62. Potassium chloride has solubility of 32 g at room temperature in water. However, its solubility decreases to 2.4 g in alcohol at the same temperature. It becomes completely insoluble in benzene. How do you account for this variation?

63. Why does boiling of water expel the dissolved gases?

64. Two samples each of substances A and B are kept in an open container and air-tight container. Sample A in the first container became sticky and in the second container remained as such. Sample B in both the containers remained without any change. Comment on the above observations.

Level 3: Assess Your Concepts

65. Identify the products given below in the order of the reactions as follows.

(i) Neutralization of CO_2 by caustic soda.
(ii) Combination of CO_2 and water in the presence of sunlight.
(iii) Reaction of CO_2 with Cl_2 gas.
(iv) Oxidation of Carbon by CO_2.
(v) CO is passed through blood.

(A) Lower oxide of carbon
(B) Carbohydrate
(C) Carbonate of sodium
(D) Carboxy haemoglobin
(E) Phosgene

66. (a) Water remains as drops on the polythene surface but it forms a thin layer on the surface of a properly cleaned glass plate. Explain.

(b) Hydrogen gas obtained in the laboratory process contains AsH_3, PH_3, H_2S, CO_2, SO_2, NO_2 and water vapour as impurities.

(A) Mention the reagents used to remove these impurities.

(B) State the reasons for using those reagents.

67. Two containers A and B contain same kind of matter and kinetic energy of molecules in A is more than that of B. Explain in which container the specific heat of matter is more. Give a reason.

68. Why does water appear blue in deep waters, but transparent in shallow waters?

69. Impure granulated zinc is preferred to pure zinc for the preparation of hydrogen. How do you account for this?

70.

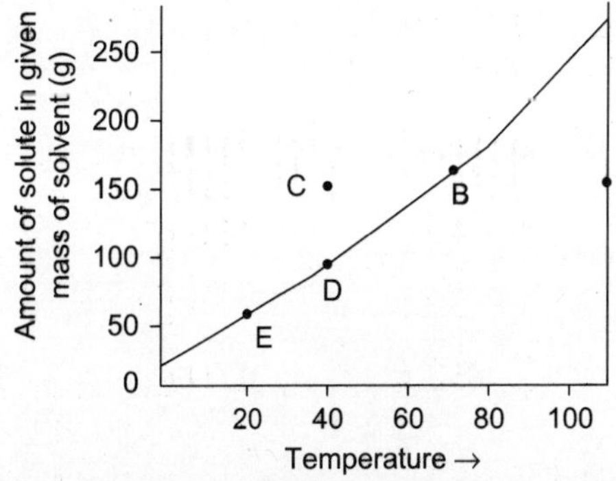

In the above graph, identify the states of solution at the various points A, B, C, D, E. If the solution is cooled from point A, at which temperature precipitation normally starts? Also find out the amount of solute precipitated at 40°C and the amount of solute in the solution at point E. What would be the maximum amount of solute that can be precipitated in the process?

71. A sample of common salt obtained from sea water contains 39 g of NaCl and 1 g of KCl. If it is dissolved in 100 g of water and then 90 g of water is evaporated, what observation do you find at 0°C? What is the maximum amount of pure NaCl that can be obtained by the above method? (solubilities of NaCl and KCl are 40 g, 55 g at 100°C and 35 g and 28 g at 0°C, respectively)

72. (a) Explain why temperature in the coastal region is moderate throughout the year.

(b)

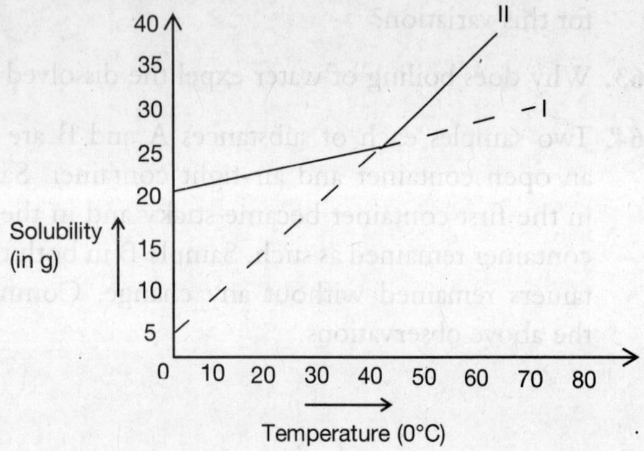

Solubility curves of two salts are shown above. Two processes A and B are carried out in the following ways. In process A, saturated solution of salts I and II are taken at 30°C and cooled slowly to 10°C. In process B hot saturated solutions of I and II are cooled from 70°C to 50°C.

(A) Identify the salt precipitated in process A and give reason.

(B) Are the precipitated crystals in processes A and B same? Justify your answer.

(C) 750 g of saturated solution of salt I and II is prepared at 40°C. Calculate the mass of the each salt present in the solution.

73. A desiccating material is used as a dehumidifying agent for absorbing moisture from highly humid air and again it is made reusable by low humid air. What is the principle involved in this process?

74. Some of the hydrated crystals are efflorescent. How do you account for this?

AT

PRACTICE QUESTIONS JEE-NEET SPECIAL WING

Multiple-Answer Type Questions

Directions for questions 1 to 5:
Select one or more correct alternative(s) from the given choices.

1. In which of the following reactions, the catalytic property of water is exploited?
   (a) Reaction of sulphur with oxygen to give sulphur dioxide
   (b) Formation of HCl from hydrogen and chlorine
   (c) Reaction of phosphorus with oxygen to give phosphorus pentoxide
   (d) Reaction of hydrogen with oxygen to form water

2. Two metals 'M' and 'N' on exposure to moisture catch fire. When dropped in water, metal 'M' produces golden yellow flame while metal 'N' produces lilac colour flame. Identify the statements which comply with the metal.
   (a) The metal 'M' is placed just above calcium in the metal reactivity series
   (b) Both 'M' and 'N' float on water in the form of silvery globules
   (c) The metal 'N' releases greater amount of heat than the metal 'M' during the reaction
   (d) Both 'M and 'N' displace magnesium from its aqueous solution

3. *'x' g* of water is present in certain mass of hydrated copper sulphate crystals. Identify the amounts of other hydrated salts which contain same mass of water.

Name of the hydrated salt	Mass of water
(a) Sodium sulphate (Glauber salt)	161 g
(b) Magnesium chloride	95 g
(c) Ferrous sulphate	152 g
(d) Sodium carbonate(Washing soda)	143 g

4. Identify the electronic configurations of metals which react with hydrogen to form respective binary compounds.
   (a) 2, 8, 18, 2 (b) 2, 8, 8, 2
   (c) 2, 8, 1 (d) 2, 8, 14, 2

5. Four solid substances A, B, C, D are taken in measured quantities in four closed containers and kept for some time under atmospheric conditions. Later, the wights of the substances were measured. The observations are as follows:
   A → Showed increase in mass without change in physical state
   B → No change in mass
   C → Showed decrease in mass
   D → Showed increase in mass and found to be in liquid state
   Which among the following sets of substances comply with the above experimental results?

	A	B	C	D
(a)	$Na_2SO_4.7H_2O$	$Na_2CO_3.10H_2O$	$CuSO_4.5H_2O$	$CaCl_2.6H_2O$
(b)	$CaCl_2.6H_2O$	$FeSO_4.7H_2O$	$Na_2CO_3.10H_2O$	NaOH
(c)	CaO	$CuSO_4.5H_2O$	$Na_2SO_4.10H_2O$	$MgCl_2.6H_2O$
(d)	$CaSO_4.2H_2O$	$MgCl_2.6H_2O$	$ZnCl_2$	KOH

Comprehension-Based Questions

Directions for questions 6 to 11:
Observe the solubility curves of the substances given and answer the following questions.

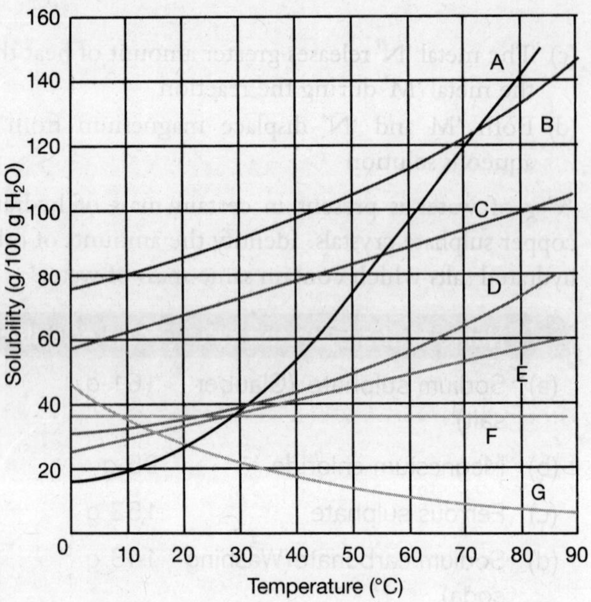

6. The saturated solutions of the salts given in the above graph are cooled from 80°C to 30°C. Identify the salts which were not found to precipitate during cooling.
   (a) A; B (b) C; D
   (c) D; E (d) F; G

7. Identify the correct order of solubilities of salts at the respective temperatures.
   (a) D<C<B<A at 50°C
   (b) A<E<D<F at 10°C
   (c) E<D<A<C at 60°C
   (d) A<G<D<E at 20°C

8. 500 g of water is taken at different temperatures and the various salts are dissolved in it to form the respective saturated solutions. It is found that the amount of 'A' dissolved is found to be same as that of the other salts at different temperatures. Identify the salt which does not comply with this condition.
   (a) B at 75°C (b) C at 85°C
   (c) D at 40°C (d) G at 10°C

9. At 50°C, 800 g of saturated solution of C is considered. Identify the amount of the salt present in the solution.
   (a) 640 g (b) 525 g
   (c) 355 g (d) 175 g

10. Equal quantities of saturated solutions of various solutes are prepared at 55°C. Certain amount of 'B' was precipitated when it was cooled to 30°C. Which among the following salts was precipitated in the same amount on cooling in the same temperature range?
    (a) D (b) C
    (c) A (d) E

11. 'x' g of A is dissolved in 200 g water to make a saturated solution at 10°C. 'y' g of B is dissolved in 200 g water to make a saturated solution at 10°C. Give the solubilities of A and B at 70°C in terms of 'x' and 'y'.

	A	B
(a)	$6x$	$1.25x$
(b)	$3x$	$1.25x$
(c)	$3x$	$0.75x$
(d)	$6x$	$0.75x$

Directions for question 12:
Interpret the data given in the paragraph given below and the match the entries in column I with those in column II

Consider the solubility of the salt 'G' as '$0.1x$' at 60°C. The various salts taken are given in column I and the amounts of solutes dissolved in 200 g of water at the same temperature are given in column II. (Consider the values of solubility to approximation)

12. Match the entries in column I with those in column II

	Column I		Column II
(a)	A	(i)	$0.7x$
(b)	B	(ii)	$1.2x$
(c)	C	(iii)	x
(d)	D	(iv)	$2.2x$
(e)	E	(v)	$1.8x$
(f)	F	(vi)	$2x$

Directions for questions 13 to 17:

Interpret the data given in the table given below and answer the questions given below.

Some thermal properties of substances A, B and C are given in the following table. Based on the data given in the following table, answer the questions given below.

Substance	Specific heat (cal/g)		Latent heat (cal/g)		Melting point (°C)	Boiling point (°C)
	Solid	Liquid	Fusion	Vaporisation		
A	0.03	0.3	2.7	70	-40	360
B	0.5	1	80	540	0	100
C	0.33	0.5	45	100	18	118
D	0.05	0.04	15	39	115	185

13. 10 g of substance 'A' is taken at room temperature (30°C) and it is subjected to complete vaporisation. Identify the heat utilised for the entire process.

(a) 3.72 kcal (b) 1.69 kcal
(c) 1 kcal (c) 0.7 kcal

14. Same mass of substances 'A' and 'B' are taken at −40°C. They are subjected to heating till the entire samples pass into liquid state. The heat required for substance 'A' is considered as 'x' Joule. What should be the amount of heat required for sample 'B' in terms of 'x'?

(a) 0.135 x (b) 7.5 x
(c) 5.13 x (d) 37 x

15. 11 g sample of the substance 'A' is considered in liquid state at its freezing point. Same amount of sample of substance 'C' is also taken in its liquid state at its freezing point. Both are subjected to heating with the same source of heat. Find the approximate ratio of time taken to vaporise the samples A and B.

(a) 5 : 9 (b) 2 : 5
(c) 3:7 (d) 4:5

16. Which among the given substances is likely to pass through imperceptible liquid state?

(a) D (b) C
(c) B (d) A

17. Identify the substance which is expected to give a steep line in the heat curve from liquid to vapour state.

(a) D (b) C
(c) B (d) A

Match The Column

18. The substances in the respective physical states are given in column I and the thermal characteristics are given in column II.

Column I		Column II	
(a)	Solid A	(i)	Cools down at the slowest rate
(b)	Liquid B	(ii)	Rises temperature at the fastest rate
(c)	Solid C	(iii)	Easiest to undergo phase change
(d)	Solid D	(iv)	Maximum thermal expansion in liquid state
(e)	Liquid A	(v)	Can exist in solid state under normal atmospheric conditions

ANSWER KEYS

Crossword

Across

1. Potassium
4. Yellow
8. Aluminium
10. High calorific value
14. Cubic
15. Dielectric constant
16. Tungsten
17. Crystalliation
18. Water gas
19. Iron
20. Adsorption

Down

2. Anhydrous salt
3. Deliquescence
5. Low critical temperature
6. Calcium
7. Efflorescence
9. High specific heat
11. Latent heat of fusion
12. Hydrogenation
13. Binary solution

Classroom Wing

Very Short Answer Type Questions

1. C_4H_{10}
2. H_3PO_4
3. moisture

Competition Wing

Level 1: Apply Your Concepts

1. False
2. False
3. True
4. True
5. False
6. False
7. True
8. True
9. False
10. True
11. False
12. False
13. deliquescent
14. bases
15. supersaturated
16. dielectric constant
17. 2O
18. $Na_2SO_4.10H_2O$
19. hydrated
20. (i) → (C), (ii) → (D), (iii) → (E), (iv) → (A), (v) → (B)
21. (b)
22. (a)
23. (a)
24. (b)
25. (c)
26. (d)
27. (a)
28. (b)
29. (b)
30. (a)
31. (b)
32. (c)
33. (c)
34. (a)
35. (d)
36. (b)
37. (a)
38. (a)
39. (b)
40. (c)

JEE-NEET Special Wing

Multiple-Answer Type Questions

1. (b; c; d)
2. (a; b; c; d)
3. (a; d)
4. (b; c)
5. (b; c)

Comprehension-Based Questions

6. (d)
7. (b)
8. (d)
9. (c)
10. (b)
11. (c)
12. (a) ↔ (vi), (b) ↔ (iv), (c) ↔ (v), (d) ↔ (ii), (e) ↔ (iii), (f) ↔ (i)
13. (b)
14. (d)
15. (a)
16. (a)
17. (d)

Match The Column

18. (a) ↔ (ii), (b) ↔ (i), (c) ↔ (v), (d) ↔ (iii), (e) ↔ (iv)

Hints and Explanations

CLASSROOM WING

Very Short Answer Type Questions

1. The general formula corresponding to saturated hydrocarbons should be $C_nH_{2n} + 2$. According to this, the formula corresponding to the one with 4 carbon atoms should be C_4H_{10}.
2. H_3PO_4
3. moisture
4. Marsh gas (methane) is a harmful gas released in coal mines.
5. Pyrolysis
   Methane on pyrolysis gives carbon black.
   $CH_4 \rightarrow C + 2H_2$
6. 6 carbon atoms. The general formula corresponding to saturated hydrocarbons should be $C_nH_{2n} + 2$. According to this, the given hydrocarbon with 14 hydrogen atoms should be C_6H_{14}.
7. Pyrolysis is the process of heating hydrocarbon in the absence of air.
8. 20.7 g of $CuSO_4$ is present in 100 g of water.
9. decreases
10. K, Na
11. Reducing agent
    e.g., $WO_3 + 3H_2 \longrightarrow W + 3H_2O$
12. 4.2 Joule $g^{-1}°C^{-1}$, 21 Joule $g^{-1}°C^{-1}$
13. Catalytic addition of hydrogen to some carbon compounds.
14. Heated steam is passed over red hot coke.
15. Heat energy required for converting 1 g of ice to water. Latent heat of fusion of ice = 80 cal/g.

    Heat energy required for converting 1 g of water to vapour. Latent heat of vaporization = 540 cal/g
16. The smallest repeated pattern of a crystal.
17. Boiling point of water decreases. Reason is decrease in pressure.
18.

Solvents	Solutes
(a) water	sugar
(b) water	alcohol
(c) $CuSO_4$	H_2O
(d) Cu	Zn
(e) Platinum	Hydrogen

19. $SO_2 + H_2O \longrightarrow H_2SO_3$ (Sulphurous acid)
20. Reaction of acid with pure zinc is vigorous at the beginning and then stops after sometime as acid does not come in contact with zinc. To get more amount of H_2, granulated zinc is taken as it possesses more surface area.
21. Hydrated copper sulphate does not lose its water of crystallization when exposed to air.
22. $Mg + H_2O \longrightarrow MgO + H_2$
23. There are some hydrated crystals which lose some of the water of crystallization or all the water of crystallization on exposure to air at normal temperature. This phenomenon is known as efflorescence and the hydrated crystals which lose water molecules are called efflorescent substances.

    Some crystalline salts absorb moisture on exposure to air and ultimately dissolve in it to form an aqueous solution. This phenomenon is called deliquescence and these crystalline salts are called deliquescent substances.
24. The accumulation of molecules of one compound over the surface of another compound. For example, Hydrogen gas gets adsorbed on the surface of some metals, like, palladium, platinum, nickel, etc.
25. Mixture

Short Answer Type Questions

26. Thermal decomposition. Baking powder contains sodium bicarbonate as a major component, which, on heating, decomposes to release CO_2.
27. Due to the sparingly soluble nature of CO_2 in water, the little amount of CO_2 present dissolved in water is utilized for photosynthesis by aquatic plants.

28. x does not decompose on heating, whereas y de-composes to give CO_2. By analysing the metals, x and y should be K_2CO_3 and $ZnCO_3$.

29. Due to the sparingly soluble nature of CO_2 in water, the little amount of CO_2 present dissolved in water is utilized for photosynthesis by aquatic plants.

30. Hard water is water that has high mineral content. Hard water is formed when water percolates through deposits of limestone and chalk which are largely made up of calcium and magnesium carbonates.

31. (i) nature of solute
(ii) nature of solvent
(iii) temperature

32. physical state of water

33. (i) constituents of water
(ii) synthesis of water

34. Natural gas contains methane as a major constituent. Methane on mixing with superheated steam at high temperature followed by compression to 30 atm pressure also gives water gas. This is subjected to Bosch process for getting pure hydrogen gas.

35. Pure water is a bad conductor of heat and electricity. The electrical conductivity of water is due to the presence of dissolved salts in water.

36. With the increase in temperature, the solubility of a gas in a particular liquid decreases. The effect of pressure on the solubility of a gas in a liquid is given by Henry's law, which states that at constant temperature the increase in pressure on the surface of the liquid increases the solubility of the gas in the liquid.

37. Water is distilled through a process in which the water is boiled, evaporated and the vapour is condensed. The distillation process does remove many unhealthy contaminants in source water, but it also removes naturally occurring minerals.

38. $ZnO + H_2 \rightarrow Zn + H_2O$;

$2Fe_2O_3 + 6H_2 \rightarrow 4Fe + 6H_2O$;

$PbO + H_2 \rightarrow Pb + H_2O$;

$CuO + H_2 \rightarrow Cu + H_2O$

Essay Answer Type Questions

40. (A) Principle: Water gas is a mixture of carbon monoxide and hydrogen. Catalytic oxidation of carbon monoxide gives hydrogen gas. Water gas can be prepared by passing steam over red hot coke.

Process

(a) Superheated steam at 170°C when passed through white hot coke or charcoal gives a mixture of CO gas and hydrogen known as water gas.

(b) Water gas obtained is made to pass over Fe_2O_3 or Cr_2O_3 along with superheated steam at 500°C. Carbon monoxide gets oxidized to CO_2 leaving hydrogen gas.

(B) In cold countries where the temperature goes below 0°C, upper layer of water freezes. This is because the density of water is maximum at 4°C and gradually decreases on cooling as well as on heating. When the temperature of the upper layer of water reaches 4°C, convection current gets generated and water from upper layer goes to the lower region. Thus, the temperature of water at the bottom most layer remains at 4°C and gradually decreases in upper layers upto 0°C and upper layer freezes. Since, the density of water is less than that of water, it floats on water. The water in the lower layer does not freeze. Since ice is a bad conductor of heat and it does not allow the heat of the water below it to be dissipated, thus the aquatic animals can survive below the layer of ice.

41. Coal, on destructive distillation, gives various products. X should be coke since it can reduce iron oxide to iron, whereas Y should be coal tar since it gives benzene as the final product on fractional distillation.

42. The graphs which show variation of solubility with temperature are called solubility curves.

Importance of Solubility Curves

(i) The solubility of a particular solute in a given solvent at a given temperature can be found out.
(ii) Solubilities of different solutes in a given solvent at a particular temperature can be compared.
(iii) It is possible to determine the amount of solute that can be precipitated by cooling the saturated solution of that solute to a certain temperature.
(iv) From the solubility curves, it is possible to know the preferential precipitation of different salts during the fractional crystallization process since the solution contains more than one salt dissolved in it.

43. (i) method
(ii) chemical equations
(iii) observations
(iv) reactivity of reactants

44. (i) vapour pressure
(ii) changes involved

Competition Wing

Level 1: Apply Your Concepts

1. **False.** High ignition temperature is not the characteristic of an ideal fuel. It should always have a low ignition temperature.

2. **False.** Phosgene and CO are poisonous gases coal gas contains CO and CH_4 which are harmful. Butane is not a harmful gas.

3. Except sodium and potassium carbonates, all other carbonates, on heating, decompose to produce CO_2.

4. True. Reaction of carbonic acid with NaOH results in the formation of Na_2CO_3 which is highly soluble in water. Therefore, it does not involve the formation of white precipitate, whereas all other reactions result in the for-mation of insoluble carbonates, which are obtained as white precipitates.

20. (i) → (C), (ii) → (D), (iii) → (E), (iv) → (A), (v) → (B)

21. Diamond is a good thermal conductor because of its compact three-dimensional structure. Mere tetravalency of carbon does not make it a good thermal conductor.

    Hence, the correct option is (b).

22. Dry ice undergoes sublimation by taking heat from the surroundings, thereby causing cooling, which results in the condensation of water vapour and ul-timately results in rain.

    Hence, the correct option is (a).

23. Graphite is a good electrical conductor because carbon shows a valency of three, leaving one free electron on each carbon.

    Hence, the correct option is (a).

24. A sealed bottle with dry ice explodes after some time as it undergoes sublimation at room temperature and the resultant pressure develops due to the accumulation of gaseous CO_2 in the bottle. Dry ice producing low temperature has no relevance to the above.

    Hence, the correct option is (b).

36. Sodium catches fire and burns with a golden yellow flame.

    Hence, the correct answer is (b)

37. Aluminium metal on reaction with steam provides a coating over the metal which prevents further reaction.

    Hence, the correct answer is (a)

38. $PbO + H_2 \rightarrow Pb + H_2O$
    yellow grey

    $Fe_2O_3 + H_2 \rightarrow Fe + H_2O$
    brown grey

    $CuO + H_2 \rightarrow Cu + H_2O$
    black red

    $ZnO + H_2 \rightarrow Zn + H_2O$
    white bluish white

    Hence, the correct answer is (a)

39. Amount of solutes A, B, C and D that crystallizes out are 5 g, 40 g, 20 g and 25 g, respectively.

    Hence, the correct answer is (b)

40. In metals, which have lesser affinity towards oxygen, their oxides can be reduced by hydrogen. Among the given metals, copper has less affinity towards oxygen. Hence, its oxide can be reduced by hydrogen.

    Hence, the correct answer is (c)

Level 2: Review Your Concepts

41. Both soda-acid fire extinguishers and foam-type fire extinguishers involve a neutralization reaction between sodium bicarbonate and H_2SO_4 or $Al_2(SO_4)_3$. However, foam-type fire extinguishers can be used for extinguishing petrol or oil fires due to the presence of saponin which traps the oil vapour in the froth.

42. Usage of graphite as a lubricant in machines, especially where high temperature is produced, involves both its layer lattice structure and high thermal resistance.

43. Action of HCl on magnesium bicarbonate results in the formation of insoluble $MgCO_3$ which is obtained as a precipitate along with the release of CO_2 as a gaseous product.

44. (i) comparison of change in solubilities with change in temperature
    (ii) comparison of change in solubilities with decrease in temperature from 100°C to 30°C
    (iii) effect of cooling on nature of the solutions of A, B and C, respectively.
    (iv) relation between extent of solubility and crystallization

45. (i) change of state of matter
    (ii) energy content of water molecules at 100°C
    (iii) energy content of steam molecules at 100°C
    (iv) comparison of energy

46. (i) components present in rain water and tap water
(ii) effect of constituents on metallic containers due to boiling
(iii) changes that take place in metallic containers due to boiling
(iv) changes that are observed with respect to boiling when rain water is again taken in containers

47. (i) changes that takes place in particle size of solute in respective solutions
(ii) comparison of amount of solutes present in respective solutions
(iii) relation between changes with respect to crystal of solute and nature of the solution

48. (i) property of water
(ii) condition required for a substance to conduct electricity
(iii) composition of pure water

49. (i) principle of dissolution of solids in liquids
(ii) process of dissolution
(iii) movement of molecules during solubility
(iv) effect of temperature on the movement of molecules

50. (i) vapour pressure of $CuSO_4.5H_2O$
(ii) Comparison between atmospheric pressure and vapour pressure of hydrated copper sulphate
(iii) Changes in hydrated $CuSO_4$ at lower pressure conditions

51. (i) change in physical property
(ii) colour of cobalt chloride
(iii) capour pressure of cobalt chloride
(iv) changes in cobalt chloride in humid atmosphere
(v) effect on colour of $CoCl_2$ due to these changes

52. (i) vapour pressure of solution
(ii) comparison of composition of solution to pure solvent
(iii) forces acting in solution and pure solvent
(iv) relation between forces acting and vapour pressure
(v) relation between vapour pressure and boiling point

53. (i) factors affecting the solubility of gases in water
(ii) composition of aerated water
(iii) pressure condition in aerated water can

54. (i) impurity present in hydrogen gas
(ii) reactivity of lead nitrate with the impurity present in hydrogen

55. Water has high specific heat and it is available in the liquid state in temperature ranging between 0°C and 100°C.

Hence, it can be conveniently used in cooling systems.

56. $Na_2CO_3.10H_2O$ on exposure to air loses 9 water molecules from its water of crystallization because initially vapour pressure of the compound is more than vapour pressure of the moisture present in the atmospheric air. It is an example of an efflorescent substance. After the release of nine molecules of water of crystallization its vapour pressure becomes equal to the pressure of the moisture present in the atmosphere. Hence, removal of the 10th water molecule requires heating.

57. Both calcium oxide and calcium chloride absorb moisture, and hence, act as hygroscopic substances. Calcium chloride absorbs moisture and dissolves in it and changes its physical state. So, it is called deliquescent substance. No change in physical state takes place when calcium oxide absorbs moisture.

58. Weight of saturated solution of KCl = 63 – 25 = 38 g

Weight of crystal of KCl = 40 – 25 = 15 g

Weight of water contained in saturated solution

= 38 – 15 = 23 g

$$\text{Solubility of KCl} = \frac{\text{Weight of KCl crystals}}{\text{Weight of water}} \times 100$$

$$= \frac{15}{23} \times 100 = 65.2 \text{ at } 40°\text{C}.$$

59. Silica gel can absorb the moisture present in the air-tight container, and thus, air present in the container is free from the moisture. Metals, Na and K can react with air only when the reaction is initiated with moisture. Therefore, when metals are kept in an air-tight container having silica gel, no reaction takes place since the air is absolutely dry.

60. The water vapour present inside the air-tight container is limited. After absorbing the water vapour, the deliquescent substances again release the water molecules to maintain the equilibrium of water vapour pressure. Hence, it cannot become sticky in the air-tight container.

61. (a) Since the rain water is pure, it does not have any dissolved salts present in it. So, it does not leave any scales on boiling.
(b) Presence of impurities decreases the melting point of ice. The more the amount of impurities, the lower

the melting point is. Hence, ice cubes made up of sea water will start melting first. During melting a large amount of heat is absorbed from the surroundings because of high latent heat of fusion of ice. Therefore, the temperature of water in A will be less.

62. Water has a high dielectric constant. KCl being an ionic compound is highly soluble in water. Alcohol has a lower dielectric constant. Hence, solubility of KCl in alcohol is less. Benzene has still lower value of dielectric constant. Therefore, KCl becomes completely insoluble in benzene.

63. As temperature increases, the solubility of a gas in a liquid decreases. Hence, boiling of water expels the dissolved gases.

64. Substance A in an open container becomes sticky and that means it is a deliquescent substance and absorbs sufficient moisture in the open container. In an air-tight container, it absorbs little moisture but again loses some moisture for maintaining equilibrium of vapour pressure. Therefore, it does not become sticky. Substance B does not become sticky even in the open container. The fact that it remained without any change in the open container indicates that it is neither efflorescent nor deliquescent. It may be a hygroscopic salt or may not absorb moisture at all.

Level 3: Assess Your Concepts

65. (i) Neutralization of CO_2 by caustic soda → Carbonate of sodium
(ii) Combination of CO_2 and water → Carbohydrate
(iii) $CO_2 + Cl_2 \rightarrow COCl_2$ (Phosgene)
(iv) $C + CO_2 \rightarrow CO$ (Lower oxide of carbon)
(v) CO is passed through blood → Carboxy haemoglobin

66. (a) (i) cohesive, adhesive forces
(ii) composition of polythene
(iii) composition of glass
(iv) forces between water and polythene
(v) forces acting between water and glass
(vi) comparison of these forces

(b) (A) AsH_3, PH_3 → Sliver nitrate solution
H_2S → Lead nitrate solution
CO_2, NO_2, SO_2 → Caustic potash
Water vapour → $CaCl_2/P_2O_5$

(B) $AsH_3 + AgNO_3 \rightarrow H_3AsO_3 + Ag + HNO_3$
$PH_3 + AgNO_3 + H_2O \rightarrow H_3PO_4 + Ag + HNO_3$

None of the products are in gaseous state.
$H_2S + Pb(NO_3)_2 \rightarrow PbS + HNO_3$
Products of the above reaction does not exist in gaseous state
CO_2, SO_2 and NO_2 are acidic oxides. They react with strong base like caustic potash or caustic soda. Water vapour is absorbed by $CaCl_2$ or P_2O_5 which are drying agents.

67. (i) relation between specific heat and intermolecular force of attractions
(ii) relation between kinetic energy and temperature
(iii) relation between kinetic energy and intermolecular forces of attraction in A and B
(iv) relation between intermolecular forces of attraction and the heat required

68. (i) nature of water molecules
(ii) relation between light absorbed/emitted/scattered and colour
(iii) light absorbed/emitted by water
(iv) comparison of amount of light absorbed/emitted in deep waters and shallow waters

69. (i) the mode of reaction between zinc and acid
(ii) role of Zn
(iii) change in property of Zn in granulated and pure forms.
(iv) comparison of the reactivity of hydrogen in presence of granulated zinc and pure zinc

70. The curve indicates that the solubility of the solute at 100°C is 250 g. However, the given solution contains only 150 g of solute. The solution at point A is an unsaturated solution. Therefore, no precipitation takes place up to point B at 80°C, where the solution becomes saturated with just 150 g of the solute. Point B indicates a saturated solution. Point C at 40°C indicates that the solution still contained 150 g of solute which is a supersaturated solution. That means, it is possible to cool solution from 80°C to 40°C without any crystallization by maintaining suitable conditions. At 40°C, when crystallization starts, the solution ultimately becomes saturated represented by point D. At point D (40°C), the solubility is 75. That means, 75 g of solute would have been precipitated out. At E also the solution remains saturated by precipitating 25 g more of solute.

71. At 100°C, the solubilities of NaCl and KCl are 40 and 55, respectively. Therefore, the entire sample dissolves in 100 g of water. When 90 g of water is evapo-

rated, 10 g of water remains and since the solution is to cooled to 0°C, it can contain 3.5 g NaCl and 2.8 g KCl. That means the entire KCl (1 g) remains in the solution which remains unsaturated with respect to KCl. In 10 g of water only 3.5 g remains in dissolved state thereby making the solution saturated with respect to NaCl. The rest of the NaCl, i.e., 35.5 g gets precipitated out. This is the maximum amount of NaCl that can be obtained in pure form.

72. (a) In coastal regions, the amount of water is more and the specific heat of water is much higher than that of the land. Hence, a major part of heat coming from the sun is absorbed by water. The increase in temperature of water is less because of its high specific heat. Hence, the temperature of the land does not change much.

(b) (A) In process A, salt I will be crystallized since its solubility decreases at a faster rate in that temperature range.

(B) In process B, salt II will be crystallized because of higher rate of decrease of solubility in this range of temperature when compared to salt I.

(C) From the given graph, it is clear that the solubility of each salt at 40°C is 25.

∴ (25 + 25) g = 50 g of solutes (I & II) should be present in (100 + 50)g = 150 g of saturated solution.

∴ 750 g of saturated solution contains

$$\frac{50}{150} \times 750 \text{ g} = 250 \text{ g of solutes (I \& II)}$$

The mass of each solute in 750 g of solution is 125 g

73. Desiccant materials have a high affinity for water vapour. The process involves exposing the desiccant material to humid air stream, allowing it to attract and retain some of the water vapour and then exposing the same desiccants to a dry air stream which has the effect of drawing the retained moisture from the desiccant. The first air stream is the air that is being dehumidified while the second air stream is used only to regenerate the desiccant material.

74. The vapour pressure of these hydrated crystals is greater than that of the water vapour present in the atmosphere at room temperature.

JEE-NEET Special wing

Multiple-Answer Type Questions

1. Except the reaction of sulphur with oxygen, all the rest of the reactions given are catalysed by the presence of moisture.

2. The metal 'M' and 'N' are identified as sodium and potassium respectively. They both are lighter than water and hence float on water in the form of silvery globules. The reaction of potassium with water is more vigorous and releases greater amount of energy than the reaction of sodium. Sodium is placed above calcium in the metal reactivity series. Both sodium and potassium displace magnesium from its aqueous solution as they are more reactive metals than magnesium.

3. The formula of hydrated copper sulphate is $CuSO_4.5H_2O$. Its molecular mass is 250 g. 90 g of water is present as water of crystallisation. The masses of other hydrated salts which contain 90 g of water are given in the table below.

	Salt		Molar mass	Amount of salt with 90 g water
(a)	Sodium sulphate (Glauber salt)	$Na_2SO_4.10\ H_2O$	322	161 g
(b)	Magnesium chloride	$MgCl_2.\ 6H_2O$	203	169
(c)	Ferrous sulphate	$FeSO_4.\ 7H_2O$	278	198 g
(d)	Sodium carbonate	$Na_2\ CO_3.\ 10\ H_2O$	286	143 g

4. Calcium with electronic configuration 2, 8, 8, 2 forms hydride of the formula CaH_2 and sodium with electronic configuration 2, 8, 1 forms hydride of the formula NaH.

5.

A	Hygroscopic	$CaCl_2.6H_2O$ CaO
B	Neither deliquescent nor hygroscopic	$FeSO_4.7H_2O$ $CuSO_4.5H_2O$
C	Efflorescent	$Na_2CO_3.10H_2O$ $Na_2SO_4.10H_2O$
D	Deliquescent	NaOH $MgCl_2.6H_2O$

Comprehension-Based Questions

6. The salt 'F' does not show appreciable change in solubility with temperature. The salt 'G' shows decrease in solubility with temperature. Therefore, these salts do not show precipitation on cooling the saturated solutions at higher temperature.

7. A < E < D < F at 100°C is the correct order of solubilities at that temperature.

8. The salts which possess same solubility as that of 'A' at a particular temperature are identified as B at 75°C, C at 85°C, D at 40°C and D at 25°C.

9. The solubility of C at 50°C is found to be approximately 80.

Amount of salt C present in 180 g of saturated solution at 500C = 80 g

Amount of salt C present in 800 g of saturated solution at 50°C = 355 g

10. The solubilities of 'B' at 55°C and 30°C are 110 and 90 respectively while those of salt C are found to be 90 and 70 respectively. In both the cases, cooling the respective saturated solutions yields 20 g of the precipitates.

11. Solubility of 'A' at 10°C = $x/2$ =20

Solubility of 'B' at 10°C = $y/2$ =80

Solubility of 'A' at 700C = 120 = $3x$

Solubility of 'B' at 700C = 120 = $0.75y$

12.

Column I			Column II
(a)	A	(vi)	$2x$
(b)	B	(iv)	$2.2x$
(c)	C	(v)	$1.8x$
(d)	D	(ii)	$1.2x$
(e)	E	(iii)	x
(f)	F	(i)	$0.7x$

13. The substance 'A' is a liquid at 30°C. It has to be heated to its boiling point(360°C) to start getting vapourised.

Then when the amount of heat equal to latent heat is supplied, the substance completely gets vapourised.

q_1 = mass × difference in temperature × specific heat = 10 × 330 × 0.3 = 990 cal

q_2 = mass × L_v = 700 cal

Total heat required = 990 + 700 = 1690 cal = 1.69 kcal

14. Substance 'A' has –40°C as its melting point. The heat required includes only the latent heat.

$Q = m \times 2.7 = x$ Joule

Substance 'B' is a solid at –40°C. The heat required is the sum of the heat required to rise the temperature to its melting point and the latent heat required to pass the substance into liquid state.

$q_1 = 40 \times 0.5 \times m$

$q_2 = 80 \times m$

Total heat = 100 m kj = 100 m/2.7m = $37x$

15. Heat required for sample of substance 'A' for vaporisation

q_1 = 11 × 0.03 × 400 = 132 cal

q_2 = 70 × 11 = 770 cal

Total heat = 132 + 770 = 902 cal

Heat required for sample of substance 'C' for vaporisation

q_1 = 11 × 0.5 × 100 = 550 cal

q_2 = 100 × 11 = 1100 cal

Total heat = 550 + 1100 = 1650 cal

Ratio of heat content = 902/1650 ≈ 5 : 9

Ratio of time taken (source of heat same) = 5 : 9

16. The substance 'D' has very low specific heat and also has very less difference between latent heat of fusion and latent heat of vapourisation. As a result, the liquid state lasts for a very short span of time and hence becomes imperceptible or unnoticed. It appears that the substance goes directly from solid to vapour state.

17. The substance which has less specific heat and maximum difference between the freezing point and boiling point shows a steep line in the heat curve. It is solid 'A'.

Match The Column

18.

Column I		Column II	
(a)	Solid A	(ii)	Rises temperature at the fastest rate
(b)	Liquid B	(i)	Cools down at the slowest rate
(c)	Solid C	(v)	Can exist in solid state under normal atmospheric conditions
(d)	Solid D	(iii)	Easiest to undergo phase transition
(e)	Liquid A	(iv)	Maximum thermal expansion

CHAPTER

6

Carbon and its Compounds

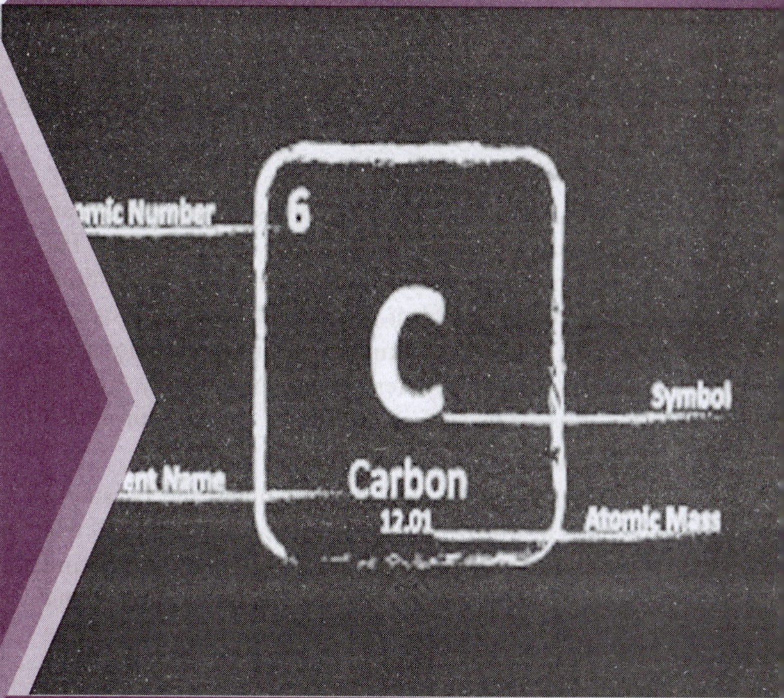

Remember

Before beginning this chapter, you should be able to:

- define metals and non-metals.
- classify substances as metal or non-metals and explain their properties.

Key Ideas

After completing this chapter, you should be able to:

- learn the carbon cycle.
- know the preparation, properties and uses of different allotropic forms of carbon and different commercially important compounds of carbon.
- describe the oxides of carbon, their laboratory preparation, properties and uses.
- explain fossil fuels, coal and petroleum.
- understand working principle of different types of fire extinguishers.
- know the occurrence, preparation and properties of methane.

Scientific Crypt

A Tribute to Edward Goodrich Acheson (1856 – 1931)

In 1884, Edward Goodrich Acheson, an American chemist, was born in Washington, Pennsylvania. He was the inventor and manufacturer of carborundum (silicon carbide), which is the second hardest substance. In 1880, he started working at the research laboratory of Thomas Edison in Menlo Park, New Jersey. Edison used a conducting carbon developed by Acheson in his electric bulbs.

In 1884, Acheson left Edison's employ and became a supervisor at a plant involved in manufacture of electric lamps. In 1891, Acheson built an electricity generating plant and used electricity to heat a mixture of clay and coke and found some shiny hexagonal crystalline substance i.e. silicon carbide which he named as "Carborundum". Carborundum is an excellent abrasive.

In 1894 he established the carborundum company in Monaghela, Pennsylvania for the manufacture of different products like grinding wheels, knife sharpeners, powdered abrasive etc. In his electric furnace he subsequently produced artificial graphite. He had an unimaginable inventive genious and extraordinary entrepreneurial mind. Throughout his life he received 70 patents related to abrasive, graphite products, refractory etc. His contribution to industrial world is enormous in shaping and finishing all metal works. He took his last breath on July 6, 1931, in New York city.

FUN TIME

CROSSWORD

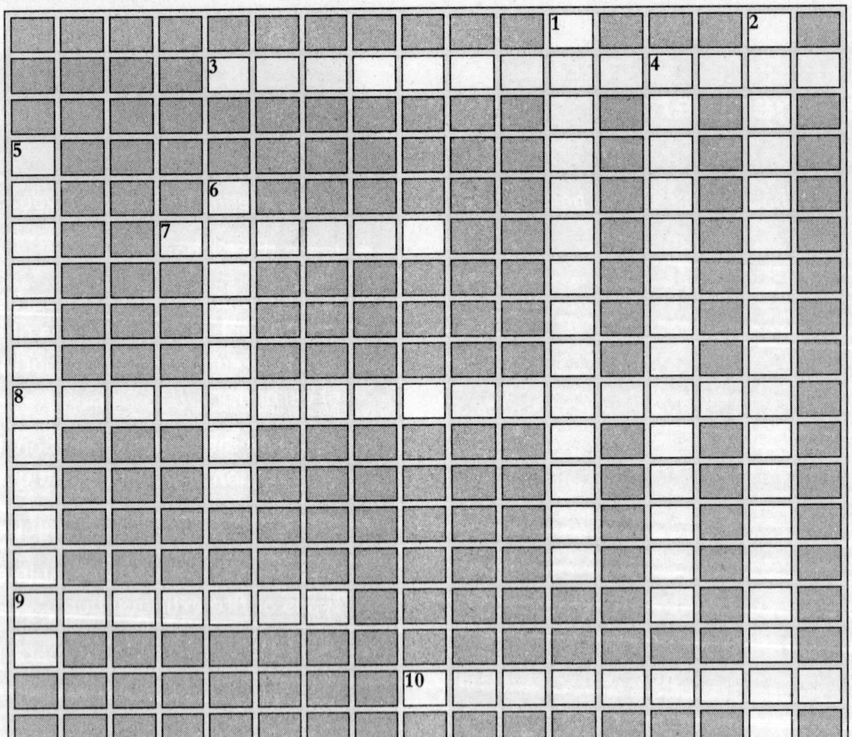

Across

3. Purest form of charcoal
7. Solid form of carbon dioxide
8. Solid substance produced when carbon dioxide is passed through lime water
9. The hardest naturally occuring solid
10. Name of the process in which methane on heating decomposes into its constituents in absence of air.

Down

1. The gas used in the preparation of phosgene
2. The substance formed when haemoglobin combines with carbon monoxide
4. Substance that produces acetylene gas on hydrolysis
5. Substance that is produced when silicon dioxide and coke is heated in an electric furnace.
6. Nonmetal used as solid lubricant.

INTRODUCTION

All the biomolecules invariably possess carbon and hydrogen as the major constituents, making carbon one of the most important non-metallic elements. The special significance of carbon lies in the fact that it forms two types of compounds—Organic and inorganic compounds. Inorganic Chemistry deals with the compounds which are analogous with the corresponding compounds of other non-metallic elements. The chemistry of the wide range of the allotropic forms of carbon also comes in the realm of inorganic chemistry. The chemistry of compounds of carbon present in the living systems are studied under the scope of organic chemistry.

Carbon

As discussed above, carbon is one of the most important non-metallic element. Some of its properties are described below.

Occurrence

Carbon occurs in both free and combined states.

Free State

Carbon exists as the native element in the form of coal in the earth's crust. It occurs in a very small amount in its allotropic forms, such as, diamond and graphite. Diamond and graphite are pure forms of carbon. Coal is an impure form of carbon. Another allotropic form of carbon, fullerene, has been discovered by geologists in a crater made by a meteorite in Germany and in ancient rocks in New Zealand.

Combined State

Carbon exists in the combined state in all the three physical states, namely, solid, liquid and gas.

1. **Solid State:** Carbon occurs in the solid state in the form of mineral carbonates, like, calcium carbonate ($CaCO_3$), magnesite ($MgCO_3$), calamine ($ZnCO_3$), etc. In plants and animals, carbon occurs in the form of fats, proteins, carbohydrates and various other complex chemical compounds.
2. **Liquid State:** Carbon commonly exists in liquid state in fuels and vegetable oils. The fuels mainly comprise petrol, diesel, kerosene, LPG, etc.
3. **Gaseous State:** In gaseous state, carbon exists either in the form of oxides, hydrocarbons or in water as dissolved carbon dioxide. Carbon dioxide and carbon monoxide are the oxides of carbon. About 0.03% by volume of atmosphere is of carbon dioxide while carbon monoxide is present in volcanic gases and furnace emissions of industries.

A wide variety of hydrocarbons occur naturally. The naturally occurring hydrocarbons are natural gas, petroleum gas, marsh gas and others. Carbon dioxide dissolves in water to form carbonic acid, which is present in all kinds of natural waters.

Carbon Cycle

The various compounds of carbon are responsible for the growth and development of living organisms. Though the various life processes involve complex organic reactions, carbon dioxide, which is basically an inorganic compound, is invariably associated with them.

Atmosphere acts as a reservoir of carbon dioxide. Plants make use of this gas for the process of photosynthesis, thereby producing carbohydrates. These carbohydrates, being the sources of energy, are consumed by animals. During the process of respiration, they break down and carbon dioxide gas is released back into the atmosphere. Apart from this, a major part of the food taken up by the animals is also assimilated into the basic organ systems of living beings. The decomposition of the dead organic matter also results in the release of CO_2 into the atmosphere. Some proportion of CO_2 gets dissolved in sea water, which is used up by the aquatic plants. The degradation of the dead aquatic plants and animals over a long period of time under specific conditions results in the formation of fossil fuels, like, coal and petroleum. Further, the burning of these fossil fuels releases CO_2 into the atmosphere.

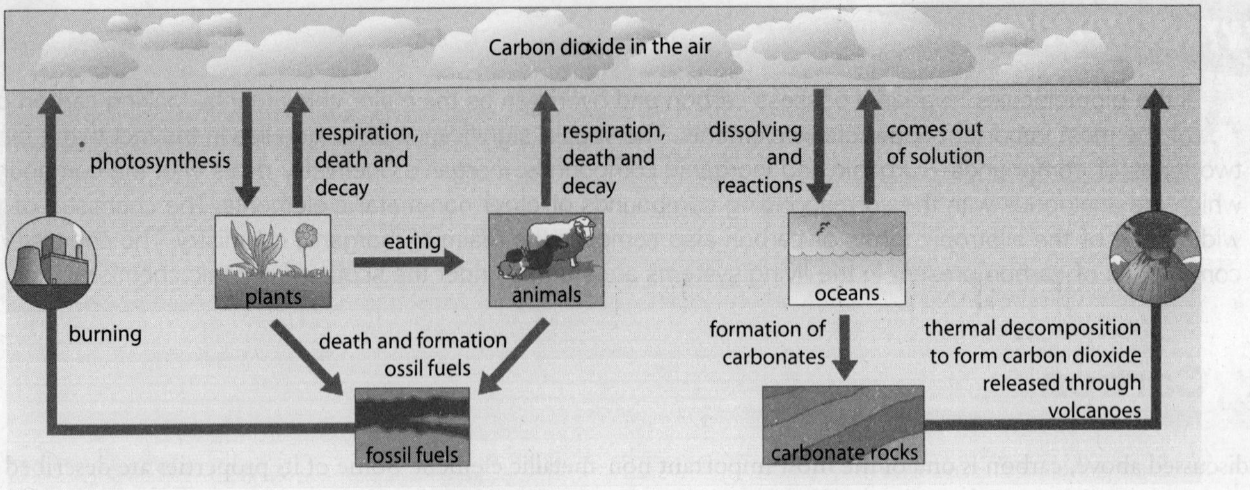

Figure 6.1 Carbon cycle

Allotropy Of Carbon

Allotropy is a phenomenon in which an element exhibits different physical forms with almost similar chemical properties. Some elements, like, carbon, phosphorous, sulphur, iron, etc., exhibit this phenomenon. The different physical forms exhibited by the element are called **allotropes**. Carbon is an element that can exhibit various allotropic forms which have a wide variety of applications. The allotropic forms exhibited by carbon are broadly of two types, namely, crystalline forms and non-crystalline forms or amorphous forms.

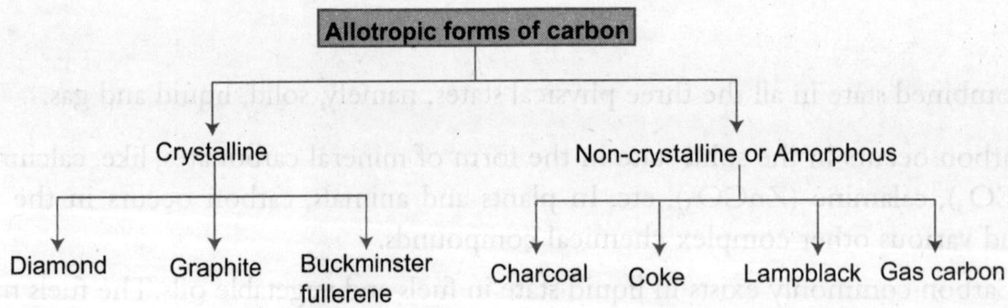

Figure 6.2 Allotropes of carbon

Crystalline Allotropic Forms of Carbon

They have well-defined regular geometrical arrangements of carbon atoms. Diamond and graphite are the widely known crystalline allotropes of carbon. A third form of crystalline allotrope of carbon called fullerene was discovered in recent times. They have extensive technological applications in various fields.

Synthesis of Various Crystalline Allotropes

Formation and Synthesis of Diamond

Diamonds are formed in nature by the crystallization of carbon. The carbon present beneath the surface of the earth under specific conditions dissolves in the molten rock material present there. The liquid so formed is commonly called **magma**. When the magma containing carbon is pushed up to the surface of the earth due to the volcanic eruption, it gets solidified. The iron present in the magma expands on solidification, exerting a great pressure on carbon, which, in turn, crystallizes to form diamonds.

Diamonds are also synthesized artificially for specific applications. In the synthesis of diamond, carbon is prepared from sugar and molten iron is obtained by melting iron in an electric furnace by raising its temperature to the range of 3000°C–3500°C. Carbon prepared from sugar is added to the molten iron to form a homogeneous solution. This solution is suddenly cooled by pouring it into molten lead at 327°C. On sudden cooling, the molten iron on outer surface suddenly cools, whereas the inner surface remains at high temperature. On further cooling, the expansion of iron takes place which exerts a great pressure on carbon producing diamonds.

Formation or Manufacture of Graphite By Acheson Process

The raw material taken for the manufacture of graphite is a mixture of powdered coke, sand and ferric oxide along with saw dust. This mixture is filled in an electric furnace lined inside with fire clay bricks. The carbon rods act as cathode and anode in the furnace. These rods are inserted in such a way that they are held in contact with each other through the particles of coke, which is commonly called **coke bed**. The mixture is covered with a layer of sand and coke on the top so as to cut off the entry of air into it.

When an electric current is passed through the electrodes, the temperature of the furnace increases to 3500°C. The coke bed connecting the two electrodes offers large resistance to the flow of the electricity.

When the current is allowed to pass through the reaction mixture for a period of 30 hours, the following reactions take place with the formation of graphite:

$$\underset{\text{(Sand)}}{SiO_2} + \underset{\text{(Coke)}}{3C} \xrightarrow{3500°C} \underset{\text{(Silicon carbide)}}{SiC} + 2CO$$

$$SiC \xrightarrow{3500°C} Si(s) + C(s)$$

The silicon formed gets evaporated and graphite is left behind.

Synthesis of Fullerenes

The first step in the synthesis of fullerene is the evaporation of graphite using laser radiation and subsequent condensation of carbon vapour. When these vapours are cooled in the atmosphere of noble gases, fullerene molecules consisting of mainly C_{60}, with smaller amount of C_{70} and traces of other fullerene molecules consisting of even number of carbon atoms up to 350 are formed. From these, C_{60} and C_{70} are separated through chromatographic separation.

Comparative Study of Various Crystalline Allotropes

Structure

Following table describes the structure of various crystalline allotropes of carbon.

Physical Properties

Following table describes the physical properties of various crystalline allotropes of carbon.

Table 6.1 Description of structures of diamond, graphite and fullerene

Diamond	Graphite	Fullerenes
Diamond has a regular tetrahedral arrangement. This is due to the bonding of each atom of carbon with four other carbon atoms, forming a single unit of crystal. These crystal units lie in different planes accounting for a rigid three-dimensional structure. Carbon has a valency of four and each carbon is bonded to four other carbon atoms forming a tetrahedral unit. These tetrahedral units lie in different planes, thus, forming a rigid three-dimensional structure.	In graphite, each carbon atom is bonded covalently to three other carbon atoms resulting in the arrangement of hexagonal rings in a single plane. The bonds between the atoms of two single crystals, in the parallel planes are weak. Each carbon is bonded to three carbon atoms only leaving behind one free valency. A three-dimensional arrangement of hexagonal rings is resulted. These rings lie on a single plane. The entire structure is such that the layers of hexagonal rings are arranged parallel to each other.	Fullerenes are large spherical carbon cage molecules and were named Buckminster fullerenes in honour of American architect Robert Buckminster Fuller. The name fullerene originated from the structure that resembled the geodesic dome structures designed by the architect. The fullerenes are broadly categorised into two major types. They are buckyballs and nanotubes. Buckyballs are the most common type of fullerenes and are called Buckminster fullerenes. They constitute C_{60} molecules generally comprised of 20 hexagonal rings and 12 pentagonal rings where no two pentagons share a common edge. This kind of arrangement of rings imparts a cage structure to the fullerene molecule and hence it is hollow in nature and resembles a football. Therefore, these are commonly called buckyballs. Nano tubes can be visualised as layers of hexagonal rings rolled into cylindrical structures.

(Continued)

Table 6.1 Continued

Diamond	Graphite	Fullerenes
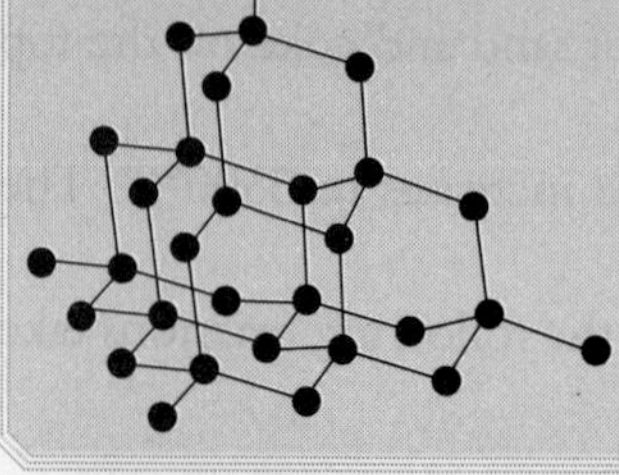	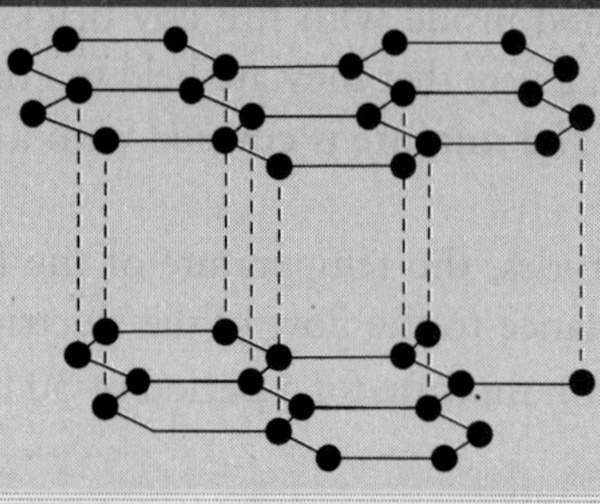	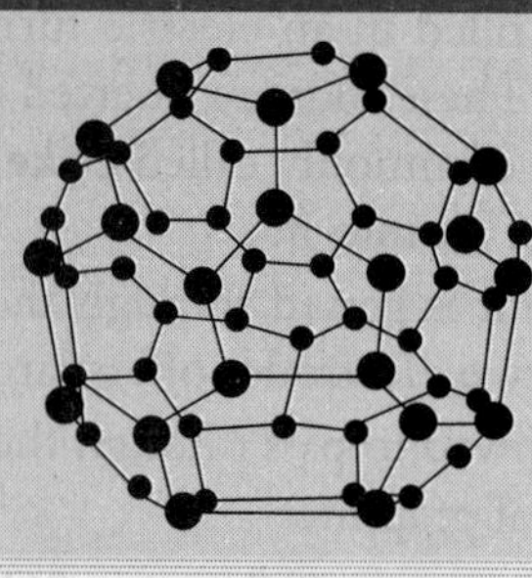

Table 6.2 Description of physical properties of diamond, graphite and fullerene

Diamond	Graphite	Fullerenes
A pure diamond is a colourless and transparent crystal. It is the hardest among naturally occurring solids.	Graphite is a dark grey and very soft solid with metallic lustre.	Brown or black powder.
Diamond is a good conductor of heat and a bad conductor of electricity.	It is a good conductor of heat and electricity.	It becomes a super conductor when it forms compounds with noble gases.
It has a high-refractive index of 2.5.	It is opaque.	Refractive index of fullerene is 2.2.
It is insoluble in common solvents.	It is insoluble in common solvents.	Soluble in common solvents, such as, benzene, toluene or chloroform.
Diamond is the densest form of carbon with a density of 3.5 g/cm^3.	Density is 2.26 g/cm^3.	Density is 1.65 g/cm^3.
The melting point of diamond is about 3700°C.	It has a melting point of about 3600°C.	It undergoes sublimation at about 527°C.
Presence of impurities impart colour to diamonds.	–	–

Chemical Properties

Following table describes the chemical properties of various crystalline allotropes of carbon.

Table 6.3 Description of chemical properties of diamond and graphite

Reactions	Diamond	Graphite
Action with oxygen	Diamond catches fire at 900°C; when heated in oxygen, it catches fire at 800°C to form CO_2 (carbon dioxide). $C(s) + O_2(g) \xrightarrow{800°C} CO_2(g)$	Graphite on heating in the presence of pure oxygen catches fire at 700°C and burns brightly forming a mixture of carbon dioxide and carbon monoxide. $3C(s) + 2O_2(g) \xrightarrow{700°C} CO_2(g) + 2CO(g) + \Delta Q$
Reaction with sodium carbonate	On heating diamond very strongly with solid sodium carbonate, sodium oxide and carbon monoxide are formed. $Na_2CO_3(s) + C(s) \longrightarrow Na_2O(s) + 2CO(g)$	Graphite does not burn in air. On heating the fused mixture of sodium carbonate and graphite, sodium oxide and carbon monoxide gas are formed. $Na_2CO_3(s) + C(s) \xrightarrow{Fuse} Na_2O(s) + 2CO(g)$

Uses of Crystalline Allotropes

Uses of Diamond

1. Diamonds are used for making various kinds of jewellery as they sparkle brilliantly.
2. Diamond is used as an abrasive for cutting glass.
3. It is used as a tip of deep boring drills.
4. It is used for making dies for drawing wires.
5. It is used in generating laser beams in electronics.
6. It is used by surgeons to perform delicate operations.

Uses of Graphite

1. Graphite is used in making leads of pencils.
2. It is used as a dry lubricant as ordinary lubricating oil gets charred at high temperature.
3. It is used in making refractory crucibles which can withstand very high temperatures.
4. Graphite is used to make suitable black paint and printer's ink.
5. Graphite fibres can be used to reinforce plastic as they are strong.
6. A strong, light-weight composite material of graphite and plastic is used to make fishing rods, bicycle frames, spacecraft parts, dish antennae and tennis rackets.
7. It is used in nuclear reactors as a moderator.

Conversion of Graphite into Diamond

Graphite can be transformed into diamond by applying a pressure greater than 1,00,000 times the atmospheric pressure at the sea level and by burning at a temperature of about 3700°C. These conditions of temperature and pressure help in rearranging the atoms of carbon in graphite into a diamond structure.

Amorphous Allotropes of Carbon

Charcoal, coke, lamp black and gas carbon are amorphous forms of carbon. In these forms of carbon, the carbon atoms are not arranged in an orderly manner. Recent X-ray study reveals that these allotropic forms are tiny graphite crystals cemented together by impurities.

Charcoal

Charcoal is one of the man-made amorphous forms of carbon. It is used as a fuel. Depending on the source from which charcoal is obtained, it is of three types.

Preparation of Various Types of Charcoal

1. **Wood Charcoal — Laboratory Preparation:** A dry, hard glass test tube is taken, and it is filled half with wood shavings. These wood shavings are subjected to heating in the absence of air using a Bunsen burner. Wood shavings get charred, and fumes are evolved. These fumes get condensed in the conical flask placed in cold water and form two separate layers. A matchstick is brought near the jet tube, and the gas coming out of it catches fire. This gas is wood gas. The products of destructive distillation of wood are wood charcoal, wood tar, pyroligneous acid and wood gas.

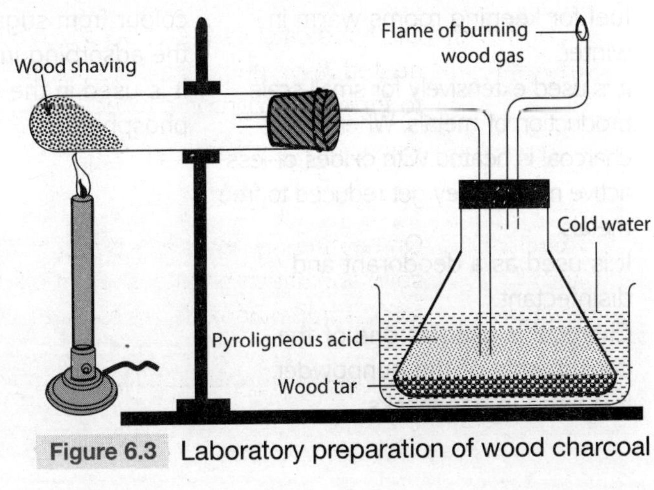

Figure 6.3 Laboratory preparation of wood charcoal

2. **Bone Charcoal:** Bone charcoal is also known as **animal charcoal** or **bone ash** or **ivory black**. Animal bones contain organic matter and calcium phosphate. The crushed fine powder of the animal bones if subjected to destructive distillation produces residue. This residue is called **bone charcoal**.

4. **Sugar Charcoal:** One of the purest forms of amorphous allotropes of carbon is sugar charcoal and it is prepared by destructive distillation of sugar. Sugar

crystals lose water and get converted to pure carbon. This pure carbon obtained from sugar is known as sugar charcoal. The chemical reaction of sugar with concentrated sulphuric acid produces sugar charcoal.

$$C_{12}H_{22}O_{11} \xrightarrow{H_2SO_4} 12C + 11H_2O$$

Physical Properties of Charcoal

Charcoal is a porous black solid. It has a huge surface area due to its porosity. It has the ability to adsorb specific substances, like, coloured impurities, poisonous substances, etc.

Chemical Properties of Charcoal

1. **Reaction with Non-Metals:** Charcoal reacts with non-metals, like, oxygen, sulphur and hydrogen.
   (a) **With Oxygen**: Oxides of carbon are formed:

$$\underset{\text{(Excess)}}{C + O} \longrightarrow CO_2$$

$$C + O_2 \longrightarrow 2CO$$

   (b) **With Sulphur**: On passing sulphur vapour through red hot charcoal, a vapour of carbon disulphide is formed:

$$C + 2S \longrightarrow CS_2$$

   (c) **With Hydrogen**: On reaction with hydrogen gas, charcoal gives methane:

$$C + 2H_2 \longrightarrow CH_4$$

2. **Reducing Property:** Both wood charcoal and sugar charcoal behave as good reducing agents when they react with steam or oxides of metals or with oxyacids:

$$C + \underset{\text{steam}}{H_2O(g)} \longrightarrow CO + H_2$$

$$ZnO + C \longrightarrow Zn + CO$$

$$C + 2H_2SO_4 \xrightarrow{\text{boiling}} CO_2 + 2H_2O + 2SO_2$$

Konnect

Since bone charcoal contains maximum percentage of calcium phosphate, it cannot act as a good reducing agent.

Uses of Charcoal

Uses of different types of charcoal are tabulated below.

Table 6.4 Uses of different types of Charcoal

Wood charcoal	Bone charcoal	Sugar charcoal
It is used as an excellent household fuel for keeping rooms warm in winter.	Bone charcoal is used to remove colour from sugar cane juice due to the adsorbing impurities.	It is used for extracting metals from their oxides.
It is used extensively for small-scale production of metals. When wood charcoal is heated with oxides of less active metals, they get reduced to free metals.	It is used in the extraction of yellow phosphorous.	It is used as an adsorbent material in place of activated charcoal.
It is used as a deodorant and disinfectant.		
Charcoal is used as one of the constituents of the gunpowder.		
It is used in gas masks.		

Other Amorphous Forms of Carbon

Table 6.5 Description of amorphous forms of carbon

Parameter	Lamp black	Coke	Gas carbon
Preparation	Lamp black is prepared by burning mustard oil, turpentine oil and petroleum in the absence of oxygen. The preparation of lamp black can be done at home by placing a clean dry glass slide over the flame of mustard oil lamp. After some time, a deep black powdery substance is coated on the slide, which is known as **lamp black**.	Coke is prepared by heating coal in the absence of air up to a temperature of 1300°C in huge iron retorts. The products obtained by the decomposition of coal are coal gas, carbon, coal tar, liquor ammonia and coal gas.	Gas carbon can be prepared by destructive distillation of coal. The thermal vaporization of small amounts of carbon from coal on condensation produces a grey solid. This grey solid obtained is called **gas carbon**.
Properties	Lamp black is a light, powdery black substance, having a velvet touch. It has an oily feel due to the presence of the vapours of some amount of oil.	It is greyish black porous solid.	It is a dull grey solid. It is a good conductor of electricity.
Uses	(i) Lamp black is used as a stabilizing filler for rubber in making tyres and plastics. (ii) It is used as a black pigment in inks and paints. (iii) It is used for making black shoe polishes. (iv) It is used in the manufacture of black carbon papers and carbon ribbons for type writers.	(i) It is used as a household fuel. (ii) It is used extensively in the extraction of metals, like, iron copper, lead, etc., from their oxides and sulphide ores as it is an excellent reducing agent. (iii) It is used in the manufacture of graphite and calcium carbide. (iv) It is used in the manufacture of water gas and producer gas.	It is used for making electrodes for dry cells.

Compounds of Carbon

The compounds of carbon are basically classified into two categories, namely, inorganic carbon compounds and organic compounds. In contrast to the vast number of organic compounds, the number of inorganic carbon compounds is very limited. Among them, oxides, carbides, carbonate and bicarbonate salts, and cyanides are important.

Oxides of Carbon: Carbon monoxide and carbon dioxide are the two stable oxides formed by carbon.

Carbon Monoxide

Occurrence

Carbon monoxide is not a natural component of atmospheric air. It is mainly added to the atmosphere due to the incomplete combustion of fossil fuels, like, wood, coal, petrol, etc., Degradation of organic matter in swamps also gives out minor proportions of carbon monoxide along with carbon dioxide. Since carbon monoxide is found to be one of the components of volcanic eruptions, the atmosphere in the volcanic regions contains slightly greater proportions of carbon monoxide.

Laboratory Method of Preparation

Method I

Principle: When CO_2 gas is passed over red hot charcoal, charcoal gets oxidized and forms carbon monoxide. This is a highly endothermic reaction.

$$\underset{\text{(red hot)}}{C(s)} + CO_2(g) \longrightarrow 2CO(g) - Q$$

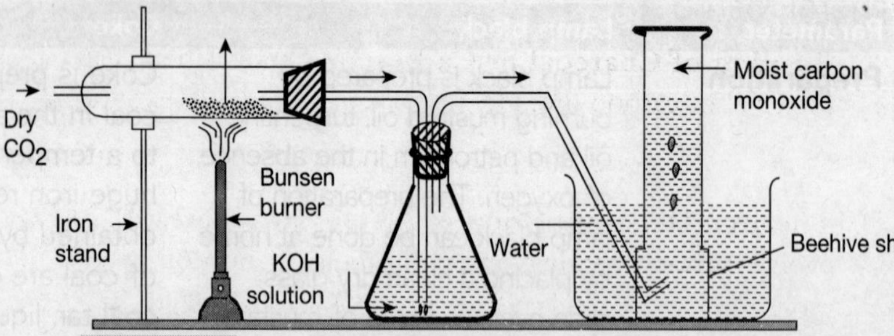

Figure 6.4 Laboratory preparation of carbon monoxide

Process: Powdered charcoal is taken in a hard glass test tube and is heated. Then, carbon dioxide gas is passed over this. CO_2 gas oxidizes carbon and turns it into carbon monoxide.

Purification: Carbon monoxide prepared by the above process may contain CO_2 gas as an impurity. This can be removed by passing the products through caustic potash solution.

Precautions:

1. The powdered charcoal is kept red hot throughout the reaction.
2. The initial bubbles of the gas are left out and only then the collection of the gas is started.
3. Carbon monoxide being a poisonous gas, the entire process of preparation is carried out in a fume chamber.

Info Bytes!

Carbon monoxide is often termed the 'silent killer' because it's colourless, odourless, and tasteless, making it very hard to detect without specific equipment.

Method II

In the laboratory, CO can also be prepared from oxalic acid and formic acid.

(a) From Oxalic Acid: Sulphuric acid absorbs water from oxalic acid, producing carbon monoxide and carbon dioxide.

$$\begin{matrix} COOH \\ | \\ COOH \end{matrix} + H_2SO_4 \xrightarrow{\Delta} H_2SO_4.H_2O + CO + CO_2$$

(b) From Formic Acid: Sulphuric acid absorbs water from formic acid, forming carbon monoxide.

$$HCOOH + H_2SO_4 \xrightarrow{100^\circ C} H_2SO_4.H_2O + CO$$

Uses of Carbon Monoxide

1. Carbon monoxide can be used as a fuel as it produces a large amount of heat on combustion. The fuels, like, coal gas, water gas and producer gas contain carbon monoxide as an important constituent.
2. Carbon monoxide is used in the extraction of metals like nickel from the mixture of other metals. This is done by passing carbon monoxide through the mixture of other metals.
3. In the manufacture of chemicals.
4. It behaves as a reducing agent in the extraction of metals.
5. In the preparation of war gas like phosgene.

Carbon Dioxide

Occurrence

Carbon dioxide occurs in nature both in free and combined states.

Free State

1. Atmospheric air contains 0.03% of CO_2.
2. Dry wells, mines and caves near lime kilns contain larger proportions of CO_2.
3. Dissolved CO_2 in water in oceans, lakes, etc.

Combined State

Minerals, such as, limestone, magnesite, etc., contain large amount of CO_2 in the form of carbonate salts.

General Methods of Preparation of Carbon Dioxide

1. **Burning of Charcoal or Carbon or Coke:** When charcoal or coke is burnt in adequate supply of air, it enhances the level of carbon dioxide. The reaction is highly exothermic.

$$C + O_2 \longrightarrow CO_2 + Q$$

2. **Thermal Decomposition of Metal Carbonates:** All carbonates except those of sodium or potassium on heating evolve carbon dioxide along with the formation of metal oxide.

$$CaCO_3 \longrightarrow CaO + CO_2$$

$$ZnCO_3 \longrightarrow ZnO + CO_2$$

3. **Thermal Decomposition of Bicarbonates:** Bicarbonates on strong heating evolve carbon dioxide along with the formation of the corresponding carbonate and water

$$NaHCO_3 \rightarrow Na_2CO_3 + H_2O$$

4. **Action of Dilute Mineral Acids on Carbonates and Bicarbonates:** Dilute HCl or H_2SO_4 when added to the carbonate or bicarbonate salt, neutralization reaction takes place with the liberation of carbon dioxide gas:

$$Na_2CO_3 + H_2SO_4 \longrightarrow Na_2SO_4 + CO_2 + H_2O$$

$$NaHCO_3 + HCl \longrightarrow NaCl + H_2O + CO_2$$

Laboratory Method of Preparation

Principle: Marble chips contain calcium carbonate which, on the addition of dilute hydrochloric acid, releases CO_2 gas:

$$CaCO_3 + 2HCl \longrightarrow CaCl_2 + H_2O + CO_2$$

Process: Marble chips are taken in a conical flask. A two-holed rubber cork is introduced into this. Through onc hole, a thistle funnel is inserted and through another hole, a delivery tube is inserted. Dilute hydrochloric acid is added dropwise through the thistle funnel. CO_2 gas generated during the reaction comes out through the delivery tube.

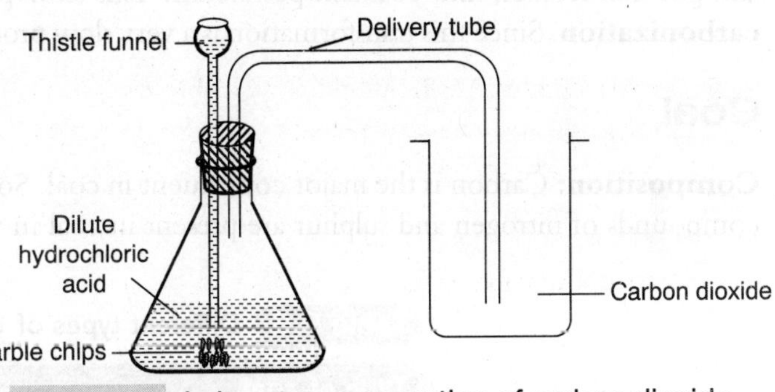

Figure 6.5 Laboratory preparation of carbon dioxide

Collection of Gas: It can be collected by the upward displacement of air since it is heavier than air.

Uses of Carbon Dioxide

Apart from being the natural and indispensable raw material for photosynthesis, CO_2 finds many important applications in various fields.

1. Carbon dioxide is used for the hardening of mortars (mixture of $Ca(OH)_2$, sand and water). Thus, the mortar applied to join bricks slowly hardens due to the absorption of carbon dioxide from the atmosphere forming calcium carbonate.
2. Carbogen, a mixture of 95% of oxygen and 5% of carbon dioxide, is used to stimulate respiratory system.
3. It is used in soft drinks or aerated drinks to give them a tangy taste.
4. Solid carbon dioxide called **dry ice** is used as a refrigerant.
5. Carbon dioxide is extensively used in the production of industrial compounds, such as, washing soda, baking soda, white lead, etc.
6. Atmosphere of carbon dioxide can be used in the preservation of food grains, fruits, etc.

7. Carbon dioxide is used in fire extinguishers to put off fires since it is a non-combustible gas and does not support combustion.
8. Baking powder which contains sodium bicarbonate produces carbon dioxide gas on heating. This gas helps in the aeration of dough.

Natural Sources of Energy

The existence of life on earth primarily owes to the various sources of energy. There are some sources of energy which remain inexhaustible and are replenished continuously at the rate at which they are consumed. These are called **renewable sources of energy**. Solar energy, hydel energy and wind energy come under this category. The sources of energy which get exhausted at much larger rate than the rate at which they are replenished. These are called non-renewable **sources of energy**. A large majority of **non-renewable** sources derive their energy from plant and animal remains and hence are called **fossil fuels**. In view of their limited availability, various researches are going on in the direction of generation of alternative sources of energy. Inspite of the great demand for alternative sources of energy, fossil fuels still constitute major proportion of worldwide energy consumption.

Info Bytes!

The coal-rich regions of Jharkhand, Chhattisgarh, and West Bengal in India have been fundamental to the country's industrial growth. These regions power a large chunk of India's energy needs.

Formation of Coal and Petroleum

The dead plants and animals were buried beneath the surface of earth millions of years ago. Due to the extreme conditions of temperature and pressure existing in the deep layers of earth's crust, the organic matter undergoes anaerobic degradation and got transformed into coal and petroleum. This slow process of transformation of dead vegetation in to coal is called **carbonization**. Since this transformation is a very slow process, these are considered to be non renewable sources of energy.

Coal

Composition: Carbon is the major constituent in coal. Some hydrocarbons are also present along with carbon. Inorganic compounds of nitrogen and sulphur are present in coal in varying proportions.

Table 6.6 Different types of coal with their carbon percentage

Type of coal	Percentage of carbon
Anthracite	90%
Bituminous	70%
Lignite	40%
Peat	10 – 15%

Processing of Coal: Processing of coal involves heating of coal at high temperature in the range of 1300–1700 K in the absence of air. This process is called **destructive distillation** which gives volatile products such as coal gas, ammonia and coal tar along with a non-volatile residue called **coke**. The volatile products can be separated by passing through water. Coal tar is insoluble in water and gets settled at the bottom.

(i) **Coal Tar:** Coal tar is a black viscous liquid with a characteristic odour. Coal tar is subjected to fractional distillation. The products obtained are again subjected to further distillation to give a number of organic compounds like benzene, naphthalene, etc.

(ii) Coal Gas: Coal gas consists of methane, carbon monoxide and hydrogen. These gases are insoluble and hence coal gas is isolated from the rest of the products. Ammonia being highly soluble in water gets dissolved in water and is removed. Being a mixture of various combustible gases like methane, carbon monoxide and hydrogen, coal gas is used as in industrial fuel, domestic fuel and also as an illuminant.

Petroleum

Petroleum is a dark viscous oily liquid with an unpleasant odour formed under the sea by the anaerobic degradation of dead organic matter from the remains of marine plants and animals. This is also known as **rock oil or crude oil**.

> **Info Bytes!**
> The word petroleum originated from Greek words – petra meaning rock and oleum meaning oil.

Composition: The composition of petroleum is variable and depends on the place of origin. It is in any way considered a mixture of hydrocarbons containing trace amounts of oxygen, nitrogen and sulphur.

Extraction and refining of petroleum: Petroleum deposits are inevitably associated with layers of natural gas. The extraction of natural gas and petroleum is done by drilling deep wells through the deep layers of earth's crust. As a result of this process, the high pressure developed in those layers results in the extraction of natural gas and petroleum.

As petroleum is drilled out from earth's crust, it consists of many impurities. These impurities should be removed and then the different fractions containing different hydrocarbons are separated. The entire process is called **refining of petroleum**. The crude oil is passed between highly charged electrodes to remove water from the sample. It is then treated with copper oxide to remove sulphur compounds.

Since the different hydrocarbons possess different boiling points, the process of refining is done by subjecting petroleum to fractional distillation. The equipment used for this purpose is called **fractionating tower** which is a tall cylindrical tower made up of a number of horizontal steel troughs.

After removing the impurities, the crude oil is fed into the fractionating tower at high temperature. The various components of crude oil vapourise and the vapours get condensed at different heights of the tower. The component which have higher boiling points get condensed first and the components which have lower boiling points are carried to the top and then get condensed.

Important Fuels Obtained from Petroleum

(i) Natural Gas: The major constituent of natural gas is methane. Methane undergoes rapid combustion releasing large amount of heat. It can be used as an automobile fuel like CNG (Compressed Natural Gas). It can also be used as domestic fuel in the form of biogas.

Apart from these, natural gas can also be used us a raw material for the manufacture of carbon black and hydrogen. This hydrogen can be used for manufacture of ammonia which can in turn be used for the manufacture of nitrogenous fertilisers.

(ii) Petroleum Gas: The major constituent of petroleum gas is butane. Since this can easily get liquefied by subjecting to high pressure, it is very much suitable for uses as domestic fuel as LPG (Liquified Petroleum Gas). It has high calorific value.

(iii) Petrol or Gasoline: It is the most important product of refining of petroleum which is used as automobile fuel.

The various fuels differ with respect to the amount of heat released on combustion. Obviously, the efficiency of a fuel mainly depends upon the amount of heat produced during combustion.

Thus, a fuel is a combustible substance and is characterised by its calorific value which is the amount of heat given out.

Calorific Value

Calorific value may be defined as the amount of heat liberated by 1 kg of a fuel when it undergoes complete combustion. It is expressed in kilojoules per kg. The calorific values of some of the fuels are given below.

Table 6.7 Few fuels with their calorific values

Name of the fuel	Calorific value (kJ/kg)
Charcoal	34000
Wood	17000 – 22000
Kerosene	50000
Petrol	45000
LPG	50000
Hydrogen	150000

Economic importance of a fuel mainly depends upon its relative calorific value, its ease of combustion and the products of combustion.

Characteristics of an Ideal Fuel:

(i) High calorific value

(ii) Low ignition temperature

(iii) Formation of least amount of objectionable biproducts

The various components obtained by the process of fractional distillation of petroleum contain mixtures of hydrocarbons having different lengths of carbon chains. These fractions are used as fuels for different purposes after further purification. Purification makes the fuels devoid of corrosive constituents and unpleasant odours. The characteristics of various fuels depend on the type of combustion they undergo and their calorific values.

The slow combustion of fuels which produce flame gives rise to heat and light which can be utilised for various purposes. However, rapid uncontrolled combustion of fuels sometimes leads to the uncontrolled flames which result in fire accidents. In that case, it becomes absolutely essential to put off these fires in order to prevent loss of lives and property. For this purpose, a device called **fire extinguisher** is used.

Fire Extinguishers

A **fire extinguisher** is a device used for putting off fires. Though many kinds of fire extinguishers are available, carbon dioxide is the basic source for extinguishing fires in most of the extinguishers.

Principle: Carbon dioxide gas is not a supporter of combustion. Being heavier than air, it forms a layer below air. Thus, CO_2 layer formed between the flames and air cuts off the contact between air and fire. As a result of this, the fire is prevented from spreading and is finally put off due to the shortage of the supply of oxygen to the fire.

Types of Fire Extinguishers

The most important types of fire extinguishers in use are the following:

1. **Soda Acid Fire Extinguisher:** A fire extinguisher consists of a metallic cylinder filled with a solution of sodium bicarbonate. At the bottom of the cylinder, a thin sealed glass tube containing concentrated sulphuric acid is placed. This tube is surrounded by a fixed wire gauze cage. A plunger with a sharp end is placed at the bottom of the cylinder in such a way that the sharp end is placed at the sealed thin glass tube, as shown in the figure given below. On the top of the cylinder, a nozzle which is sealed with wax is provided.

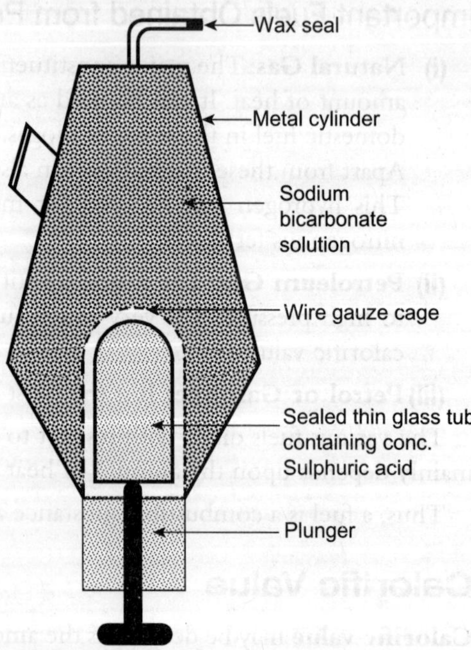

Figure 6.6 Soda acid fire extinguisher

When the plunger is hit against the floor, the sharp tip of the plunger breaks the glass test tube. The acid in the test tube reacts with sodium bicarbonate solution to produce carbon dioxide gas. Carbon dioxide gas is forced out through the nozzle. The wax seal is broken off, thus, forcing CO_2 gas out through the nozzle. The fire is put off when the gas is directed against the fire.

Limitations: This fire extinguisher is used to extinguish fire caused by solid inflammable materials only. In the case of extinguishing fires caused by inflammable liquids, such as petrol, it is rendered useless because the solution coming out of the cylinder, being denser than oil sinks in the oil and disables it to cut off the supply of air to the fire. It should not be used to extinguish the flames caused by electricity as the solution is a good conductor of electricity.

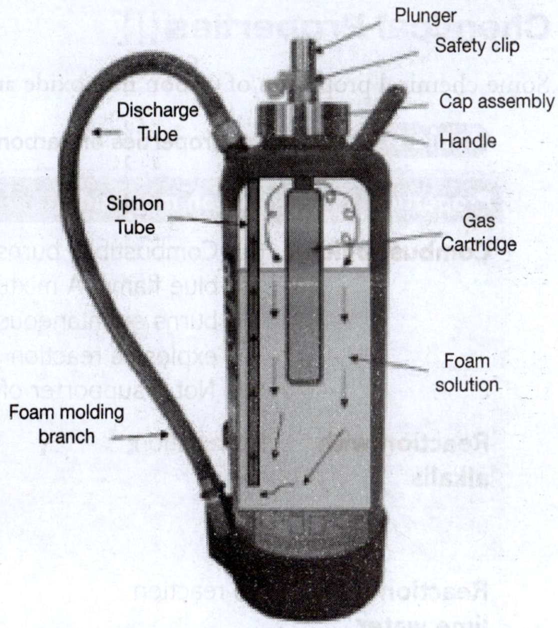

Figure 6.7 Fire Extinguisher

2. **Foam Type Extinguisher:** Foam type extinguisher is used to extinguish fire caused by inflammable liquids, such as, petrol, alcohol, diesel, etc. The construction and working of the extinguisher is similar to that of soda acid fire extinguisher. However, the solution of sodium bicarbonate contains saponin (a material which produces lot of foam). Sulphuric acid is replaced by aluminium sulphate solution. As a result, the following reaction takes place, which helps in extinguishing fire:

$$Al_2(SO_4)_3 + 6NaHCO_3 \longrightarrow 3Na_2SO_4 + 2Al(OH)_3 + 6CO_2$$

Limitation: This fire extinguisher cannot be used to extinguish fire caused by electricity.

Comparative Study of Carbon Monoxide and Carbon Dioxide

Physical Properties

Some physical properties of carbon monoxide and carbon dioxide are compared below.

Table 6.8 Physical properties of carbon dioxide and carbon monoxide

Properties	Carbon monoxide	Carbon dioxide
Colour	Colourless	Colourless
Odour	No characteristic smell	No characteristic smell
Vapour density (VD)	Slightly lighter than air, VD = 14	Heavier than air, VD = 22
Solubility	Insoluble in water	Highly soluble in water
Nature	Neutral and does not respond to litmus test	Acidic. Changes blue litmus to red
Boiling point	−192°C	−78.5°C

Chemical Properties

Some chemical properties of carbon monoxide and carbon dioxide are compared below.

Table 6.9 **Chemical properties of carbon dioxide and carbon monoxide**

Properties	Carbon monoxide	Carbon dioxide
Combustibility	(a) Combustible, burns in air with a pale blue flame. A mixture of CO and air burns spontaneously resulting in an explosive reaction (b) Not a supporter of combustion	Non-combustible Not a supporter of combustion
Reaction with alkalis	No reaction	Neutralization takes place with the formation of salt and water: $CO_2 + 2NaOH \longrightarrow Na_2CO_3 + H_2O$
Reaction with lime water	No reaction	Turns milky due to the formation of insoluble $CaCO_3$: $CO_2 + Ca(OH)_2 \longrightarrow CaCO_3 + H_2O$
Reaction with metals	When CO gas is passed over the finely divided metals, like, nickel, chromium and iron, metal carbonyls are formed: $Ni + 4CO \xrightarrow{\Delta} Ni(CO)_4$ $Cr + 6CO \longrightarrow Cr(CO)_6$ $Fe + 5CO \longrightarrow Fe(CO)_5$	Na, K and Ca combine with CO_2 to form their respective carbonates along with carbon, whereas Mg and Al give their respective oxides and carbon: $4Na + 3CO_2 \longrightarrow 2Na_2CO_3 + C$ $2Mg + CO_2 \longrightarrow 2MgO + C$
Reaction with non-metals	Reaction with oxygen gives CO_2 gas and reaction with Cl_2 gas gives phosgene: $2CO + O_2 \longrightarrow 2CO_2$ $CO + Cl_2 \longrightarrow COCl_2$	No reaction with O_2 and Cl_2
As reducing agent/oxidizing agent	CO reduces oxides of less active metals: $Fe_2O_3 + 3CO \longrightarrow 2Fe + 3CO_2$	Oxidizes carbon to carbon monoxide: $CO_2 + C \longrightarrow 2CO - Q$
Biochemical process	Combines with haemoglobin of blood to form carboxyhaemoglobin. This makes CO gas poisonous	Green plants synthesize carbohydrates by the combination of CO_2 and water in the presence of sunlight. The process is called **photosynthesis.** $6CO_2 + 6H_2O \longrightarrow C_6H_{12}O_6 + 6O_2$

Action of Carbon Dioxide When it is Passed through Lime Water

Limited Amount of Carbon Dioxide

When limited amount of CO_2 is passed through lime water, it turns milky due to the formation of insoluble $CaCO_3$:

$$Ca(OH)_2(aq) + CO_2(g) \longrightarrow CaCO_3 + H_2O$$

Excess Amount of Carbon Dioxide

When an excess amount of CO_2 is passed through lime water, it first turns milky, and then the milkiness disappears due to the formation of soluble $Ca(HCO_3)_2$:

$$Ca(OH)_2 + CO_2 \longrightarrow CaCO_3 + H_2O$$

$$CaCO_3 + CO_2 + H_2O \longrightarrow Ca(HCO_3)_2$$

EXAMPLE 6.1 What reactions occur when carbon interacts with carbon dioxide?

SOLUTION

Carbon, a non-metal, reacts with carbon dioxide under specific conditions to produce carbon monoxide: $C + CO_2 \rightarrow 2CO$

EXAMPLE 6.2 How is dry ice manufactured?

SOLUTION

Dry ice can be prepared by liquifying CO_2 below 31°C by compression and then the liquid is allowed to evaporate rapidly, a portion of it solidifies to dry ice.

Other Inorganic Compounds of Carbon

Calcium Carbide (CaC_2)

Preparation: Calcium carbide is prepared by heating pulverized calcium oxide and coke:

$$2CaO + 6C \longrightarrow 2CaC_2 + 2CO$$

Physical Properties: Greyish black crystalline solid.

Chemical Properties: Hydrolysis gives acetylene.

$$CaC_2 + 2H_2O \longrightarrow Ca(OH)_2 + C_2H_2$$

Uses

1. It is used to prepare acetylene gas in laboratory.
2. It is used as a dehydrating agent.
3. It is used in the manufacture of graphite and hydrogen.

Konnect

Calcium carbide, when mixed with water, produces acetylene gas. This gas is used for welding purposes and in old carbide lamps.

Silicon Carbide (SiC)

Preparation: SiC is produced by heating silicon dioxide and coke in an electric furnace. It is also known as **carborundum**.

$$SiO_2 + 3C \longrightarrow SiC + 2CO\uparrow$$

Physical Properties

1. It is a very hard substance with high melting point nearly 2700°C.
2. It is insoluble in water.
3. Its density is 3.22 g/cm^3.

Chemical Properties: Silicon carbide is oxidized by fused sodium hydroxide in the presence of air:

$$SiC + O_2 + 4NaOH \longrightarrow Na_2CO_3 + Na_2SiO_3 + 2H_2O$$

Uses

1. It is used as an abrasive.
2. It is also used as a grinding stone to cut and sharpen tools.

Calcium Carbonate ($CaCO_3$)

Preparation

1. Carbonic acid reacts with calcium hydroxide to produce $CaCO_3$.
2. It is prepared by passing CO_2 into a solution of calcium hydroxide, calcium carbonate precipitates out:

$$Ca(OH)_2 + CO_2 \longrightarrow CaCO_3 + H_2O$$

Physical Properties

1. It is a white crystalline solid with melting point of 825°C.
2. It is insoluble in water.

Chemical Properties

1. It reacts with strong acids releasing CO_2:

$$CaCO_3 + 2HCl \longrightarrow CaCl_2 + CO_2 + H_2O$$

2. It reacts with water that is saturated with CO_2 to form the soluble calcium bicarbonate:

$$CaCO_3 + CO_2 + H_2O \longrightarrow Ca(HCO_3)_2$$

Uses: It is used as an antacid.

Sodium Carbonate (Na_2CO_3)

Preparation: It is prepared by heating carbonic acid with NaOH:

$$H_2CO_3 + 3NaOH \longrightarrow Na_2CO_3 + 2H_2O$$

Physical Properties

1. It is a white crystalline solid with melting point of 851°C.
2. It is soluble in water.

Chemical Properties

1. It reacts with water to form carbonic acid and sodium hydroxide:

$$Na_2CO_3 + 2H_2O \longrightarrow H_2CO_3 + 2NaOH$$

2. It reacts with metal salts to form insoluble basic carbonates.

Uses

1. It removes greasy dirt from clothes and vessels.
2. It is used in the manufacture of glass.
3. It is used to soften hard water.

Sodium Bicarbonate ($NaHCO_3$)

Preparation: It forms when sodium hydroxide reacts with carbonic acid:

$$H_2CO_3 + NaOH \longrightarrow NaHCO_3 + H_2O$$

Physical Properties

1. It is a white crystalline substance.
2. It is sparingly soluble in water.

Chemical Properties

1. It reacts with water to form carbonic acid and sodium hydroxide:

$$NaHCO_3 + H_2O \longrightarrow H_2CO_3 + NaOH$$

2. It reacts with acids to evolve CO_2:

$$NaHCO_3 + HCl \longrightarrow NaCl + H_2O + CO_2$$

Uses

1. It is used in the preparation of sodium carbonate.
2. It is used as an antacid.
3. It is used in the preparation of baking powder.

Compounds of Carbon and Hydrogen

Carbon has the unique capability of forming long chains by means of self-linkage among the atoms. This ability of an element to form either straight chains or branched chains is called **catenation.**

Due to this unique feature of catenation, carbon can form an innumerable number of compounds. The compounds containing only carbon and hydrogen are called **hydrocarbons.**

Depending on the relative proportions of carbon and hydrogen, hydrocarbons are further classified into saturated and unsaturated hydrocarbons. Saturated hydrocarbons have larger proportions of hydrogen and have a general formula, C_nH_{2n+2}. The saturated hydrocarbons containing 1, 2, 3 and 4 carbon atoms are called **methane**, **ethane**, **propane** and **butane**, respectively. All these compounds exist in a gaseous state at room temperature.

The unsaturated hydrocarbons have lesser proportion of hydrogen. They are characterised by the presence of at least one multiple bond between the carbon atoms. If a double bond is present in the carbon chain, those unsaturated hydrocarbons are known as **alkenes** with a general formula, C_nH_{2n} . The unsaturated hydrocarbons with a triple bond between the carbon atoms are known as **alkynes** with a general formula C_nH_{2n-2}.

Methane

It is the simplest member of saturated hydrocarbons with the molecular formula CH_4.

Occurrence

Natural gas contains mainly methane. Natural gas is formed by the anaerobic decomposition of organic matter by bacteria present inside the earth's crust.

Methane is also found in marshy places. Hence, it is commonly known as **marsh gas.** In coal mines, methane which causes explosions and fire, accumulates.

Info Bytes!

For the safety of miners, Davy's safety lamp is used for illumination inside the mines. This lamp was designed by Sir Humphrey Davy.

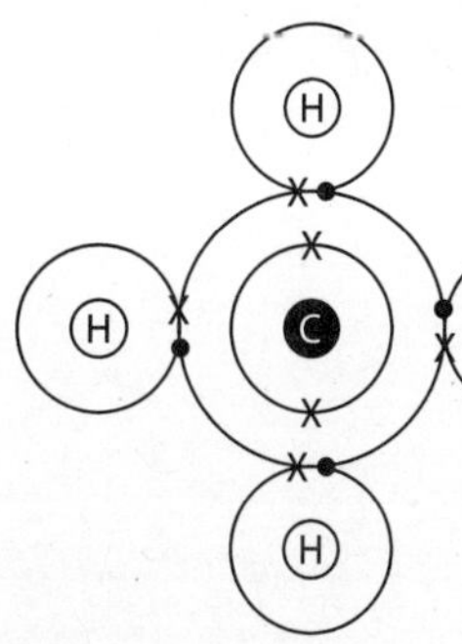

Figure 6.8 A molecule of methane

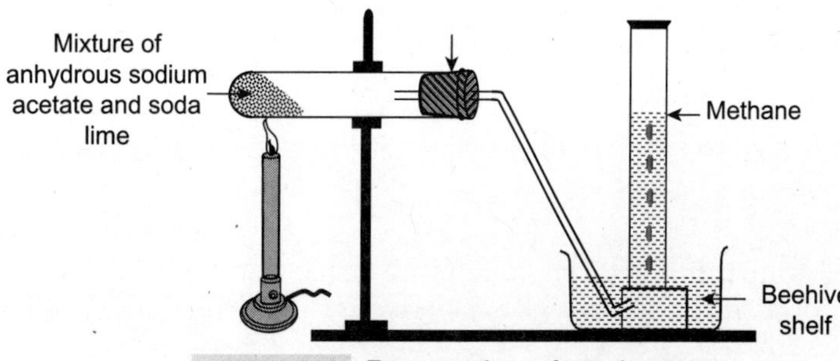

Figure 6.9 Preparation of methane

Preparation of Methane

On heating anhydrous sodium acetate (sodium salt of acetic acid) with soda lime (a mixture of sodium hydroxide and calcium oxide), methane is formed along with sodium carbonate.

$$\underset{\text{Sodium acetate}}{CH_3COONa} + NaOH \xrightarrow{\Delta} \underset{\text{Methane}}{CH_4} + Na_2CO_3$$

Methane gas produced during the reaction is collected over water by the downward displacement of water since it is lighter than air and insoluble in water.

Physical Properties

1. Methane is a colourless and odourless gas.
2. It is insoluble in water.
3. It is lighter than air.
4. It causes global warming as it is a greenhouse gas.
5. CNG which contains mainly methane can be stored in cylinders.

Chemical Properties

1. Methane on combustion burns with a blue flame giving out carbon dioxide and water:

$$CH_4 + 2O_2 \longrightarrow CO_2 + 2H_2O + \text{Energy}$$

2. Methane reacts with chlorine gas in the presence of sunlight, by displacing one, two, three or all of its hydrogen atoms:

$$CH_4 + Cl_2 \xrightarrow{\text{Sunlight}} CH_3Cl + HCl$$

$$CH_3Cl + Cl_2 \xrightarrow{\text{Sunlight}} CH_2Cl_2 + HCl$$

$$CH_2Cl_2 + Cl_2 \xrightarrow{\text{Sunlight}} CHCl_3 + HCl$$

$$CHCl_3 + Cl_2 \xrightarrow{\text{Sunlight}} CCl_4 + HCl$$

3. Methane on heating in the absence of air decomposes into carbon and hydrogen. The carbon so obtained is called **carbon black**. This reaction is called **pyrolysis** or **cracking**.

$$CH_4 \longrightarrow C + 2H_2$$

POINTS TO REMEMBER

- ✔ Allotropy is a phenomenon in which an element exhibits different physical forms with almost similar chemical properties.
- ✔ The different physical forms exhibited by the element are called allotropes.
- ✔ Diamond, graphite, and fullerene are the widely known crystalline allotropes of carbon.
- ✔ Charcoal, coke, lamp black and gas carbon are amorphous forms of carbon.
- ✔ The crushed fine powder of the animal bones if subjected to destructive distillation produces residue. This residue is called bone charcoal.
- ✔ The ability of an element to form either straight chains or branched chains is called catenation.
- ✔ The compounds containing only carbon and hydrogen are called hydrocarbons.
- ✔ Depending on the relative proportions of carbon and hydrogen, hydrocarbons are further classified into saturated and unsaturated hydrocarbons.
- ✔ Saturated hydrocarbons have larger proportions of hydrogen and have a general formula, C_nH_{2n+2}.
- ✔ Methane is the simplest member of saturated hydrocarbons with the molecular formula CH_4.
- ✔ Methane is also found in marshy places. Hence, it is commonly known as marsh gas.
- ✔ Methane, on heating in the absence of air, decomposes into carbon and hydrogen. The carbon so obtained is called carbon black. This reaction is called pyrolysis or cracking.

PRACTICE QUESTIONS CLASSROOM WING

Very Short Answer Type Questions

Direction for questions from 1 to 6:
Fill in the blanks.

1. The major component of CNG is ______.
2. ______ acid on reaction with H_2SO_4 gives only carbon monoxide gas.
3. Melting point of diamond is ______.
4. Colour is imparted to diamond due to the presence of ______.
5. The composition of lime mortar is ______.
6. The poisonous gas, phosgene is prepared from ______ and ______ gases.

Direction for questions from 7 to 25:
Answer the following questions.

7. What is the common feature between blue vitriol and washing soda?
8. Under certain conditions, when a mixture of hydrogen and chlorine was exposed to sunlight, no reaction occurred. Why?
9. When a glass full of ice is subjected to melting, the water level in the glass decreases due to an increase in density.
10. Is the collection of hydrogen by downward displacement of water related to the effect of pressure on the solubility of gases?
11. Why does, brine solution when taken in equal volumes freeze at the lowest temperature?
12. When iron metal is taken in place of zinc for the laboratory preparation of hydrogen, the volume of hydrogen collected is found to be lower. Why?
13. Mention two physical properties of methane.
14. Give the chemical properties of calcium carbide.
15. How is bone charcoal prepared?
16. Explain the structure of graphite.
17. What are fullerenes?
18. Name the purest form of charcoal.
19. Explain the reducing property of wood charcoal.
20. Mention the chemical properties of sodium carbonate.
21. Name the different allotropes of carbon.
22. How is coke formed? Give two uses of coke.
23. Write the reaction involved in the preparation of silicon carbide.
24. Mention any two physical properties of carbon dioxide.
25. Give two properties and two uses of lamp black.

Short Answer Type Questions

26. The solubility of a substance is 40 at 25°C. What amount of the substance is present in 210 g of a saturated solution of that substance at the same temperature?
27. 10 g of water obtained by melting of ice is subjected to heating. What is the amount of heat required to be supplied to this water to reach its boiling point?
28. Which type of water (Saline/Distilled) when taken in equal volumes freezes at the highest temperature and where (hill station/plains)?
29. Explain the reactivity of graphite with oxygen and sodium carbonate with chemical equations.
30. (a) What are the different products formed when methane and chlorine are made to react in the presence of sunlight?
    (b) Write the principles involved in the usage of CO_2 for the following purposes. Write the chemical reactions where applicable.
    (a) Soft drinks or aerated drinks
    (b) As a refrigerant
    (c) Baking cakes
    (d) Hardening of mortar

31. Mention the chemical properties of diamond.

32. How is methane prepared in the laboratory?

33. Write short notes on gas carbon.

34. Discuss the reactivity of carbon monoxide with metals and non-metals.

35. Explain the reactivity of carbon dioxide with metals.

36. What are the physical properties of carbon monoxide?

37. State the physical properties of diamond.

38. Give the preparation method of the following compounds:

(i) CaC_2 (ii) SiC
(iii) $CaCO_3$ (iv) Na_2CO_3
(v) $NaHCO_3$

39. Discuss three important uses of

(i) graphite (ii) wood charcoal
(iii) carbon monoxide (iv) sugar charcoal
(v) bone charcoal (vi) carbon dioxide
(vii) methane

40. Discuss the physical properties of

(i) CaC_2 (ii) SiC
(iii) $CaCO_3$ (iv) Na_2CO_3
(iv) $NaHCO_3$

Essay Answer Type Questions

41. 80 g of a saturated solution of a substance contains 16 g of the substance. What is the solubility of the substance at that temperature?

42. Explain the manufacture of graphite by Acheson process.

43. Discuss the laboratory preparation of carbon monoxide.

44. Discuss carbon cycle in nature.

45. (a) Explain the working of the two types of fire extinguishers.

(b) Explain the working principle of liquid carbon dioxide fire extinguisher.

PRACTICE QUESTIONS COMPETITION WING

Level 1: Apply Your Concepts

Directions for questions from 1 to 11:
State whether the following statements are true or false.

1. The floating of the human body in the Dead Sea is an application of anomalous expansion of water.
2. Fullerene is the amorphous allotrope of carbon.
3. Lamp black is used as filler in making rubber tyres.
4. Carbon monoxide is neither combustible nor a supporter of combustion.
5. In methane, all the hydrogen atoms can be replaced by chlorine atoms when the reaction takes place in presence of sunlight.
6. Sugar charcoal is a good reducing agent.
7. Foam type extinguisher is used to extinguish any kind of fire.
8. Carbon has no allotropes.
9. Graphite is a good conductor of electricity.
10. Lamp Black is used in the manufacture of black carbon papers.
11. Bone charcoal contains maximum percentage of inorganic matter.

Directions for questions from 12 to 18:
Fill in the blanks.

12. Crystallization of carbon to form diamonds takes place when ______________ metal expands during solidification.
13. Carbon monoxide is slightly ______ than air.
14. The compound of carbon used to soften hard water is ________.
15. ______________ acid on reaction with H_2SO_4 gives only carbon monoxide gas.
16. Methane is prepared in a laboratory by heating anhydrous sodium acetate with ______.
17. Sugar on reaction with ______________ gives sugar charcoal.
18. Gas carbon is used as ______ in dry cells.

Directions for question 19:
Match the entries in column A with the appropriate ones in Column B.

19. Match the statements of Column A with those of Column B.

	Column A (Reaction)		Column B (Observation)
(i)	Potassium + water	(a)	Yellow substance and turns to white on cooling
(ii)	Sodium + water	(b)	Brown substance
(iii)	Magnesium + boiling water	(c)	Catches fire with lilac flame
(iv)	Zinc + steam	(d)	Catches fire with yellow flame
(v)	Iron + steam	(e)	Brilliant white light and ash

Directions for questions from 20 to 42:
For each of the questions, four choices have been provided. Select the correct alternative.

20. Although all active metals liberate hydrogen gas with acids, zinc is preferentially used in the laboratory preparation of hydrogen. Various metals are not suitable for different reasons. The metals and the reasons for their non-suitability are given below. Which of the following is/are incorrectly matched?
    (a) Potassium—Violent explosion
    (b) Lead—Reversible reaction
    (c) Aluminium—Formation of protective coating
    (d) None of these

21. **Assertion (A):** Calcium sulphate shows the same solubility at two different temperatures.
    Reason (R): Water of crystallization of salt changes with a change in temperature.
    (a) Both A and R are true and R is the correct explanation of A.
    (b) Both A and R are true, but R is not the correct explanation of A.
    (c) A is true and R is false.
    (d) A is false and R is true.

22. **Assertion (A):** Glucose is highly soluble in water.
Reason (R): Water has a high value of dielectric constant.
(a) Both A and R are true and R is the correct explanation of A.
(b) Both A and R are true, but R is not the correct explanation of A.
(c) A is true and R is false.
(d) A is false and R is true.

23. **Assertion (A):** Glauber's salt shows the same solubility at two different temperatures.
Reason (R): Glauber's salt is a hydrated salt.
(a) Both A and R are true and R is the correct explanation of A.
(b) Both A and R are true, but R is not the correct explanation of A.
(c) A is true and R is false.
(d) A is false and R is true.

24. **Assertion (A):** Many ionic compounds show appreciable solubility in water.
Reason (R): Water has a high value of dielectric constant.
(a) Both A and R are true and R is the correct explanation of A.
(b) Both A and R are true, but R is not the correct explanation of A.
(c) A is true and R is false.
(d) A is false and R is true.

25. Nature of the products obtained by complete combustion of methane is
(a) acidic, basic (b) acidic, neutral
(c) basic, neutral (d) both are neutral

26. Which of the following carbonates does not decompose to give CO_2?
(a) $NaHCO_3$ (b) $CaCO_3$
(c) K_2CO_3 (d) $ZnCO_3$

27. A compound X made of two non-metals in a reaction with another non-metal Y gives the hardest substance and carbon monoxide. Identify the compound X and the non-metal Y.
(a) CO_2, Si (b) SiO_2, C
(c) SiC, O_2 (d) CO, Si

28. Which of the following allotropes of carbon is used for the manufacture of fullerenes?
(a) graphite (b) diamond
(c) coke (d) charcoal

29. Graphite cannot be used as a lubricant in space because
(a) absence of external pressure transforms crystalline graphite to amorphous form
(b) there is no atmosphere in space, and hence, graphite sublimes in space
(c) there is no atmosphere in space, and hence, there is no adsorbed air and water between layers of graphite
(d) none of the above

30. Coke can be used as
(a) an oxidizing agent
(b) a household fuel
(c) printer ink
(d) electrodes

31. In the reaction:

$$2CaO + C \longrightarrow CaC_2 + 2CO$$

$$2CaC_2 + 2H_2O \longrightarrow A + B$$

if A is involved in the neutralization reaction with acid, then B may be
(a) CH_4 (b) C_2H_2
(c) $Ca(OH)_2$ (d) CaH_2

32. Carbon occurs as the native element in the earth's crust in the form of
(a) diamond (b) methane
(c) carbon dioxide (d) gas carbon

33. Why shouldn't we light a candle in a closed room with people?
(a) The CO_2 formed causes breathlessness.
(b) Carbon particles are formed which are dangerous for respiratory tract.
(c) Methane gas, which is poisonous, is formed.
(d) Carbon monoxide gas which reduces the ability of blood to carry oxygen is formed.

34. Why do black shoe polishes have an oily feel?
(a) Shoe polish is a mixture of oil and powdered graphite.
(b) On exposure to air, these undergo chemical changes and produce oily substances.
(c) Vapour of some amount of oil is left over after its preparation.
(d) These are formed by dissolving charcoal in oil.

35. Arrange the steps in the process of carbon cycle, starting from the abundant state of existence of carbon in the combined state in their correct sequence.

(1) dead remains (2) CO_2 in atmosphere
(3) organic matter (4) plants
(5) fossil fuels
(a) 2 1 3 4 5 (b) 2 4 1 3 5
(c) 4 2 3 1 5 (d) 4 5 2 3 1

36. Arrange the steps in the process of carbon cycle starting from the substances which possess a mixture of hydrocarbons in a proper sequence.
(1) sea water (2) dead remains
(3) aquatic plants (4) CO_2 in the atmosphere
(5) organic matter (6) fossil fuels
(a) 3 1 4 5 6 2 (b) 6 3 4 1 2 5
(c) 4 1 3 2 5 6 (d) 6 4 1 3 2 5

37. Graphite fibres are used to reinforce plastic as they
(a) have weak carbon bonds
(b) have high-tensile strength
(c) are brittle
(d) have weak forces of attraction between layers

38. In the manufacture of graphite by Acheson process, the charge filled between the cathode and anode consists of
(a) powdered coke, sand and ferric oxide
(b) powdered coke
(c) sand
(d) ferric oxide

39. Arrange the different types of coal in sequence in the increasing order of the quality coal.
(1) lignite (2) peat
(3) anthracite (4) bituminous
(a) 1 3 4 2 (b) 4 2 3 1
(c) 2 1 4 3 (d) 2 3 4 1

40. Graphite is a greasy, soft lubricant because it
(a) has low density
(b) has weak forces of attraction between layers
(c) is greyish-black in colour
(d) has a three-dimensional structure

41. Arrange the given combustible substances in decreasing order of calorific value:
(1) hydrogen (2) charcoal
(3) petrol (4) LPG
(5) wood
(a) 2 3 1 4 5 (b) 1 4 3 2 5
(c) 2 1 4 5 3 (d) 2 1 3 5 4

42. Graphite is used in a nuclear reactor as
(a) a moderator (b) a fuel
(c) an electrode (d) a lubricant

Level 2: Review Your Concepts

43. What are the maximum amounts of 'X' and 'Y' that can be precipitated during the process?

44. Two substances 'X' and 'Y' are exposed to air for a long time. X forms an anhydrous salt, whereas Y forms a monohydrate and on heating, its anhydrous salt is obtained. Identify X and Y.

45. 2.1 kJ of heat is supplied to 100 g of water. What would be the expected increase in the temperature of water?

46. Identify the amounts of 'X' and 'Y' precipitated when the solutions are cooled up to 60°C.

47. Burning more and more fossil fuels creates an imbalance in the natural carbon cycle as well as in the natural water cycle. Give reasons.

48. Carbon monoxide gas can be detected by passing it through a blood sample. Explain.

49. A building constructed from mortar becomes stronger on long standing. Give a reason.

50. Why is CNG replacing petrol as an automobile fuel?

51. Dry ice should not be stored in a sealed bottle. Explain with an appropriate reason.

52. Two non-metal atoms contain the same number of electrons in their valence shells. One of the non-metals in its most abundant form reacts with the other non-metal forming a very stable compound A. Compound A on reaction with oxygen and fused sodium hydroxide gives two products B and C. B is used as a raw material for the manufacture of glass and C is the major constituent of glass. Identify A, B and C. Write balanced chemical equations for the above reactions.

53. Burning more and more fossil fuels creates an imbalance in the natural carbon cycle as well as in the natural water cycle. Give reasons.

54. Tiny diamonds find applications in coating the tips and edges of cutting tools. Which properties of diamonds are made use of for this purpose?

55. Explain the role of baking soda as a leavening agent and as an antacid?

56. An oxide of a bivalent metal on heating with coke gives a compound X and a gas Y. The gas Y reacts with chlorine gas to give a poisonous gaseous compound. X undergoes hydrolysis to give a hydrocarbon Z with two carbon atoms. Identify the compounds X, Y and Z. Also, give the reactions involved.

57. Graphite is used as a solid lubricant. Give reasons.

58. How does a dry powder type fire extinguisher work?

59. A naturally occurring mineral of sedimentary rocks on heating to high temperatures decomposes giving a solid A and a gas. The solid on dissolution in water undergoes chemical reaction which is associated with hissing sound and the solution appears to be boiling. Compound B formed during this reaction on long standing forms a layer of white powder. When excess CO_2 is passed through this milky white solution, a clear solution is formed again. Identify the substances and justify the above observations. Give reasons wherever required.

60. In the manufacture of silicon carbide by Acheson process, sawdust is used along with sand and coke in the electric furnace. What is the main purpose of using sawdust as one of the constituents of the mixture?

61. The genuineness of a pearl can be verified by dipping it in lemon juice. Why?

62. (a) Why does fogging occur while using a soda acid fire extinguisher?

(b) With what material are pencil leads made of? Justify its usage and also explain why it is called 'lead'. Also explain why different pencils give different shades of darkness?

63. Why is wood charcoal considered to be an excellent household fuel?

64. Two compounds X and Y, when dissolved in water, produced sodium bicarbonate. If hydrochloric acid is added to compound X, compound Y is liberated. Identify X and Y.

65. A student of VIII class broke a dry cell to examine its parts and correlate them with his teacher's explanations about dry cells. In the chemistry class, the student asked his teacher that though graphite is a non-metal, why is it used as electrodes in the electrolytic process, especially where a high temperature is maintained. Write down the explanation the teacher gave to the student.

66. Sam and his family went to watch a Hollywood movie in which the hero along with his friends rescues 76 people trapped in mines where poisonous gas was being released. During the process, gas masks containing wood charcoal were given to the people. In the movie the hero and his friends were research students in the nearby university. Sam asked his scientist father regarding the role of wood charcoal in gas masks. Write the scientist's explanation in this regard.

67. An eleven-year old naughty boy Krish took keys of his father's car without his father's permission. He went inside the garage, closed it and started the ignition. After a few minutes, he started coughing. His father fortunately went into the garage, opened it, immediately brought him out and rescued him. Krish's mother asked her husband the reason for Krish's condition. What explanation did the father give?

Level 3: Assess Your Concepts

68. Which of the following changes will require the highest energy? Specific heat of ice = 0.5 cal/g/°C and specific heat of water vapour = 0.9 cal/g/°C

(a) 100 g ice into water at 30°C

(b) 50 g boiling water into water at 120°C

(c) 100 g boiling water into water vapour at 100°C

(d) 50 g ice into water at 0°C

69. (a) Wood charcoal floats on water, but if it is boiled in water it sinks. Explain with appropriate reasons.

(b) Diamonds when taken out from mines appear as black chunks of charcoal. However, the diamonds studded in jewellery sparkle brilliantly and hence considered to be the most precious gem stones. How do you account for the uniqueness of diamonds among all the gem stones?

70. Compare and contrast the principle involved in the usage of $NaHCO_3$ and dry ice for cleaning industrial equipment by blasting the given substances with compressed air.

71. Why is molten iron used in the preparation of artificial diamond?

72. What is the advantage of liquid CO_2 fire extinguisher over soda–acid fire extinguisher? Explain.

73. Though coke is made from coal, it is used for metallurgical processes instead of coal. Give reasons.

74. Draw a comparison among petrol, LPG and CNG as automobile fuels.

75. Compare and contrast the principle involved in the usage of $NaHCO_3$ and dry ice for cleaning industrial equipment by blasting the given substances with compressed air.

76. Pinku and Rinku are TIME IIT-F students. They went to a jewellery shop with their mother. They were delighted to see the lustrous gold ornaments. Pinku peeped through the showcase to see a diamond necklace and told Rinku—Really, the glitterance of diamonds is incomparable to the lustre of gold! Rinku complained that their chemistry teacher explained the lustre of metals in detail but didn't mention about diamonds at all. They both decided to ask their chemistry teacher the next day. What explanation will the teacher give?

77. Ocean acidification due to the disposal of industrial waste has a negative effect on oceanic calcifying organisms. Why?

AT

PRACTICE QUESTIONS JEE-NEET SPECIAL WING

Multiple-Answer Type Questions

Directions for questions 1 to 5:

Select one or more correct alternative(s) from the given choices.

1. Identify the purposes to which sugar charcoal is put to use in industries.
   (a) Purification of sugar
   (b) Reducing agent
   (c) Gas masks
   (d) Synthesis of artificial diamonds

2. A gaseous product is obtained by passing CO_2 gas through red hot charcoal. Which among the following statements comply with this product?
   (a) The gas cannot be collected by downward displacement of water
   (b) The entire process of preparation is carried out in fume chamber
   (c) This gas is a common component of water gas and producer gas
   (d) The reaction involved in the above preparation is endothermic

3. Identify the electronic configurations of metals which form carbonates which on strong heating liberate a gas that reacts with aqueous potassium hydroxide solution.

	Electronic configuration
(a)	2, 8, 18, 2
(b)	2, 8, 8, 1
(c)	2, 8, 18, 1
(d)	2, 8, 13, 2

4. Some metals react with carbon monoxide to form metal carbonyls of different formulae. Identify the correctly matched sets among the following.

Metal	Electronic configuration
(a) Ni	$M(CO)_4$
(b) Cr	$M(CO)_6$
(c) Fe	$M(CO)_5$
(d) Zn	$M(CO)_7$

5. Identify the correct match with respect to the major constituents of the respective industrially useful materials.

	Useful material	Major constituent
(a)	LPG	Ethane
(b)	Phosgene	Carbonyl chloride
(c)	Carbogen	Oxygen
(d)	CNG	Methane

Comprehension-Based Questions

Directions for questions 6 to 12:

Read the content given in the following passage and answer the questions given below.

The ability of carbon to form long chains known as catenation is responsible for the formation of innumerable number of compounds by this element in combination with few other elements. These are known as organic compounds. The organic compounds which possess only carbon and hydrogen are known as hydrocarbons. The hydrocarbons can be categorised into various types. The hydrocarbons with only single bonds are called saturated hydrocarbons. The hydrocarbons with a double bond between any two of the carbon atoms are known as alkenes. The hydrocarbons with a triple bond between any two of the carbon atoms are known as alkynes. Alkenes and alkynes are together known as unsaturated hydrocarbons. The alkanes, alkenes and alkynes are represented by a general formula C_nH_{2n+2}; C_nH_{2n} and C_nH_{2n-2} respectively. The alkanes with cyclic or ring structures are called cycloalkanes which possess the same general formula as alkenes. The other classes of organic compounds can be obtained by replacing the hydrogen by another atom or group of atoms. The series of compounds with progressively increasing number of carbon atoms is known as homologous series. In any class of compounds, the successive members of a homologous series differ by a unit of $-CH_2$.

6. The molecular mass of a hydrocarbon is 40. What should be the molecular formula of the succeeding homologue of that compound?
(a) C_3H_4 (b) C_3H_6
(c) C_4H_6 (d) C_4H_{10}

7. The percentage of carbon increases by 5% in the successive members of homologous series. Identify the pair of homologues among the following.
(a) Ethyne; Propyne (b) Methane; Ethane
(c) Ethene : Propene (d) Propane; Butane

8. The alkanes can be prepared by treating the sodium salt of the carboxylic acid with soda lime. In this reaction, a molecule of carbon dioxide is eliminated from the carboxylic acid. Predict the molecular mass of carboxylic acid which should be taken to prepare second member of alkanes.
(a) 60 (b) 46
(c) 88 (d) 74

9. Identify the hydrocarbon which has the same molecular formula as the first member of cycloalkanes.
(a) Propene (b) Propane
(c) Ethene (d) Butene

10. The gram molecular mass of an alkane is 58. What should be the molecular mass of the compound in which one of the hydrogens is replaced by -OH group?
(a) 74 (b) 72
(c) 68 (d) 60

11. Identify the wrongly matched set among the following.

Description	Molecular mass
(a) 3rd homologue of alkynes	54
(b) 4th homologue of alkenes	56
(c) 3rd homologue of alkanes	44
(d) 2nd homologue of alkynes	40

12. Match the entries in column I with those in column II.

Column I Description of hydrocarbon		Column II Ratio of carbon and hydrogen
(a) Alkane with 2 carbons	(i)	8:1
(b) Alkene with 3 carbons	(ii)	12:1
(c) Alkyne with 4 carbons	(iii)	5:1
(d) Alkane with 5 carbons	(iv)	6:1
(e) Alkyne with 2 carbons	(v)	4:1

Directions for questions 13 to 17:

Read the content given in the following passage and answer the questions given below.

Fire extinguisher is an amazing equipment which prevents the destruction of lives and property at the time of fire accidents. We observe that generally fire engines reach the site of the accident and use water propelled with great force to put of the fire. But this is not suitable for all kinds of fires. The fire extinguishers are of different types. That is why different types of fire extinguishers are available which work with different mechanisms. The appropriate type of extinguisher is used for the fire depending on the source of fire. For example, the fires caused mostly by paper or wood or such kind of material can be controlled by water. In all other types of extinguishers, carbon dioxide acts as the extinguishing material.

The schematic diagrams of the different types of extinguishers are given below.

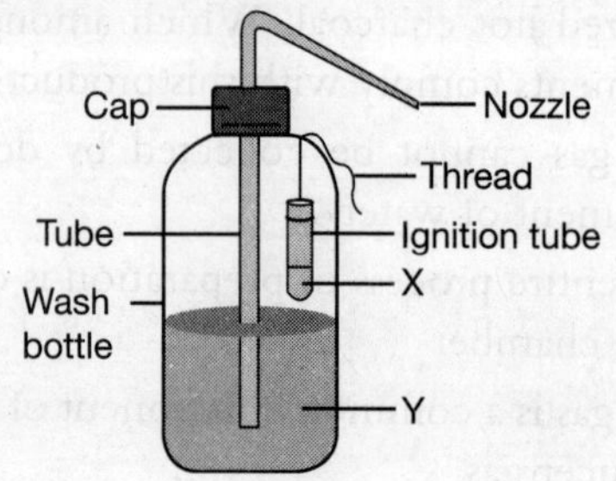

A

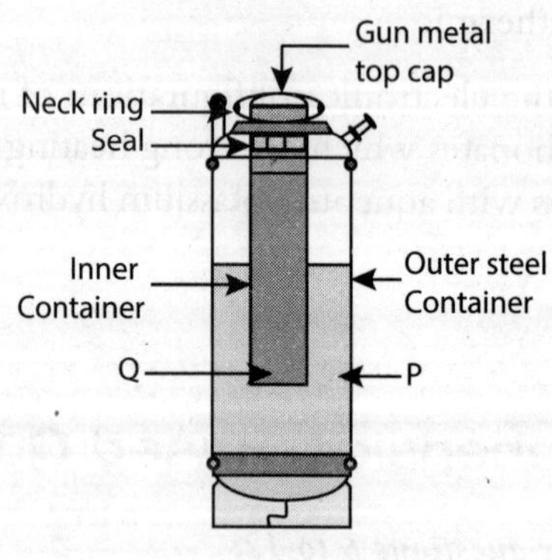

B

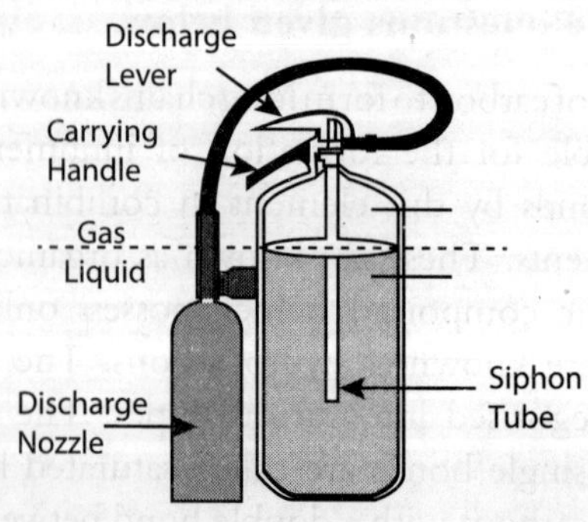

C

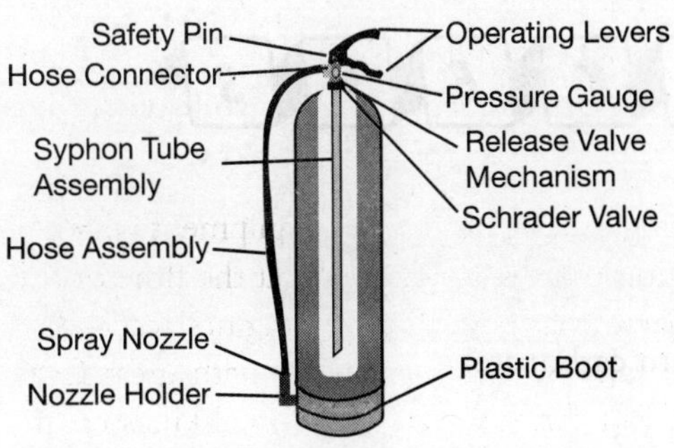

D

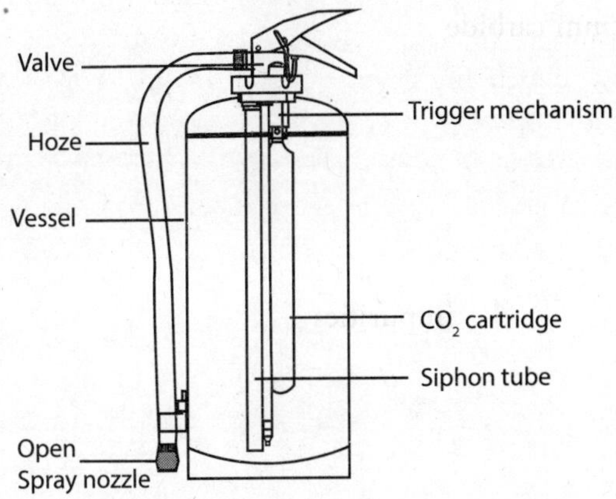

E

13. **Assertion (A):** Water cannot be used for extinguishing fires caused by petrol.

Reason (R): Petrol and water are miscible liquids

(a) Both A and R are correct, and R is the correct explanation of A

(b) Both A and R are correct, and R is not the correct explanation of A

(c) A is correct and R is wrong

(d) R is correct and A is wrong

14. In the extinguisher indicated by 'A' two substances are taken which when come in contact with each other produce a gas which extinguishes fire. The substance indicated by 'Y' is sulphuric acid. Identify the substance 'X'.

(a) Calcium carbonate (b) Sodium bicarbonate

(c) Carbonic acid (d) Liquid CO_2

15. Identify the type of extinguishers suitable for extinguishing fires caused by electrical equipment.

(a) A; D (b) E; D

(c) B; C (d) C; E

16. Identify the extinguishers suitable for extinguishing fires caused by petrol or such flammable liquids.

(a) B (b) C

(c) E (d) All of these

17. Gases when subjected to sudden expansion, produce cooling and results in lowering temperature thereby facilitating the liquefaction of the gas taken. Working of which among the following fire extinguishers is based on this principle?

(a) D (b) C

(c) E (d) B

Match the Column

18. Study the following diagram of carbon cycle given and match the entries in column I with those in column II.

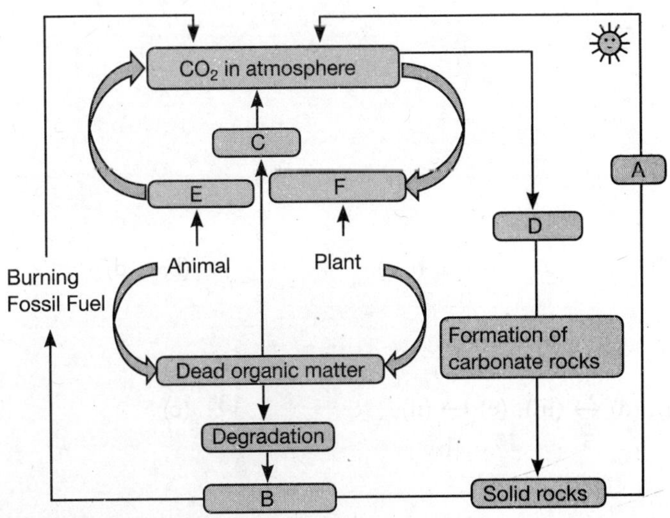

Column I		Column II	
(a)	A	(i)	Oceans
(b)	B	(ii)	Respiration
(c)	C	(iii)	Photosynthesis
(d)	D	(iv)	Volcanoes
(e)	E	(v)	Fossil fuels
(f)	F	(vi)	Decomposition

ANSWER KEYS

Crossword

Across

3. Sugar charcoal 7. Dry ice 8. Calcium carbonate
9. Diamond 10. Pyrolysis

Down

1. Carbon monoxide 2. Carboxyhaemoglobin 4. Calcium carbide
5. Silicon carbide 6. Graphite

Classroom Wing

Very Short Answer Type Questions

1. methane 2. formic 3. 3700°C 4. impurities
5. $Ca(OH)_2$ + Sand + water 6. CO and Cl_2

Competition Wing

Level 1: Apply Your Concepts

1. False 2. False 3. True 4. False 5. True
6. True 7. False 8. False 9. True 10. True
11. False 12. iron 13. lighter 14. Na_2CO_3 15. formic
16. soda lime 17. conc. H_2SO_4 18. electrodes
19. (i) → (C), (ii) → (D), (iii) → (E), (iv) → (A), (v) → (B) 20. (b) 21. (b)
22. (b) 23. (b) 24. (a) 25. (b) 26. (c)
27. (b) 28. (a) 29. (c) 30. (b) 31. (b)
32. (a) 33. (d) 34. (c) 35. (b) 36. (d)
37. (b) 38. (a) 39. (c)
40. (b) 41. (b) 42. (a)

JEE-NEET Special Wing

Multiple-Answer Type Questions

1. (a, d) 2. (b, c, d) 3. (a, c, d) 4. (a, b, c) 5. (b, c, d)

Comprehension-Based Questions

6. (c) 7. (b) 8. (d) 9. (a) 10. (a)
11. (b) 12. (a) ↔ (v), (b) ↔ (iv), (c) ↔ (i), (d) ↔ (iii), (e) ↔ (ii) 13. (c)
14. (b) 15. (d) 16. (d) 17. (b)

Match the Column

18. (a) ↔ (iv), (b) ↔ (v), (c) ↔ (vi), (d) ↔ (i), (e) ↔ (ii), (f) ↔ (iii)

Hints and Explanations

CLASSROOM WING

Very Short Answer Type Questions

1. methane
2. formic
3. 3700°C
4. impurities
5. $Ca(OH)_2$ + Sand + water
6. CO and Cl_2
7. The formulae of blue vitriol and washing soda are $CuSO_4\ 5H_2O$ and $Na_2CO_3\ 10H_2O$, respectively. Both of them possess water of crystallization.
8. Moisture catalyses the reaction between hydrogen and chlorine to form hydrogen chloride. Therefore, no reaction takes place between dry hydrogen and chlorine even in the presence of diffuse or intense sunlight
9. When a glass full of ice is subjected to melting, the water level in the glass will be lower than the ice. This is because ice has a lower density than water and occupies a greater volume than water. The water formed is denser than ice and occupies a lesser volume.
10. No. The collection of hydrogen by the downward displacement of water is due to the insoluble nature of hydrogen in water.
11. As brine solution is a saturated solution of sodium chloride, it contains the maximum amount of dissolved salt and hence, freezes at the lowest temperature.
12. When iron is taken in place of zinc for the laboratory preparation of hydrogen, the reaction becomes slow and yields only a lesser volume of hydrogen as the reaction of iron with acid becomes reversible.
13. colourless, odourless insoluble in water and lighter than air
14. (i) Hydrolysis of CaC_2:

$$CaC_2 + 2H_2O \longrightarrow Ca(OH)_2 + C_2H_2$$

(ii) $CaC_2 + N_2 \longrightarrow \underset{\text{Nitrolim}}{Ca(CN)_2} + C$

(iii) $3MgO + CaC_2 \longrightarrow 3Mg + CuO + 2\ CO\uparrow$

15. destructive distillation of animal bones
16. layered structure of hexagonal rings arranged parallel to each other
17. crystalline allotrope of carbon, C_{60}, C_{70} up to C_{350} with hexagonal and pentagonal rings with football structure
18. sugar charcoal
19. When wood charcoal is heated with oxides of less active metals, they get reduced to free metals.
20. (i) $Na_2CO_3 + 2H_2O \longrightarrow H_2\ CO_3 + 2NaOH$

    (ii) reacts with metal salts to form insoluble basic carbonates
21. Crystalline: diamond, graphite and fullerene. Amorphous: charcoal, coke, lampblack and gas carbon.
22. Destructive distillation of coal. Fuel, reducing agent, manufacture of graphite, CaC_2, water gas and producer gas.
23. $SiO_2 + 3C \longrightarrow SiC + 2CO\uparrow$
24. highly soluble in water, heavier than air
25. Light, powdery black, having a velvet touch. Manufacture of black carbon papers, carbon ribbons and black shoe polish.

Short Answer Type Questions

26. Solubility = 40

    Mass of saturated solution = 210 g

    140 g of solution → 40 g of substance

    210 g of solution → ______ 60 g
27. 1 g of water requires 4.2 J of heat for a rise in the temperature by 1°C. 10 g of water requires 42 J of heat for the same rise in temperature. For reaching the boiling point (100°C), 4200 J or 4.2 kJ of heat is required.
28. The presence of dissolved salts decreases the freezing point of water. Distilled water freezes at a higher temperature than saline water. An increase in pressure decreases the freezing point. As pressure is low at higher

altitudes, the water freezes at a higher temperature at hill stations than on plains.

29. $3C + 2O_2 \rightarrow CO_2 + 2CO + H_2O + \Delta Q$;

$Na_2CO_3 + C \rightarrow Na_2O + 2CO$

30. (a) Methane reacts with chlorine gas in the presence of sunlight, by displacing one, two, three or all of its hydrogen atoms:

$CH_4 + Cl_2 \rightarrow CH_3Cl + HCl$

$CH_3Cl + Cl_2 \rightarrow CH_2Cl_2 + HCl$

$CH_2Cl_2 + Cl_2 \rightarrow CHCl_3 + HCl$

$CHCl_3 + Cl_2 \rightarrow CCl_4 + HCl$

(b) (a) CO_2 is dissolved at high pressure in soft drinks or aerated drinks. This imparts tangy taste to the beverages due to the formation of carbonic acid.

$CO_2 + H_2O \rightarrow H_2CO_3$

(b) CO_2 in the form of dry ice is used as a refrigerant as it produces a very low temperature of –20°C due to the sublimation of dry ice under normal conditions.

(c) Sodium bicarbonate is used as an additive to the dough for making cakes. During the process of baking, it decomposes to give CO_2 which makes the dough rise and imparts puffiness to the dough.

(d) Mortar is a mixture of lime and sand. Lime or calcium hydroxide absorbs atmospheric CO_2 to form $CaCO_3$. This results in hardening of mortar.

$Ca(OH)_2 + CO_2 \rightarrow CaCO_3 + H_2O$.

31. (i) reaction with O_2
(ii) reaction with sodium carbonate

32. (i) reactants
(ii) conditions
(iii) collection

33. Gas carbon can be prepared by destructive distillation of coal. The thermal vaporisation of small amounts of carbon from coal on condensation produces a grey solid. This grey solid obtained is called gas carbon.

34. Reaction of CO with metals: When CO gas is passed over the finely divided metals like nickel, chromium and iron, metal carbonyls are formed.

Reaction of CO with non- metals: Reaction with oxygen gives CO_2 gas and reaction with Cl_2 gas gives phosgene.

35. Reaction of metals with carbon dioxide Na, K and Ca combine with CO_2 to form their respective carbonates along with carbon, whereas Mg and Al give their respective oxides and carbon.

36. (i) colour
(ii) smell
(iii) vapour density
(iv) solubility
(v) litmus test
(vi) nature

37. (i) colour
(ii) density
(iii) refractive index
(iv) conduction of heat and electricity

38. (i) Calcium carbide is prepared by heating pulverized calcium oxide and coke.
(ii) SiC is produced by heating silicon dioxide and coke in an electric furnace.
(iii) $CaCO_3$ is prepared by passing CO_2 into a solution of calcium hydroxide, calcium carbonate precipitates out.
(iv) Na_2CO_3: It is prepared by heating carbonic acid with NaOH.
(v) $NaHCO_3$ is formed when NaOH reacts with carbonic acid.

39. (i) leads of pencils, moderator in nuclear reactors, making refractory crucibles
(ii) deodorant and disinfectant, gas masks, fuel for keeping rooms warm in winter
(iii) reducing agent in the extraction of metals, manufacture of chemicals, fuel
(iv) extracting metals from their oxides, adsorbent material, making artificial diamonds
(v) Removes colour from sugarcane juice, extraction of yellow phosphorous, fertilizer industry
(vi) Soft drinks or aerated drinks, fire extinguishers, production of industrial compounds
(vii) fuel, parent hydrocarbon for halogenation reactions, water gas preparation

40. (i) greyish black crystalline solid, melting point of 2300°C, non-conductor of electricity

(ii) insoluble in H_2O, density of 3.22 g/cm^3, hard substance, melting point of 2700°C

(iii) white crystalline solid with melting point of 825°C, insoluble in H_2O

(iv) white crystalline solid with melting point of 851°C, insoluble in H_2O

(v) white crystalline, sparingly soluble in water

Essay Answer Type Questions

41. Mass of the solution = 80 g

Mass of solute = 16 g

Mass of solvent = 80 – 16 = 64 g

Amount of substance dissolved in 64 g water = 16 g

Amount of substance dissolved in 100 g = $\frac{1600}{64}$ = 25 g

Solubility of the substance = 25

42. The raw material taken for the manufacture of graphite is a mixture of powdered coke, sand and ferric oxide along with saw dust. This mixture is filled in an electric furnace lined inside with fire clay bricks. The carbon rods act as a cathode and an anode in the furnace. These rods are inserted in such a way that they are held in contact with each other through the particles of coke, which is commonly called coke bed. The mixture is covered with a layer of sand and coke on the top so as to cut off the entry of air into it. When an electric current is passed through the electrodes, the temperature of the furnace increases to 3500°C. The coke bed connecting the two electrodes offers large resistance to the flow of electricity. When the current is allowed to pass through the reaction mixture for a period of 30 hours, the following reactions take place with the formation of graphite.

$$SiO_2 + 3C \rightarrow SiC + 2CO$$

$$SiC \rightarrow Si + C$$

43. When CO_2 gas is passed over red hot charcoal, charcoal gets oxidized and forms carbon monoxide. This is a highly endothermic reaction. Powdered charcoal is taken in a hard glass test tube and is heated. Then, carbon dioxide gas is passed over this. CO_2 gas oxidizes carbon and turns it into carbon monoxide.

44. Atmosphere acts as a reservoir of carbon dioxide. Plants make use of this gas for the process of photosynthesis, thereby producing carbohydrates. These carbohydrates, being the sources of energy, are consumed by animals. During the process of respiration, they break down and carbon dioxide gas is released back into the atmosphere. Apart from this, a major part of the food taken up by the animals is also assimilated into the basic organ systems of living beings. The decomposition of the dead organic matter also results in the release of CO_2 into the atmosphere. Some proportion of CO_2 gets dissolved in sea water, which is used up by the aquatic plants. The degradation of the dead aquatic plants and animals over a long period of time under specific conditions results in the formation of fossil fuels, like, coal and petroleum. Further the burning of these fossil fuels releases CO_2 into the atmosphere.

45. (a) Soda acid fire extinguisher and Foam type extinguisher. Soda acid fire extinguisher consists of a metallic cylinder filled with a solution of sodium bicarbonate. At the bottom of the cylinder, a thin sealed glass tube containing concentrated sulphuric acid is placed. This tube is surrounded by a fixed wire gauze cage. A plunger with a sharp end is placed at the bottom of the cylinder in such a way that the sharp end is placed at the sealed thin glass tube, as shown in the above figure. On the top of the cylinder, a nozzle which is sealed with wax is provided. Foam type extinguisher is used to extinguish fire caused by inflammable liquids, such as, petrol, alcohol, diesel, etc. The construction and working of the extinguisher is similar to that of soda acid fire extinguisher. However, the solution of sodium bicarbonate contains saponin (a material which produces lot of foam). Sulphuric acid is replaced by aluminium sulphate solution.

(b) Liquid CO_2 fire extinguisher contains CO_2 at very high pressure in a cylinder fitted with a nozzle. A valve fitted to the cylinder controls the outflow of CO_2. At such high pressure, CO_2 is maintained in liquid form. When the valve is opened, the gas come out of the nozzle. As it is coming out from high pressure region, it undergoes sudden and enormous expansion. CO_2 being heavier, drives away the air containing oxygen. Thus, by removing the supporter of combustion from the combustible material, the fire can be put off. Sudden expansion of CO_2 causes considerable reduction in the temperature of the surroundings. This results in the cooling down of the combustible material.

Competition Wing

Level 1: Apply Your Concepts

1. Floating of dead bodies in the water in the Dead Sea is due to the greater density of water in Dead Sea due to the very high salinity of that water. This is not a consequence of the anomalous expansion of water.

19. (i) → (C), $K \rightarrow H_2O \rightarrow KOH + H_2 \Rightarrow$ Catches fire with lilac flame
(ii) → (D), $Na + H_2O \rightarrow NaOH + H_2 \Rightarrow$ Catches fire with yellow flame
(iii) → (E); $Mg + H_2O \rightarrow Mg(OH)_2 + H_2 \Rightarrow$ Brilliant white light and white ash
(iv) → (A); $Zn + H_2O \rightarrow ZnO + H_2 \Rightarrow$ Yellow substance and turns to white on cooling
(v) → (B); $Fe + H_2O \rightarrow Fe_2O_3 + H_2 \Rightarrow$ Brown substance

20. Lead is not a preferred metal for the laboratory preparation of hydrogen because of the formation of insoluble $PbCl_2$ or $PbSO_4$, which stops the further reaction.
Hence, the only (b) is incorrectly matched.

21. Solubility of calcium sulphate first increases and then decreases with temperature. Therefore, it shows the same solubility at two different temperatures.
Hence, the correct option is (b).

22. Glucose is not an inorganic compound. Its high solubility in water is not due to the high dielectric constant.
Hence, the correct option is (b).

23. Glauber's salt is $Na_2SO_4.10H_2O$. Its solubility increases with an increase in temperature. At 32.6°C, it changes to anhydrous Na_2SO_4. Its solubility decreases with an increase in temperature. Change in water of crystallization is not the reason for a change in the trend of solubility.
Hence, the correct option is (b).

24. Due to the high value of the dielectric constant of water, water can break the forces of attraction between the oppositely charged ions. Therefore, many ionic compounds are highly soluble in water.
Hence, the correct option is (a).

35. (i) CO_2 in the atmosphere
(ii) plants
(iii) dead remains
(iv) organic matter
(v) fossil fuels

Hence, correct option is (b).

36. (i) fossil fuels
(ii) CO_2 in the atmosphere
(iii) sea water
(iv) aquatic plants
(v) dead remains
(vi) organic matter

Hence, correct option is (d).

37. Graphite fibres are used to reinforce plastic as they have high-tensile strength.
Hence, correct option is (b).

38. In the manufacture of graphite by Acheson process, the charge filled between the cathode and anode consists of powdered coke, sand and ferric oxide.
Hence, correct option is (a).

39. (2) peat
(1) lignite
(4) bituminous
(3) anthracite
Hence, correct option is (c).

40. Graphite is a greasy and soft lubricant because it has weak forces of attraction between layers.
Hence, correct option is (b).

41. (1) hydrogen
(4) LPG
(3) petrol
(2) charcoal
(5) wood
Hence, correct option is (b).

42. Graphite is used in a nuclear reactor as a moderator.
Hence, correct option is (a).

Level 2: Review Your Concepts

43. At 0°C, the solubilities of X and Y are 20 and 10, respectively. That means, 20 g of X and 10 g of Y will be left behind in the solution even at 0°C. Therefore, out of 50 g of the substances in the solution taken at 80°C, 30 g of X and 40 g of Y can be precipitated.

44. Glauber's salt and washing soda are efflorescent substances. On exposure to air, Glauber's salt loses water of crystallization completely and forms an anhydrous salt. However, washing soda loses only 9 water molecules and forms a monohydrate. Only on heating, it forms anhydrous salt.

45. 4.2 J of heat is required for 1 g of water for 1°C rise in temperature. 100 g of water requires 420 J of heat.
420 J of heat → 1°C
2.1 → 103 J of heat → $2 \times 10^3/420 = 5$°C

46. The solutions of X and Y contain 90 g and 70 g of solutes at 80°C as they are saturated solutions. When they are cooled up to 60°C, 20 g of X and 10 g of Y are precipitated since their solubilities are 70 and 50 at 60°C.

47. (i) products of combustion of fuels
(ii) effect of products formed on environment
(iii) reactivity of products with rain water
(iv) effect on carbon and water cycle

48. (i) interaction between carbon monoxide and haemoglobin
(ii) reaction of CO with O_2 carrier in blood
(iii) product formed
(iv) colour of the product formed

49. (i) constituents of mortar
(ii) purpose of mortar in construction
(iii) reaction between one of the components present in mortar with the component present in air
(iv) the percentage abundance of the above component present in air
(v) relation between the availability of the reactant and the time taken for the reaction

50. (i) chemical composition of CNG
(ii) energy released per unit mass due to the burning of the major component of CNG
(iii) the products formed during burning of CNG
(iv) effect of these products on the atmosphere

51. (i) properties of dry ice
(ii) change in dry ice at normal temperature and pressure conditions
(iii) comparison of volume before and after the change

52. (i) raw material used in the manufacture of glass and the major constituent of glass
(ii) identification of B and C
(iii) identification of A based on the composition of B and C

53. (i) products of combustion of fuels
(ii) effect of products formed on environment
(iii) reactivity of products with rain water
(iv) effect on carbon and water cycles

54. (i) properties of cutting tools
(ii) characteristics of tools used for cutting
(iii) arrangement of atoms in diamond

55. (i) chemical property of baking soda
(ii) reaction of baking soda with other components present in baking powder
(iii) physical state of the products formed
(iv) effect of the physical state of the product on bakery products
(v) reaction of baking soda with the excess acid produced in the stomach
(vi) nature of the reaction

56. (i) identification of hydrocarbons
(ii) identification of metal which gives hydrocarbon with two carbon atoms on hydrolysis
(iii) products formed on reaction of metal oxide with coke
(iv) reaction of gaseous product with chlorine

57. (i) properties of lubricants
(ii) structure of graphite
(iii) bonding in graphite
(iv) melting point of graphite

58. A mixture of sand and sodium bicarbonate can be used to put off the burning material. The heat released from the burning material decomposes sodium bicarbonate and the carbon dioxide produced being heavier than air puts off the flame.

$$2NaHCO_3 \rightarrow Na_2CO_3 + H_2O + CO_2$$

59. Limestone is the naturally occurring mineral in sedimentary rocks. This contains calcium carbonate which on decomposition at high temperature gives solid CaO and CO_2.
CaO on reaction with water forms $Ca(OH)_2$. This is a highly exothermic reaction and CO_2 gas is evolved during this reaction. Therefore, the solution appears to be boiling and is associated with a hissing sound. On long exposure to air, this reacts with atmospheric CO_2 to form $CaCO_3$ as a white-powdered layer. On passing excess CO_2, $CaCO_3$ reacts with this forming soluble calcium bicarbonate. Therefore, a clear solution is formed again.

60. Sawdust used in the charge increases its porosity. The increase in porosity allows a continuous escape of car-

bon monoxide that burns at the top of the charge. It also prevents heat loss.

61. Real pearl is nothing but calcium carbonate which gives effervescence of carbon dioxide when dipped in citric acid present in lemon juice. But imitation pearl is made up of plastic which does not give out carbon dioxide with lemon juice.

62. (a) Carbon dioxide comes out with great force through a small nozzle from soda acid fire extinguisher. This reduces the temperature of the carbon dioxide to a great extent and moisture present in air condenses on the carbon dioxide molecules and appears like fog.

(b) Pencil leads are made of graphite. In the layer lattice structure of graphite, the layers are bound by weak vanderwaal's force of attraction. Application of slight pressure makes the graphite layer to come out layer by layer and form an impression on paper. Therefore, a mixture of graphite and clay is used to make pencil leads. Because they resemble the metal lead in colour and lustre, they are called pencil leads. Because of this resemblance, graphite when discovered was thought to be a form of metal lead and was named Plumbago. Moreover, before pencil was invented, the ancient Romans used stylus which was made of lead. Clay is mixed with graphite for making pencil lead as clay acts as binding material. The shade of a pencil depends on the relative proportions of graphite and clay. The pencils with greater proportion of graphite and lesser proportion of clay are called 'B' pencils (Black). The pencils with lesser proportion of graphite and greater proportion of clay are called 'H' pencils (Hard). HB (Hard Black) pencil has moderate proportions of graphite and clay. **70.** When wood burns, most of the gases and tars present in wood vaporize and charcoal remains. Charcoal is almost 100% carbon and burns with a red glow and leaves very little flame or smoke. Charcoal is a good fuel that burns easily and cleanly in the presence of adequate supply of air.

64. $X + Y + H_2O \rightarrow NaHCO_3$

$$X + HCl \rightarrow Y$$

X should be the carbonate of sodium which produces bicarbonate; secondly, X on reaction with acids like HCl produces CO_2, hence, Y is CO_2. The reaction is

$$\underset{(X)}{Na_2CO_3} + \underset{(Y)}{CO_2} + H_2O \rightarrow 2NaHCO_3$$

65. Graphite is a good conductor of electricity and it is inert to most of the electrolytes. It has a very high-thermal resistivity. Due to these properties, graphite is used in making electrodes in the process of electrolysis.

66. Wood charcoal has a good adsorbing capacity. In areas where the inhaled air contains harmful gases, gas masks containing wood charcoal are used to adsorb these gases. The charcoal in the gas masks adsorbs these gases and the pure air enters the respiratory track.

67. The burning of a fuel takes place while starting a car. If the fuel is burnt in a closed system, incomplete combustion takes place resulting in the formation of CO due to an inadequate supply of air. CO is very harmful for health because of the formation of carboxyhaemoglobin.

Level 3: Assess Your Concepts

68. (a) 100 g ice → water at 0°C

$q_1 = 100 \times 80 = 8000$ cal

Water at 0°C → water at 30°C

$q_2 = 100 \times 1 \times 30 = 3000$ cal

$Q = q_1 + q_2 = 8000 + 3000 = 11000$ cal

(b) 50 g boiling water → water vapour at 100°C

$q_1 = 50 \times 540 = 27{,}000$ cal

Water vapour at 100°C → water vapour at 120°C

$q_2 = 50 \times 0.9 \times 20 = 900$ cal

$Q = q_1 + q_2 = 27{,}000 + 900 = 27{,}900$ cal

(c) 100 g boiling water → water vapour at 100°C

$q = 100 \times 540 = 54{,}000$ cal

(d) 50 g ice → water at 0°C

$q = 50 \times 80 = 4000$ cal

(d) Change will require the highest energy.

69. (a) (i) physical properties of wood charcoal

(ii) principle of floating

(iii) factors affecting density

(iv) relation between temperature and kinetic energy of gases

(b) In diamond, one carbon atom is bonded with four other carbon atoms very strongly because of significant small size of carbon atoms. This criterion gives rise to a highly compact crystal structure to diamond and therefore the optical density of diamond is significantly high. Hence light rays which are incident on diamond suffer total internal reflection. If a diamond is cut in planes in such a way that the incident rays come out through a particular plane in the form of parallel rays, it glitters brilliantly. In case of other gem stones, the phenomenon of total internal reflection does not occur due to their much lower optical density. Just because they possess metal ions which impart colours, they exhibit bright colours and not glitterance. Hence, diamond is unique and the most precious gem stone.

70. (i) effect on the unwanted coating due to the blasting of soda or dry ice
(ii) nature of sodium bicarbonate
(iii) mechanical impact on the industrial equipment due to blasting of $NaHCO_3$ and dry ice
(iv) changes that takes place in dry ice after blasting
(v) change in temperature due to the above phenomenon
(vi) effect of change in temperature on the coating of impurities on the surface of industrial equipment

71. (i) change in volume during solidification of iron
(ii) conditions required for preparation of diamond
(iii) comparison of volume of iron before and after solidification
(iv) effect of change in volume on pressure
(v) effect of pressure in preparation of diamond

72. (i) comparison of the working principle of the given fire extinguishers
(ii) comparison of composition of the materials used in soda fire extinguisher with that used in liquid CO_2 fire extinguisher
(iii) transformations that takes place during the usage of both the fire extinguishers
(iv) comparison of physical properties of the products formed
(v) types of fire where soda–acid fire extinguisher cannot be used

73. Coal is fed into the coke oven and heated in an oxygen-free atmosphere and devolatized. The heating is done in various steps which subject the coal to different temperatures for varying time periods. During each step different volatile compounds are driven off. At the end of the heating process, coke remains. It is porous with good strength. Since coke is a purer form of carbon than coal and is porous, it is a better reducing agent than coal.

74. Petrol is a fraction containing hydrocarbons with more than five carbon atoms (C_5–C_{10}). LPG contains butane as a major component with four carbon atoms. CNG contains methane with one carbon atom as a major component. With decrease in number of carbon atoms in the hydrocarbon, the calorific value increases and also the extent of incomplete combustion decreases. Therefore, the fuel efficiency increases. Apart from this, petrol contains sulphur and nitrogen which release harmful pollutants into the atmosphere, whereas LPG and CNG do not contain sulphur and nitrogen. Petrol being a liquid leaves residue in the engine. Among LPG and CNG, burning of CNG produces less amount of CO_2 than LPG. Hence, CNG is considered as the best fuel.

75. Soda blasting is a technique employed to strip off the paints and unwanted materials from all surfaces. This technique involves blasting of $NaHCO_3$ on the required surface with the help of compressed air. Dry ice blasting is also used for the same purpose. But it is more advantageous than soda blasting because dry ice pellets sublime as soon as they are blasted on any surface leaving no residual matter on the surface. Since huge amount of heat is absorbed for sublimation process, thermal shock (due to sudden contraction) in generated in the coating which is an added advantage for the removal of unwanted coating.

76. Metals possess free electrons and on absorption of light, these electrons undergo excitation and deexcitation. This gives metals their lustre. Diamond does not possess any free electrons. However, when light falls on it, the edges of the diamond reflect light at a certain angle and this phenomenon is called **total internal reflection**. This leads to the sparkling of diamond which is responsible for its unique position among all gemstones.

77. The disposal of the industrial wastes in the ocean increases the acidity of ocean water which damages the shells of the oceanic calcifying organisms. Therefore, their self-protection system becomes weaker.

JEE-NEET SPECIAL WING

Multiple-Answer Type Questions

1. Sugar charcoal is the purest form of charcoal and is used for decolourisation of sugarcane juice in the extraction of sugar from sugarcane. Due to its high purity, it is also used in the synthesis of artificial diamonds.

2. The gaseous product obtained in the given reaction is carbon monoxide. The given reaction is endothermic. This gas being poisonous, the process of preparation is carried out in fume chamber. Producer gas is a mixture of carbon monoxide and nitrogen while water gas is a mixture of carbon monoxide and hydrogen. This can be collected by downward displacement of water since it is insoluble in water.

3. All metal carbonates except those of sodium and potassium on thermal decomposition give CO_2 gas which reacts with aqueous potassium hydroxide solution.

Electronic configuration	Metal
(a) 2,8,18, 2	Zn
(b) 2,8,8,1	K
(c) 2,8,18,1	Cu
(d) 2,8,13,2	Mn

4.

Metal	Formula of carbonyl
(a) Ni	$Ni(CO)_4$
(b) Cr	$Cr(CO)_6$
(c) Fe	$Fe(CO)_5$
(d) Zn	No carbonyl formation

5.

Useful material	Major constituent
(a) LPG	Butane
(b) Phosgene	Carbonyl chloride
(c) Carbogen	Oxygen
(d) CNG	Methane

Comprehension-Based Questions

6. The hydrocarbon with molecular mass 40 should be propyne. Its molecular formula would be C_3H_4. Its succeeding homologue would be butyne with molecular formula C_4H_6.

7. Increase in percentage of carbon along the homologous series happens only in case of alkanes.
Percentage of carbon in methane = 1200/16 = 75%
Percentage of carbon in ethane = 2400/30 = 80%

8. Since a molecule of CO_2 is eliminated from the carboxylic acid during the reaction, an acid with one carbon more than the alkane should be taken. The 2nd homologue of alkanes is ethane which is prepared from the carboxylic acid with 3 carbon atoms that is C_3H_7COOH. Its molecular mass would be 74.

9. Cycloalkanes possess same molecular formulae as alkenes. The first member of cycloalkanes is cyclopropane. It has molecular formula C_3H_6 which is same as propene.

10. The alkane with molecular mass 58 is butane (C_4H_{10}). The molecular formula of the compound in which hydrogen is replaced by -OH group is $C_4H_{10}O$. Its molecular mass would be 74.

11.

Description	Molecular formula	Molecular mass
(a) 3rd homologue of alkynes	C_4H_6	54
(b) 4th homologue of alkenes	C_5H_{10}	70
(c) 3rd homologue of alkanes	C_3H_8	44
(d) 2nd homologue of alkynes	C_3H_4	40

12.

Column I Description of hydrocarbon	Formula	Column II Mass ratio of carbon and hydrogen	
(a) Alkane with 2 carbons	C_2H_6	(v)	4:1
(b) Alkene with 3 carbons	C_3H_6	(iv)	6:1
(c) Alkyne with 4 carbons	C_4H_6	(i)	8:1
(d) Alkane with 5 carbons	C_5H_{12}	(iii)	5:1
(e) Alkyne with 2 carbons	C_2H_2	(ii)	12:1

13. The petrol vapours are lighter than steam. Hence, they go above the steam and get in contact with oxygen which is the most important element of fire. Therefore, water can not effectively extinguish the fires caused by petrol. Petrol and water are not miscible liquids.

14. The substance indicated by 'Y' is Sodium bicarbonate.

15. The fires caused by electrical equipment can be extinguished by liquid CO_2 fire extinguishers (indicated by 'C') and dry powder extinguishers (indicated by 'E').

16. Foam type extinguishers (B), liquid CO_2 extinguishers (C) and dry powder extinguishers (E) are suitable for extinguishing fires caused by petrol or such flammable liquids.

17. Liquid CO_2 fire extinguisher (C) works based on the principle of cooling resulting due to sudden expansion of a gas.

Match the Column

18.

Column I		Column II	
(a)	A	(iv)	Volcanoes
(b)	B	(v)	Fossil fuels
(c)	C	(vi)	Decomposition
(d)	D	(i)	Oceans
(e)	E	(ii)	Respiration
(f)	F	(iii)	Photosynthesis

CHAPTER

7

Some Important Elements and their Compounds

Remember

Before beginning this chapter, you should be able to:

- expalin the properties of metals and non-metals, and their applications in various fields.
- know the commonly know elements such as Nitrogen, Sulphur, Chlorine; their preparation, and properties of different compounds that find wide applications in our daily life.

Key Ideas

After completing this chapter, you should be able to:

- describe the preparation, properties and uses of nitrogen, phosphorus and their compounds, like, Ammonia (NH_3), Nitric Acid (HNO_3), Phosphoric acid (H_3PO_4), etc.
- know the preparation, properties and uses of Sulphur and its compounds, like, SO_2, H_2SO_4, H_2S.
- expalin the preparation, properties and uses of chlorine and its compounds, like, HCl, $CaOCl_2$.
- study the industrial applications of chlorine and its derivatives.

Scientific Crypt

A Tribute to Fritz Haber (1868 – 1934)

Fritz Haber, a German chemist received Nobel Prize in Chemistry in the year 1918 for his contribution for the preparation of ammonia, an important component of fertilizers and explosives.

At Technical University of Karlsruhe he and his brother-in-law, Carl Bosch, who was a chemist have developed the method of catalytic synthesis of ammonia from hydrogen and atmospheric nitrogen under high temperature and pressure. This process of formation of ammonia is well known as Haber Bosch process or Haber's process and was a milestone in Industrial Chemistry as it ended the dependence on the fast disappearing natural sources of ammonia located along the coast of Chile.

In 1918, Fritz Haber received the most prestigious award, Nobel Prize for his work on the preparation of ammonia. Apart from this most prestigious award, Haber received many honours during his life time. He has also been regarded as the "father of chemical warfare" for being associated with the usages of chlorine gas and other deadly gases during World War I.

After a grave illness, Haber passed away on 29th January 1934 at Basel, Switzerland.

FUN TIME

CROSSWORD

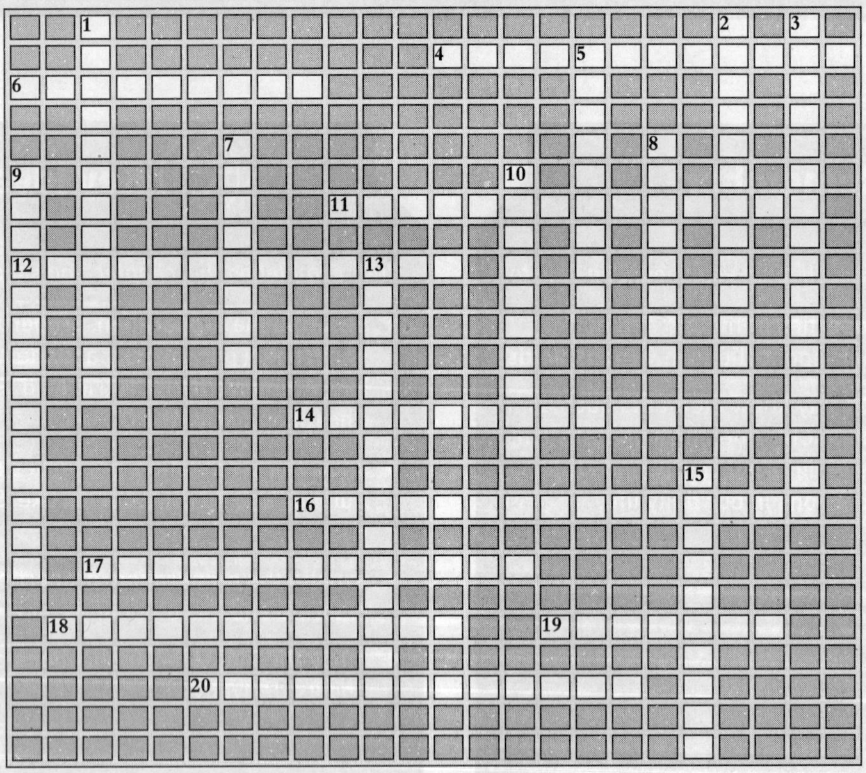

Across

4. The allotrope of phosphorus that undergo sublimation
6. The mixture of 3 : 1 volumes of conc.HCl and conc. HNO_3
11. Amorphous form of sulphur
12. Alloy of phosphorus, copper and tin
14. Calcium chlorohypochlorite is the chemical name of
16. Compound of sulphur with rotten egg smell
17. Product formed by the hydrolysis of oleum
18. Ammonia is manufactured by
19. Nonmetal used in the vulcanisation
20. Sulphuric acid is manufactured by

Down

2. Salt formed by loss of all water molecules from hydrated salt
3. Phenomenon of absorption of moisture by a salt associated with formation of solution
5. One of the constraints to use hydrogen as a fuel.
6. Metal which does not catch fire and makes the water milky and alkaline
7. Phenomenon of loss of water molecules on exposure to air
9. The property of water responsible for the use as coolant
11. Heat required to convert one gram of ice to water at 0°C
12. The reaction involved in the making of vanaspathi
13. Solution with two components

INTRODUCTION

The 118 elements that are known today and are authorized can be classified into metals and non-metals. Out of those, metals gained significance not only due to their large number but also due to their widespread use in various fields of industry. Nevertheless, the role of non-metals is not insignificant in day-to-day life. Oxygen and carbon are inevitably very important in the biosphere. Apart from this, some non-metals in the form of their compounds occupy the most pivotal position in the industrial sector and they are rightly called **industrial chemicals.**

Non-Metals and Their Compounds

Nitrogen, the element which is well known for its abundance in the atmospheric air, is the most important nutrient for plants. Therefore, the various compounds of nitrogen are manufactured for the use as fertilizers. Sulphur and phosphorous also form a part of the fertilizer industry. In addition to this common use, certain compounds are useful for specific purposes such as phosphorous in the match industry. Similarly common salt, a compound of chlorine, forms an important part of our diet.

However, there are some compounds, such as, nitric acid, sulphuric acid, hydrochloric acid, etc., which form an inevtable part of almost every chemical industry. In fact, the yearly consumption of sulphuric acid in a country is taken as an indication which reflects the status of chemical industry in that country. In this context, it should be recalled that sulphuric acid is popularly known as the king of chemicals.

Owing to the significant industrial importance attached to non-metals and their compounds, the study of these forms an important area in chemistry.

Info Bytes!

India is the third largest producer of Sulphur in Asia. The country has vast resources of Sulphur deposits, primarily in the states of Andhra Pradesh, Gujarat, and Rajasthan.

Occurrence

Table 7.1 Occurrence of some of the important elements

Elements	Free state	Combined state
Nitrogen	Nitrogen exists in a free state in the atmospheric air. It is the major constituent of air comprising 78% by volume and 75% by weight.	Nitrogen occurs in a combined state in various forms. It is present in the form of minerals, like, nitre (KNO_3) and Chile salt petre ($NaNO_3$). Nitrogen is present in major amounts in organic matter, such as, proteins, nucleic acids, enzymes and various compounds of biological importance.
Phosphorus	Phosphorous, being highly reactive, does not exist in the free state.	In the combined state, it exists in the form of phosphates, in inorganic as well as organic matter. Examples: chlorapatite $3Ca_3(PO_4)_2.CaCl_2$, fluorapatite $3Ca_3(PO_4)_2.CaF_2$, phosphorprotein of yolk, bone marrow, etc.
Sulphur	Sulphur, in the free state is found in the earth's crust (0.03% of the earth's crust is elemental sulphur). In the volcanic regions, such as, Sicily and Japan; it is present near the earth's crust and in the non-volcanic regions of the United States, such as, Texas and Louisiana; it is found much below the earth's crust (300–400 m below the earth crust).	Sulphur in the combined state is found in the form of sulphides (in ores), sulphates (in salts) and in organic matter. Examples: cinnabar (HgS), iron pyrites (FeS.CuS), gypsum $CaSO_4.2H_2O$, insulin, glucosionates, etc.
Chlorine	Chlorine does not occur in the free state in nature due to its high reactivity.	Chlorine exists in the combined state in the form of chlorides, like, common salt (NaCl), potassium chloride (KCl), Carnalite ($KCl.MgCl_2{\cdot}6H_2O$) and mineral horn silver (AgCl).

Nitrogen

Manufacture of Nitrogen

Since nitrogen is abundantly available in the atmospheric air, it is manufactured mainly by the fractional distillation of liquid air.

Procedure: The process of manufacturing of nitrogen from air involves three stages:

Stage 1: Liquefaction of Air

Before subjecting air to liquefaction, air should be free from dust particles, moisture and carbon dioxide.

Table 7.2 Removal of components during liquefaction of air

Components to be removed	Methods of removal
Dust particles	By passing through electric precipitators or filters
Moisture (water vapour)	By passing through conc. H_2SO_4 or anhydrous $CaCl_2$
Carbon dioxide gas	By passing through caustic soda (NaOH) or caustic potash (KOH)

Application of high pressure of 100 atm–200 atm over dry air and subsequent expansion of this compressed air through a fine jet results in cooling. Repeating the above process a number of times results in the conversion of this air to liquid state.

Stage 2: Isolation of Nitrogen from Liquid Air

Nitrogen and oxygen, the major constituents of air, have different boiling points of −195°C and −182.9°C, respectively and can be separated by fractional distillation. Nitrogen has a lower boiling point than oxygen, and hence, gets evaporated first leaving behind oxygen in the liquid form.

Stage 3: Detection of Nitrogen Gas

There is no direct test for the identification of nitrogen gas due to its chemical inertness. However, it is possible to identify nitrogen by an indirect method.

Table 7.3 Tests to detect nitrogen gas

Test	Reactions involved
A burning magnesium ribbon when introduced into a jar of nitrogen, continues to burn giving a pale yellow powder.	$3Mg + N_2 \longrightarrow Mg_3N_2$
The powder on treating with water evolves a colourless pungent smelling gas, which produces white dense fumes on exposure to a glass rod dipped in HCl solution.	$Mg_3N_2 + 6H_2O \longrightarrow 3Mg(OH)_2 + 2NH_3$ $NH_3 + HCl \longrightarrow NH_4Cl$

Physical Properties of Nitrogen

Physical properties of nitrogen are tabulated below.

Table 7.4 Physical properties of nitrogen

Parameter	Characteristic
Solubility	Slightly soluble in water (2.3 vol in 100 vol)
Vapour density	14.0
Liquefaction	It can be liquefied to a colourless liquid which boils at −195.8°C
Solidification	It can be solidified under high pressure to a white snow-like mass which melts at −209.8°C.
Nature	It is a chemically unreactive gas. Due to this unreactive nature, it is used in (i) filling of electric bulbs to prevent the oxidation of the filament present in it (ii) preservation of food stuffs

Chemical Properties of Nitrogen

Chemical properties of nitrogen are tabulated below.

Table 7.5 Chemical properties of nitrogen

Property	Reaction
Combustibility	(a) No reaction with oxygen under normal conditions (b) Not combustible (c) Not a supporter of combustion
Action with litmus	No response to litmus test (neutral gas)
Reaction with non-metals	**(i) Reaction with hydrogen** Nitrogen reacts with hydrogen at high temperature and pressure to give ammonia gas: $N_2 + 3H_2 \longrightarrow 2NH_3$ **(ii) Reaction with oxygen** Nitrogen and oxygen react in equal volumes to form nitric oxide: $N_2 + O_2 \longrightarrow 2NO$
Reaction with metals	**(i) Reaction with magnesium** Magnesium reacts with nitrogen to form magnesium nitride: $3Mg + N_2 \longrightarrow Mg_3N_2$ **(ii) Reaction with calcium** $3Ca + N_2 \longrightarrow Ca_3N_2$ **(iii) Reaction with aluminium** $2Al + N_2 \longrightarrow 2AlN$
Reaction with compounds	**Reaction with calcium carbide** Heating calcium carbide with nitrogen at 800°C–1000°C forms a mixture of calcium cyanamide and graphite: $CaC_2 + N_2 \xrightarrow{800°C} CaCN_2 + C$

Uses of Nitrogen

1. Dilutes the activity of oxygen in natural processes, like, combustion and respiration.
2. Manufacture of ammonia by Haber's process. Ammonia finds application in the manufacture of fertilizers.
3. Nitric oxide combines with oxygen to give various other oxides and these oxides of nitrogen react with water to give oxyacids of nitrogen.
4. The mixture of calcium cyanamide and graphite is known as **nitrolim** which is an important fertilizer.

Nitrogen is also needed in the soil for both plants and animals. The process of fixing nitrogen in the soil is called nitrogen fixation.

Info Bytes!

While Nitrogen is non-reactive and makes up a majority of our atmosphere, its compounds can be quite reactive. For instance, nitro-glycerine, a compound of nitrogen, is a powerful explosive!

Nitrogen Fixation

Though atmosphere contains large proportion of free nitrogen, it is not assimilated by either plants or animals directly. The process of conversion of the atmospheric nitrogen into the usable form either by natural or artificial means is called **nitrogen fixation**.

Natural Fixation

Natural fixation of nitrogen takes place by leguminous plants and also by lightening.

Fixation of Nitrogen by Leguminous Plants

Only leguminous plants, like, peas, beans, etc., are capable of taking in atmospheric nitrogen. These plants possess root nodules which absorb nitrogen from the atmospheric air. The symbiotic bacteria living in these root nodules convert nitrogen into various nitrogen compounds which plants can easily assimilate and the soil becomes rich in nitrogen compounds. These compounds become the source of nitrogen for the plants which are grown in that soil.

By Lightening

When discharges of lightening take place in the atmosphere, due to the high temperature the atmospheric nitrogen combines with oxygen forming nitrogen monoxide which gets oxidized further to nitrogen dioxide:

$$N_2 + O_2 \rightleftharpoons 2NO$$

$$2NO + O_2 \longrightarrow 2NO_2$$

This gas dissolves in the water droplets in clouds and forms nitric acid which comes down to soil in the form of rain water:

$$4NO_2 + 2H_2O + O_2 \longrightarrow 4HNO_3$$

Nitric acid further reacts with minerals, like, metal carbonates or basic oxides present in the deeper layers of soil to form respective metal nitrates which can be assimilated by plants:

$$2HNO_3 + MCO_3 \longrightarrow M(NO_3)_2 + CO_2\uparrow + H_2O$$

Artificial Fixation by Haber's Process

Nitrogen which is isolated from the atmospheric air by the fractional distillation of liquid air is made to react with hydrogen in the ratio of 1: 3 under high pressure (200–900 atm) in the presence of a catalyst (finely divided iron with molybdenum as a promoter) at about 450°C–500°C to produce ammonia gas:

$$N_2 + 3H_2 \rightleftharpoons 2NH_3$$

Ammonia so manufactured can be used for the manufacture of various ammonium fertilizers. The ammonia can also be converted to nitric acid which can further be converted to various nitrate fertilizers, like, calcium ammonium nitrate.

Recovery of nitrogen back to the atmosphere

Nitrate salts are assimilated by plants through their roots and are converted into proteins. These proteins are consumed by animals. Now the proteins present in the animals are decomposed into simpler substances like urea during metabolic process which are later converted to ammonium salts. Decay products of dead plants and animals are converted into ammonium salts by ammonifying bacteria which are further converted into nitrites and nitrates by nitrifying bacteria. *Nitrosomonas* bacteria help in the conversion of ammonium salts to nitrites and subsequent conversion of these nitrites to nitrates is carried out by *Nitrobacter.* The nitrates so obtained are further converted to nitrogen gas by denitrifying bacteria. Thus, the nitrogen consumed during different processes is returned to the atmosphere again.

Nitrogen Cycle

The atmospheric nitrogen is converted to nitrogenous compounds by means of nitrogen fixation. However, the percentage of nitrogen in the atmospheric air remains unaltered. That means, the nitrogen which is converted into compounds is returned back into the atmosphere by the above processes. The entire process of nitrogen fixation and the reconversion of this fixed nitrogen into free nitrogen is called **nitrogen cycle**.

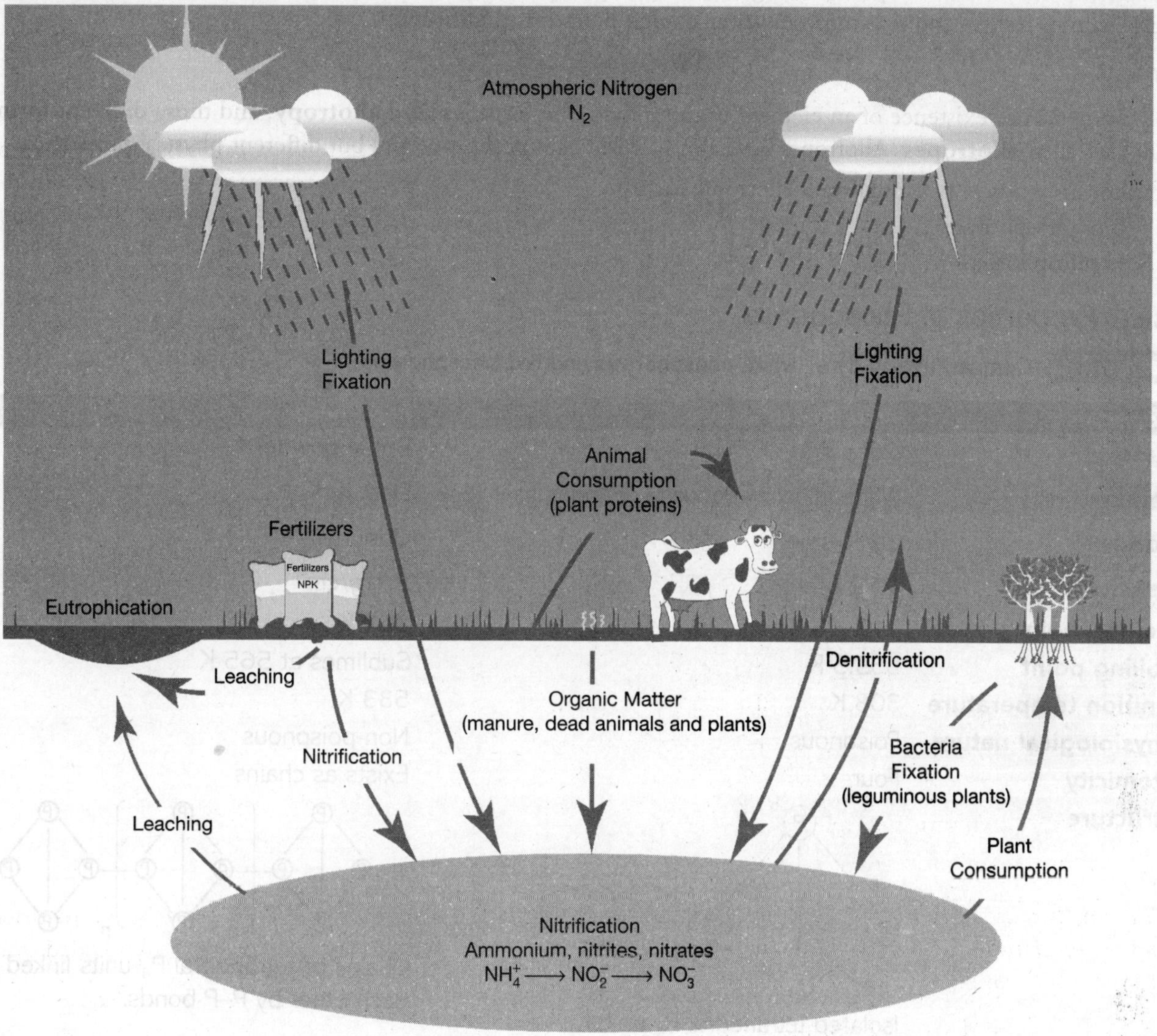

Figure 7.1 Nitrogen cycle

Phosphorus

Preparation

Phosphorous is prepared by the electrolytic reduction of mineral phosphate.

Procedure: The mineral phosphate (calcium phosphate) is mixed with sand and coke. This mixture is taken in an electric furnace with carbon electrodes. The mixture is electrically heated up to 1775 K.

The following reactions take place:

$$2Ca_3(PO_4)_2 + \underset{(sand)}{6SiO_2} \longrightarrow \underset{(Slag)}{6CaSiO_3} + P_4O_{10}$$

$$P_4O_{10} + 10C \longrightarrow P_4 + 10CO$$

> **Info Bytes!**
> Phosphate rock, a primary source of phosphorus compounds, has considerable reserves in India. Udaipur in Rajasthan is a key region known for its phosphorite mines.

The slag formed settles at the bottom and is removed. Phosphorous vapours and carbon monoxide gas formed are let out of the furnace from the top. The subsequent cooling of these vapours under water results in the condensation of phosphorous into solid phosphorous.

Purification: The phosphorous obtained is purified using potassium dichromate in an acidic medium. The impurities are oxidized and removed as vapours or slag. Pure liquid phosphorous settles at the bottom where it is collected, filtered through chamois leather and sent through water-cooled pipes for solidification.

Allotropy

The phenomenon of existence of an element in more than one form is called **allotropy**, and those different forms of an element are called **allotropes**. Allotropes have almost same chemical properties but different physical properties.

Phosphorous exists in two important allotropic forms:

1. White phosphorous
2. Red phosphorous

Physical Properties of Phosphorus

Table 7.6 Comparative study of white phosphorous and red phosphorous

Properties	White Phosphorous	Red Phosphorous
State	Soft solid	Brittle powder
Colour	White initially, gradually changes to yellow	Dark red
Odour	Garlic smell	Odourless
Density	1.82 g/cm^3	2.1 g/cm^3
Melting point	317 K	863 K
Boiling point	553.5 K	Sublimes at 565 K
Ignition temperature	308 K	533 K
Physiological nature	Poisonous	Non-poisonous
Atomicity	Four	Exists as chains
Structure	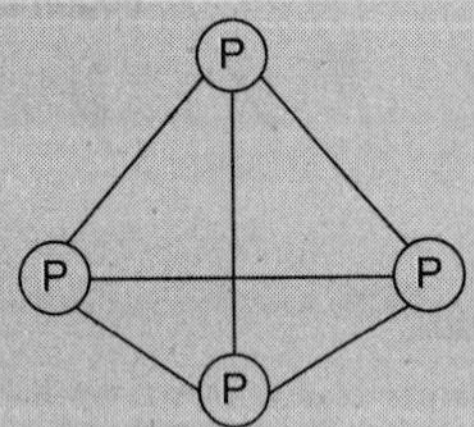 Isolated tetrahedral P_4 units	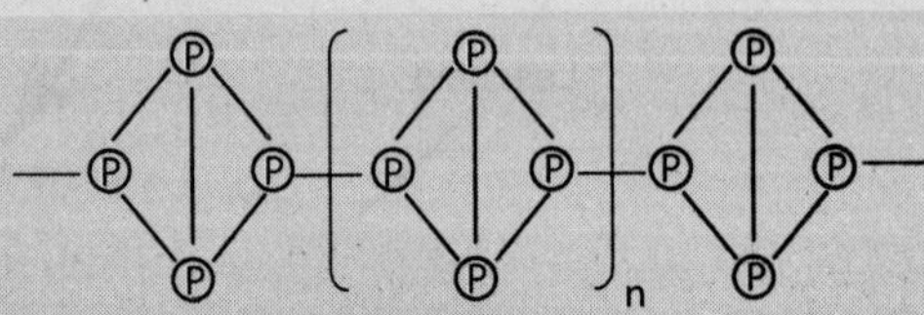 Chains of tetrahedral P_4 units linked to each other by P–P bonds.

Chemical Properties of Phosphorus

Table 7.7 Important chemical properties of phosphorus

Property	Reaction
Reaction with oxygen	Phosphorus reacts with oxygen or air and forms white dense fumes of phosphorus pentoxide: $4P + 5O_2 \longrightarrow 2P_2O_5$
Reaction with chlorine	A piece of phosphorus introduced into a jar containing chlorine reacts initially to form phosphorus trichloride and on further reaction forms phosphorus pentachloride: $2P + Cl_2 \longrightarrow 2PCl_3$

(Continued)

Table 7.7 Continued

Property	Reaction
Reaction with calcium	Phosphorus can directly combine with calcium to give calcium phosphide: $3Ca + 2P \longrightarrow Ca_3P_2$
Reaction with NaOH	Phosphorus when boiled with a solution of sodium hydroxide, phosphine gas and sodium hypophosphite are formed: $4P + 3NaOH + 3H_2O \longrightarrow PH_3 + 3NaH_2PO_2$
Reaction with HNO_3	Phosphorus on reaction with concentrated nitric acid produces phosphoric acid and nitrogen dioxide: $P + 5HNO_3 \longrightarrow H_3PO_4 + 5NO_2 + H_2O$ Phosphorus acts as a powerful reducing agent.

Uses of Phosphorus

1. Phosphor bronze, an alloy of phosphorus, copper and tin can be manufactured from phosphorus.
2. White phosphorus is used as a rat poison.
3. Phosphorus is used in the manufacture of compounds, like, hypophosphates, phosphoric acid and phosphorus chlorides.
4. Phosphorous is used in the manufacture of bombs, smoke screens and fireworks.
5. Phosphorous is very widely used in the match industry, as it has a low-ignition temperature. Depending upon the activity of the matches, they are categorized into two types:
   (a) **Lucifer Matches:** These are 'strike anywhere matches.' They are so called because they catch fire when they are rubbed against any hard surface. In these matches, the tip of the match stick is composed of antimony trisulphide, red phosphorous and potassium chlorate in addition to a binding material like glue.
   (b) **Safety Matches:** These burn only when they are made to strike on a particular surface. The chemical on the stick is composed of potassium chlorate and antimony sulphide mixed with glue. When this is rubbed on a surface made of red phosphorous, antimony sulphide and fine glass powder, a small part of phosphorous detaches and catches fire. This spark initiates the ignition of antimony sulphide which further helps in the decomposition of potassium chlorate which provides oxygen for combustion.

EXAMPLE 7.1 Farmers are advised to include bean plants in the crop rotation system. What purpose does it serve?.

SOLUTION

Nitrogen is an essential nutrient required in large quantities by plants. Nitrogen in the soil is consumed fast when a particular type of crop is grown. The bean plant belongs to leguminous family and is capable of taking atmospheric nitrogen directly and converting it to nitrate salts. Thus, they help in the replenishment of soils with nitrogen. When the bean plants are removed from the soil, the next crop can get plenty of nitrogen from the soil.

Sulphur

Occurrence

Sulphur has a wide variety of uses in the industries. It is extracted from the earth's crust by the following processes:

Sicilian Process

This process is used to extract sulphur which is near to the earth's crust (deposits in Sicily). This process is carried out in brick kilns built on sloping hill sides.

Procedure: Large amounts of clay and stone are mixed with crude sulphur and is stacked inside the brick kiln leaving small spaces in between. This is covered with a layer of powdered sulphur which is then subjected to burning. The heat evolved during the burning of this sulphur leads to melting of the remaining sulphur that lies in the bottom layers. The molten sulphur is allowed to flow down and is collected in wooden moulds.

Purification: The sulphur obtained in the above process contains about 5% of earthly impurities. Depending on the applications, it is used in the natural form or in the purified form. The purification is carried out by distillation process. The liquid sulphur obtained after distillation is collected in the form of solid rolls, and hence, called **roll sulphur**.

Frasch Process

This process is used to extract the sulphur which lies 150–400 m below the earth's crust. This process is also called **Louisiana process** as large deposits of this are found in Louisiana. A direct mining is not possible as the sulphur is present in layers of quick sand and gravel.

Procedure: In this process three, concentric pipes of diameters 25 mm, 76 mm and 152 mm are drilled through the ground to the sulphur deposits. Superheated steam (170°C) under pressure is sent through the outermost pipe. This melts the sulphur present below (melting point of sulphur = 112°C). Hot compressed air (up to 35 atm) is sent through the innermost pipe, which froths up the molten sulphur below. The sulphur foam formed rises up the middle pipe and is collected.

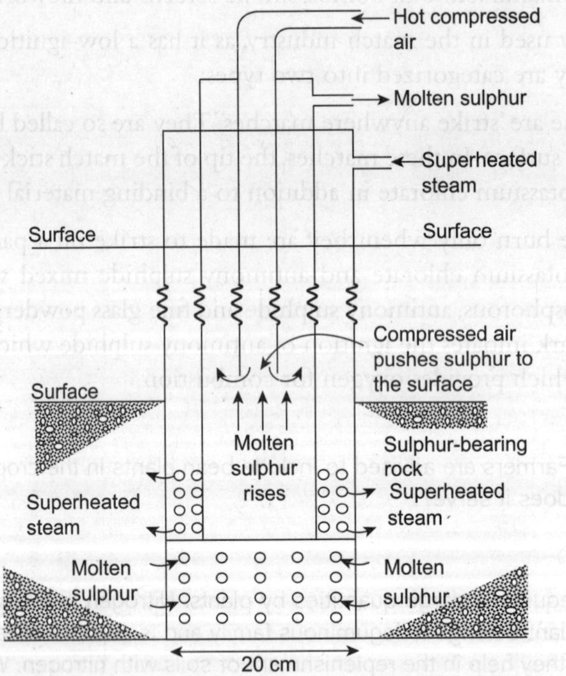

Figure 7.2 Frasch process for extracting sulphur

Advantages: The sulphur extracted in this process is 99.5% pure and does not need further purification.

Allotropes of Sulphur

Sulphur exists in different allotropic forms. Following are the three main allotropic forms of sulphur:

1. Rhombic sulphur
2. Monoclinic sulphur
3. Plastic sulphur

Info Bytes!

Rhombic sulphur and monoclinic sulphur are crystalline, whereas plastic sulphur is amorphous.

Table 7.8 Comparative study of the allotropic forms of sulphur

Parameter	Rhombic sulphur	Monoclinic sulphur	Plastic sulphur
Other names	Octahedral sulphur, alpha sulphur	Prismatic sulphur, beta sulphur	Gamma sulphur
Preparation	Roll sulphur is dissolved in carbon disulphide. This is allowed to evaporate slowly by slight heating. Rhombic sulphur crystals are left behind	Roll sulphur is heated on an evaporating dish till it melts to pale yellow liquid. This on cooling forms a crust on the surface. Holes are pierced on the crust and the molten sulphur is drained out. Needle-shaped sulphur (monoclinic sulphur) crystals are left behind	Roll sulphur is heated to above 300°C till it turns to dark brown, this is poured into cold water and the sulphur formed is plastic sulphur
Colour	Pale yellow	Amber	Dark brown
Shape/structure	Octahedral 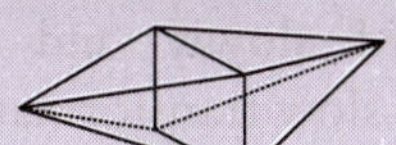	Needle shaped 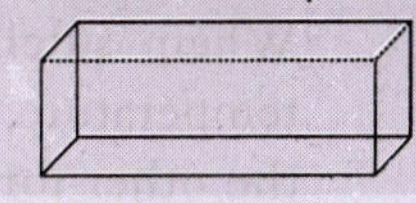	Amorphous There is no definite structure for plastic sulphur
Density	2.08 g/cm^3	1.98 g/cm^3	1.92 g/cm^3
Solubility	Soluble in carbon disulphide	Soluble in carbon disulphide	Insoluble in carbon disulphide
Melting point	112.8°C	119°C	No sharp melting point
Conductivity	Sulphur is a bad conductor of heat and electricity		
Boiling point	Sulphur boils at 444°C		

Transition Between Rhombic Sulphur and Monoclinic Sulphur

Rhombic sulphur is stable below 95.6°C and above this temperature it changes to monoclinic sulphur. Conversely, monoclinic sulphur is stable above 95.6°C, but changes to the rhombic variety below this temperature. Hence, 95.6°C is called **transition temperature** of these two allotropes of sulphur.

Puckered-Ring Structure of Sulphur: Both rhombic sulphur and monoclinic sulphur exist in the form of S_8 molecules. These S_8 molecules are in the form of a ring. It forms a crown-shaped molecule with four atoms on the top and four atoms at the bottom.

Konnect

Rhombic sulphur is the most stable form at normal temperature. Monoclinic sulphur and plastic sulphur change to rhombic form on long standing.

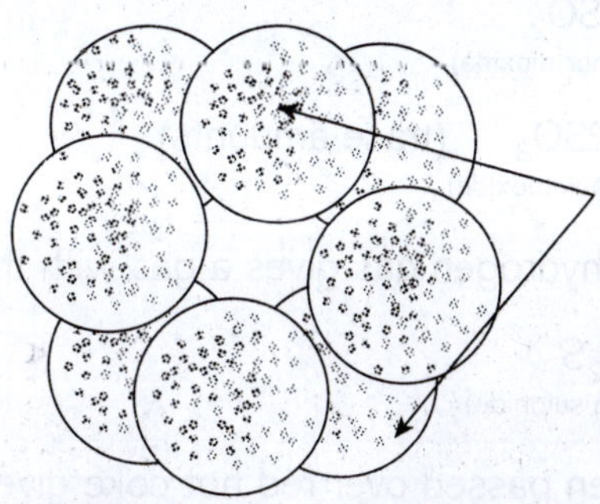

Figure 7.3 Puckered-ring structure of sulphur

The rhombic form and the monoclinic form differ in the arrangement of these S_8 puckered rings. In rhombic sulphur, these rings fit snugly into each other while in monoclinic sulphur the rings are stacked one on top of the other.

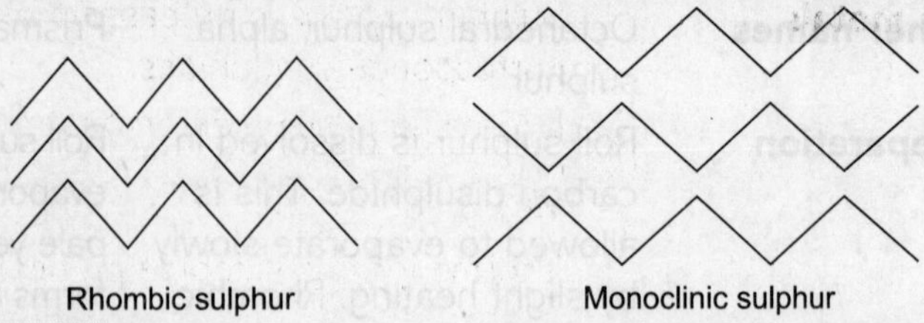

Figure 7.4 Structures Rhombic sulphur and Monoclinic sulphur

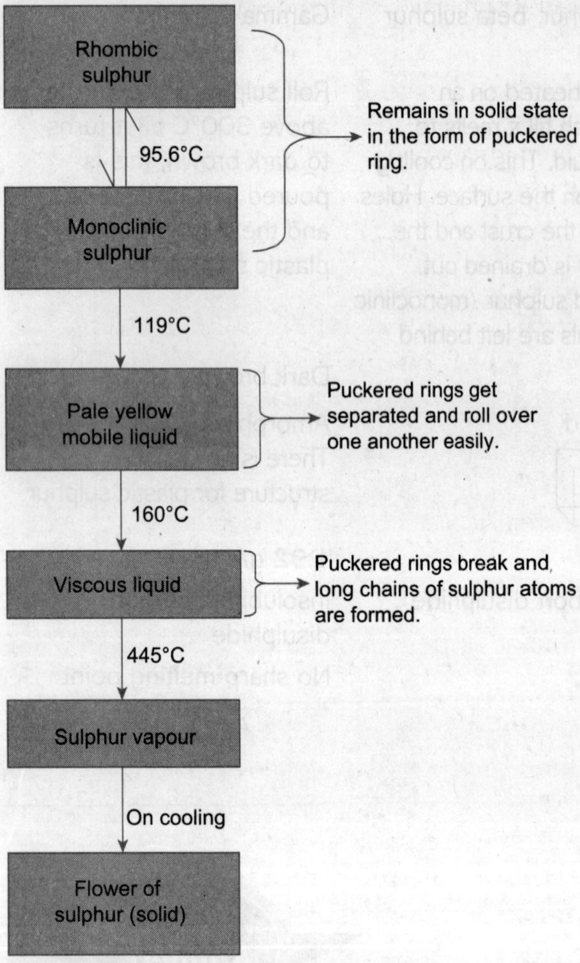

Figure 7.5 Action of heat on sulphur

Action of Heat on Sulphur

When sulphur is heated slowly and steadily from room temperature, it undergoes slow transformation from one form to the other form. At normal temperature, rhombic sulphur is the most stable allotropic form of sulphur. When this is subjected to slow heating, at 95.6°C temperature, it gets transformed into monoclinic sulphur. This is because of the separation of the puckered rings which get rearranged to give monoclinic form. 95.6°C is called **transition temperature of sulphur.** Further heating of sulphur to 118°C results in the separation of puckered rings thereby giving a pale yellow mobile liquid. If the heating is continued, at 160°C, the puckered rings break giving long chains of sulphur atoms which entangle with each other. This results in the formation of thick, viscous liquid. This on further heating till the boiling point that is 445°C, sulphur vapour is obtained. These vapours on cooling condense to form flower sulphur.

Chemical Properties of Sulphur

Table 7.9 Important chemical properties of sulphur

Properties	Reaction
With non-metals	Above 300°C, it burns with a pale blue flame giving out two oxides of sulphur.
Oxygen	$S + O_2 \longrightarrow SO_2$ (Sulphur dioxide) $2S + 3O_2 \longrightarrow 2SO_3$ (trace amounts) (Sulphur trioxide)
Hydrogen	Boiling sulphur with hydrogen gas gives a gas with the smell of rotten eggs. $S + H_2 \longrightarrow H_2S$ (hydrogen sulphide)
Carbon	Sulphur vapours when passed over red hot coke give carbon disulphide. $C + S \longrightarrow CS_2(l)$ C: Coke (red hot); CS_2: (Carbon disulphide)

(Continued)

Table 7.9 Continued

Properties	Reaction
With metals	Sulphur vapour when passed over the heated surface of certain metals gives corresponding sulphides.
Zinc	It forms zinc sulphide on heating: $Zn + S \longrightarrow ZnS$
Iron	It forms ferrous sulphide on heating: $Fe + S \longrightarrow FeS$
Copper	It forms: (a) cuprous sulphide (below 400°C) $2Cu + S \xrightarrow{< 400°C} Cu_2S$ (b) cupric sulphide (above 400°C) $Cu + S \xrightarrow{< 400°C} CuS$
Mercury	When sulphur vapour is passed over cold metallic mercury, it gives mercuric sulphide: $Hg + S \longrightarrow HgS$
With acids	
Sulphuric acid	Reduces sulphuric acid to sulphur dioxide: $S + H_2SO_4 \longrightarrow 3SO_2 + H_2O$
Nitric acid	Sulphur is oxidized to sulphuric acid and reduces nitric acid to nitrogen dioxide: $S + 6HNO_3 \longrightarrow H_2SO_4 + 6NO_2 + 2H_2O$

Uses of Sulphur

Sulphur has a wide variety of uses in various industries as listed hereunder:

1. **Rubber Industry**: It is used for the vulcanization of rubber to make it hard and elastic.
2. **Chemical Industry**: Used in making chemicals, like, sulphuric acid, carbon disulphide, etc.
3. **Explosive Industry**: Sulphur along with charcoal and nitre is used in making gunpowder.

EXAMPLE 7.2 Why does rhombic sulphur turn into monoclinic sulphur upon heating to temperatures just above room temperature?

SOLUTION

Rhombic sulphur and monoclinic sulphur are allotropes of sulphur. Rhombic Sulphur has a melting point of 112.8°C, but it is only stable at room temperature (below 96°C). However, as the temperature rises just above room temperature and approaches 96°C, rhombic sulphur starts transforming into the monoclinic form. This is because monoclinic sulphur becomes the more stable allotrope between 96°C and 119°C. This transition is due to the reorganization of the sulphur molecules in the crystal lattice in response to the increased thermal energy. Upon cooling below 96°C, the monoclinic form reverts back to the rhombic form.

It is also worth noting that Rhombic Sulphur has a melting point of 112.8°C, but it is only stable at temperatures below 96°C.

EXAMPLE 7.3 The viscosity of sulphur increases from 160°C to 195°C and subsequently decreases above this range. Explain with appropriate reasons.

SOLUTION

The viscosity of liquids usually decreases as temperature increases. When liquid sulphur is heated from 160°C to 195°C, the viscosity increases. This is due to breaking of S8 rings followed by polymerization of the chains of sulphur atoms. Due to polymerization interlocking of sulphur chains takes place with each other. The longer the chains of S atoms, the more the chains interlock with each other and the more viscous the sulphur becomes. Above 195°C, the long chains begin to break up, and thus, viscosity gradually decreases.

Chlorine

Laboratory Method of Preparation

Oxidation of Hydrochloric Acid: Hydrochloric acid on oxidation with MnO_2 or $KMnO_4$ or $K_2Cr_2O_7$ gives chlorine gas. Oxidation of HCl by MnO_2 is the most common method employed for the preparation of chlorine gas in laboratory.

When manganese dioxide is heated with concentrated HCl, HCl gets oxidized to chlorine gas:

$$MnO_2 + 4HCl \longrightarrow MnCl_2 + 2H_2O + Cl_2$$

Procedure: A round-bottomed flask fitted with a two-holed rubber cork is taken. MnO_2 is taken in this flask. A thistle funnel is introduced into the flask through one hole. Concentrated HCl can be added through this thistle funnel. Through the second hole, a delivery tube is inserted into the flask. The mixture of MnO_2 and HCl taken in the round-bottomed flask is heated gently. The liberated chlorine gas which comes out of the delivery tube is collected into a gas jar.

Collection of Gas: Chlorine gas being heavier than air is collected by the method of upward displacement of air.

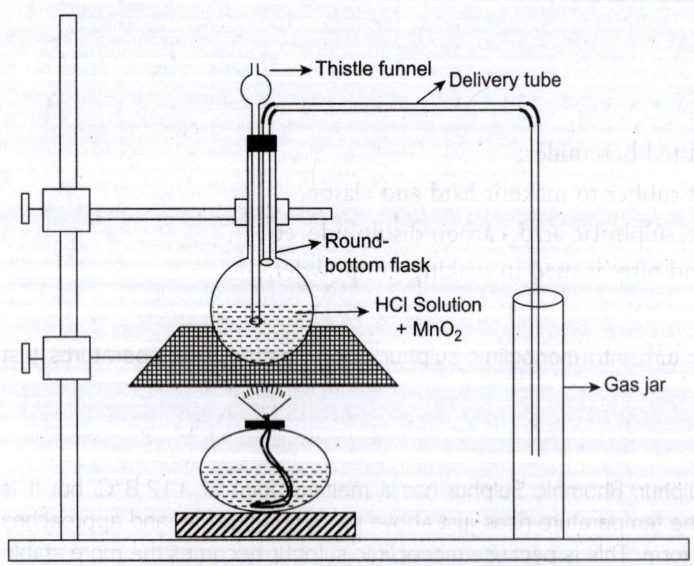

Figure 7.6 Preparation of chlorine

Konnect

India's salt industry, mainly located in the state of Gujarat, is one of the largest globally. The chlor-alkali industry, which produces compounds like Sodium Hydroxide, heavily relies on salt as a primary raw material.

Physical Properties of Chlorine

Table 7.10 Important physical properties of chlorine

Parameters	Characteristics
Colour	Greenish Yellow
Odour	Pungent smell
Solubility	Sparingly soluble in water
Density	Heavier than air. Vapour density is 35.5
Atomicity	2

Chemical Properties of Chlorine

Table 7.11 Important chemical properties of chlorine

Properties	Reaction
Reaction with air	Under normal conditions, chlorine does not react with oxygen. Chlorine is non-combustible and also not a supporter of combustion.
Reaction with water	Chlorine dissolves in water. A mixture of hydrochloric acid and hypochlorous acid is formed. This reaction is responsible for the bleaching action of chlorine since HOCl dissociates giving nascent oxygen: $Cl_2 + H_2O \longrightarrow HCl + HOCl$ $HOCl \longrightarrow HCl + [O]$
Reaction with metals	Chlorine reacts with most of the metals: $2Na + Cl_2 \longrightarrow 2NaCl$ For example, when burning magnesium ribbon reacts with chlorine gas, the corresponding metallic chlorides are formed. $MgCl_2$ is formed with the evolution of light energy: $Mg + Cl_2 \longrightarrow MgCl_2$
Reaction with non-metals	At high temperature, chlorine reacts with some non-metals E.g., $2P + 3Cl_2 \longrightarrow 2PCl_3$ $2P + 5Cl_2 \longrightarrow 2PCl_5$ Corresponding non-metallic chlorides are formed
	(a) Reaction with alkalies (cold and dilute) (a) On reaction with cold dilute NaOH, the products are sodium chloride and sodium hypochlorite: $Cl_2 + 2NaOH \longrightarrow 5NaCl + NaOCl + 3H_2O$ **(b) Reaction with alkalies (hot and concentrated)** (b) On reaction with hot concentrated NaOH, the products are sodium are sodium chloride and sodium chlorate: $3Cl_2 + 6NaOH \longrightarrow 5NaCl + NaOCl_3 + 3H_2O$

(Continued)

Table 7.11 Continued

Properties	Reaction
Reaction with other compounds	Reaction of chlorine with excess of ammonia gives ammonium chloride and nitrogen: $8NH_3 + 3Cl_2 \longrightarrow 6NH_4Cl + N_2$ Reaction of chlorine with limited amount of ammonia. Products formed are nitrogen trichloride and HCl: $NH_3 + 3Cl_2 \longrightarrow NCl_3 + 3HCl$
	On reaction with H_2S, chlorine oxidizes H_2S to sulphur and a yellow, coloured sulphur powder is formed: $H_2S + Cl_2 \longrightarrow S + 2HCl$
Reaction with turpentine	Chlorine gas is passed over a filter paper dipped in hot turpentine. It burns with a black sooty flame with the formation of black soot of carbon: $C_{10}H_{16} + 8Cl_2 \longrightarrow 10C + 16HCl$

Uses of Chlorine

1. In the manufacture of bleaching power ($CaOCl_2$).
2. For bleaching wood pulp, cotton, paper, silk, rayon, etc.
3. For preparing poisonous gases, such as, mustard gas (ClC_2H_4-S-C_2H_4Cl), phosgene ($COCl_2$) and tear gas (CCl_3NO_2).
4. In the preparation of hydrochloric acid.
5. In the extraction of metals, like, platinum, gold, titanium, etc.
6. In the manufacture of chloroform ($CHCl_3$), carbon tetrachloride (CCl_4), dichloro diphenyl trichloro ethane (DDT), etc., and also in rubber, plastic and paint industries.
7. In the purification of drinking water.

Compounds of Nitrogen

Since nitrogen is the most essential element for the growth of plants and most of the plants are incapable of absorbing nitrogen directly from the atmosphere, the manufacture of useful compounds from nitrogen has lot of industrial significance. The most important compounds are ammonia and nitric acid which form the basic raw materials for the manufacture of a number of fertilizers.

Ammonia

It is prepared by the action of quick lime on ammonium chloride:

$$NH_4Cl + CaO \longrightarrow CaCl_2 + H_2O + 2NH_3$$

Physical Properties of Ammonia

Table 7.12 Important physical properties of ammonia

Parameters	Characteristics
Colour	Colourless
Odour	Pungent smell, causes burning sensation in the upper part of nasal track and brings tears to eyes
Taste	Bitter in taste
Physiological nature	Poisonous, damages respiratory system
Density	It is lighter than air (vapour density is 8.5)
Solubility	Highly soluble in water, so, it cannot be collected by downward displacement of water. Further, 1300 volumes of NH_3 can be dissolved in 1 volume of water at STP
Boiling point	–33.4°C
Freezing point	–78°C

Chemical Properties of Ammonia

Table 7.13 Important chemical properties of ammonia

Parameters	Reaction and Observation
Combustibility	A burning match stick is introduced into ammonia gas chamber. The match stick is put off. Ammonia gas is neither combustible nor a supporter of combustion
Action with litmus	A moist red litmus paper is dipped into a jar of ammonia Red litmus is turned to blue colour. Ammonia is basic in nature
Action with acids	When ammonia gas is passed into the acids, such as, HCl or H_2SO_4, ammonium salts are formed: $NH_3 + HCl \longrightarrow NH_4Cl$ $NH_3 + H_2SO_4 \longrightarrow (NH_4)_2SO_4$
Action with non-metals	A burning match stick when introduced into a jar containing ammonia and oxygen burns with a pale blue flame: $4NH_3 3O_2 \longrightarrow 2N_2 + 6H_2O$ **(i) Reaction with oxygen** When the above mixture of ammonia and oxygen is passed over heated platinum, nitric oxide and water vapour are formed with the evolution of heat $4NH_3 + 5O_2 \xrightarrow[900^\circ C]{P} 4NO + 6H_2O$ $2NO + O_2 \longrightarrow 2NO_2$ $2NO_2 + H_2O \longrightarrow HNO_2 + HNO_3$
	(ii) Reaction with chlorine (1) Limited amount of Cl_2 White dense fumes of ammonium chloride are formed along with nitrogen: $8NH_3 + 3Cl_2 \longrightarrow 6NH_4Cl + N_2$ (2) Excess amount of Cl_2 Nitrogen trichloride and HCl are formed: $NH_3 + 3Cl_2 \longrightarrow NCl_3 + 3HCl$

(Continued)

Table 7.13 Continued

Parameters	Reaction and Observation
Reaction with metals	On reaction with active metals, corresponding amides are formed: $2NH_3 + 2Na \longrightarrow 2NaNH_2 + H_2$ $2NH_3 + 2K \longrightarrow 2KNH_2 + H_2$
Reducing properties	Ammonia gas when passed over heated metal oxides, reduces them to respective metals: $3CuO + 2NH_3 \longrightarrow 3Cu + N_2 + 3H_2O$ $3PbO + 2NH_3 \longrightarrow 3Pb + N_2 + 3H_2O$

Uses of Ammonia

1. In the manufacture of fertilizers, like, urea, ammonium sulphate, etc.
2. Used as a solvent
3. Used as a refrigerant in ice plants
4. In the manufacture of nitric acid, sodium carbonate and sodium bicarbonate

Some Important Ammonium Salts

Table 7.14 Description of some important ammonium salts

Preparation	Applications
Ammonium chloride $NH_4OH + HCl \longrightarrow NH_4Cl + H_2O$	(i) Soldering (ii) Electrolyte in dry cell and Leclanche cell (iii) Dyeing and calico printing (iv) Laboratory reagent
Ammonium sulphate $NH_3 + H_2SO_4 \longrightarrow (NH_4)_2SO_4$	(i) Fertiliser (ii) Preparation of other ammonium salts, like, ammonium carbonate and ammonium nitrate
Ammonium nitrate $(NH_4)SO_4 + 2NaNO_3 \longrightarrow Na_2SO_4 + 2NH_4NO_3$	(i) Fertiliser (ii) Explosives, like, amatol (NH_4NO_3 + 20% TNT) and ammonal (NH_4NO_3 + Al powder) (iii) Manufacture of nitrous oxide
Calcium ammonium nitrate—Mixture of calcium carbonate and ammonium nitrate	Fertiliser
Ammonium phosphate $NH_3 + H_3PO_4 \longrightarrow NH_4H_2PO_4$ $2NH_3 + H_3PO_4 \longrightarrow (NH_4)_2HPO_4$ $3NH_3 + H_3PO_4 \longrightarrow (NH_4)_3PO_4$	Fertiliser

Nitric Acid

Nitric acid is prepared by heating a mixture of potassium nitrate and concentrated sulphuric acid, when taken in a proportion in a retort. The vapours of nitric acid are passed into a receiver and cooled by water.

$$KNO_3 + H_2SO_4 \longrightarrow HNO_3 + KHSO_4$$

Physical Properties of Nitric Acid

Table 7.15 Important physical properties of nitric acid

Parameters	Characteristics
Colour	It is a colourless liquid but commercial nitric acid is yellowish brown in colour
Odour	Suffocating smell
Taste	Sour taste
Nature	Hygroscopic and fuming liquid
Density	Pure nitric acid has a density of 1.54 g/cm^3 and commercial nitric acid has lower density than the pure one, i.e., 1.42 g/cm^3
Solubility	Highly soluble in nature
Physiological action	Non-poisonous but stains skin yellow and causes very painful blisters
Boiling point	86°C
Melting point	–42°C

Chemical Properties of Nitric Acid

Table 7.16 Important chemical properties of nitric acid

Parameters	Characteristics
Action of heat	Nitric acid when subjected to simple heating decomposes to give reddish brown vapours of NO_2: $4HNO_3 \xrightarrow{\Delta} 2H_2O + 4NO_2 + O_2$
Dilution	When excess of water is added, self-ionization takes place giving hydronium ion and nitrate ion: $HNO_3 + H_2O \longrightarrow H_3O^+ + NO_3^-$
Reaction with metal oxides	Treating dilute HNO_3 with metallic oxide leads to the formation of metal nitrates and water: $CuO + 2HNO_3 \longrightarrow Cu(NO_3)_2 + H_2O$
Reaction with bases	On addition of dil HNO_3 to bases, metal nitrates and water are formed: $NaOH + HNO_3 \longrightarrow NaNO_3 + H_2O$
Reaction with metal carbonates	On addition of dil. HNO_3 to metal carbonates, metal nitrates are formed with evolution of CO_2 gas: $CaCO_3 + 2HNO_3 \longrightarrow Ca(NO_3)_2 + CO_2 + H_2O$
Oxidizing properties	It is a strong oxidizing agent due to the liberation of nascent oxygen: $2HNO_3 \longrightarrow 2HNO_2 + 2[O]$

(Continued)

Table 7.16 Continued

Parameters	Characteristics
Oxidation of non-metals	Heating a non-metal with conc. HNO_3 leads to the formation of oxyacid of that non-metal: $S + 6HNO_3 \longrightarrow H_2SO_4 + 6NO_2 + 2H_2O$ $P + 5HNO_3 \longrightarrow H_3PO_4 + 5NO_2 + H_2O$
Oxidation of metals	Metals with dilute nitric acid form metal nitrates and liberate other gases: **(i) Metals with dilute nitric acid** $3Cu + 8HNO_3 \longrightarrow 3Cu(NO_3)_2 + 2NO + 4H_2O$ $4Zn + 10HNO_3 \longrightarrow 4Zn(NO_3)_2 + N_2O + 5H_2O$ $Mg + 2HNO_3 \longrightarrow Mg(NO_3)_2 + H_2$ $Mn + 2HNO_3 \longrightarrow Mn(NO_3)_2 + H_2$
	(ii) Metals with conc. nitric acid Metals with concentrated nitric acid also form metal nitrates and liberate nitrogen dioxide gas: $Cu + 4HNO_3 \longrightarrow Cu(NO_3)_2 + 2NO_2 + H_2O$ $Zn + 4HNO_3 \longrightarrow Zn(NO_3)_2 + 2NO_2 + 5H_2O$
	(iii) With Fe, Co, Ni Certain metals, like, iron, cobalt, nickel, however, become passive and do not react with nitric acid.
Reaction with other inorganic compounds	Some inorganic compounds, like, H_2S, KI, SO_2 get oxidized by reducing HNO_3 to NO_2. $3H_2S + 2HNO_3 \longrightarrow 4H_2O + 2NO_2 + 3S$ $2KI + 2HNO_3 \longrightarrow 2KNO_3 + 2H_2O + 2NO + I_2$ $SO_2 + 2HNO_3 \longrightarrow H_2SO_4 + 2NO_2$ $6FeSO_4 + 3H_2SO_4 + 2HNO_3 \longrightarrow 4H_2O + 3Fe_2(SO_4)_3 + 2NO$ $3HCl + HNO_3 \longrightarrow 2H_2O + NOCl + Cl_2$

Konnect

Nitric acid due to its unique chemical properties and strong oxidizing nature is useful in many ways. It is used in making fertilizers, explosives, artificial silk and as a laboratory reagent.

Compounds of Phosphorous

Table 7.17 Important compounds of phosphorus

Compounds	Preparation	Uses
Phosphorous pentoxide	$4P + 5O_2 \longrightarrow 2P_2O_5$	As a dehydrating agent In making phosphoric acid
Phosphoric acid	$P_2O_5 + 3H_2O \longrightarrow 2H_3PO_4$	In the preparation of pharmaceuticals. In the manufacture of phosphates and phosphatic manures
Salts of phosphoric acid	$NaOH + H_3PO_4 \longrightarrow NaH_2PO_4 + H_2O$ Sodium dihydrogen. phosophate $2NaOH + H_3PO_4 \longrightarrow NaH_2PO_4 + H_2O$ (Disodium hydrogen phosphate) $3NaOH + H_3PO_4 \longrightarrow 3H_2O + Na_3PO_4$ (Sodium phosphate)	As anti-microbials coagulants, food preservatives, etc. In electronics, aviation, petroleum field. Used along with sodium bicarbonate in making baking powder. To clean out the intestines before a medical examination
Sodium hypophosphite	$4P + 3NaOH + 3H_2O \longrightarrow PH_3 + 3NaH_2PO_2$	As a reducing agent in electroplating
Metal phosphides	$2P + 3Ca \longrightarrow Ca_3P_2$ $2P + 3Zn \longrightarrow Zn_3P_2$	Zinc phosphide is used in making rat poison
Chlorides of phosphorus	$2P + 3Cl_2 \longrightarrow 2PCl_3$ $PCl_3 + Cl_2 \longrightarrow PCl_5$	In making $POCl_3$ and $PSCl_3$ which are used in making herbicides, insecticides and plasticisers
Superphosphate of lime	$Ca_3(PO_4)_2 + 2H_2SO_4 + 5H_2O$ ↓ $\underbrace{Ca(H2PO_4)_2.H_2O}_{\text{Super phosphate of lime}} + 2CaSO_4.2H_2O$	As a fertilizer

Compounds of Sulphur

The most important compound of sulphur are discussed below.

Sulphur Dioxide

This is an oxide of sulphur where one atom of sulphur is associated with two atoms of oxygen. It is found in exhaust emissions of internal combustion engine, in the industrial areas where coal and petroleum are used as fuels. In nature, it is found in volcanic gases.

Laboratory Preparation of Sulphur Dioxide

Sulphur dioxide is prepared in the laboratory by heating copper turning with concentrated sulphuric acid:

$$Cu + 2H_2SO_4 \longrightarrow CuSO_4 + 2H_2O + SO_2\uparrow$$

Physical Properties of Sulphur Dioxide

Table 7.18 Physical Properties of Sulphur dioxide

Parameters	Characteristics
Colour	Colourless
Odour	Pungent and suffocating
Taste	Sour
Vapour density	32 (2.2 times heavier than air)
Solubility in water	Fairly soluble
Boiling point	−10°C
Freezing point	−76°C
Physiological nature	Poisonous

Chemical Properties of Sulphur Dioxide

Table 7.19 Chemical Properties of Sulphur dioxide

Compounds	Preparation
Acidic nature	**(i) With litmus** Sulphur dioxide is acidic in nature and can change blue litmus to red **(ii) Reaction with water** Sulphur dioxide with water forms an unstable sulphurous acid: $H_2O + SO_2 \longrightarrow H_2SO_3$
Reducing properties	
Bleaching action	Sulphur dioxide is a good reducing agent. This on reaction with moisture or water produces nascent hydrogen which helps in the reducing action: $SO_2 \uparrow + H_2O \longrightarrow H_2SO_4 + 2[H]$ (reducing agent) The nascent hydrogen produced on being exposed to moisture acts as a bleach. It reduces the coloured matter to colourless. This reaction is reversible. The colourless product on exposure to atmospheric oxygen can get oxidized, and thus, regain its colour Colour vegetable + [H] ⟶ Colourless product + Water Bleached product + Atmospheric oxygen ⟶ Original colour
Addition reactions	The reducing property of sulphur dioxide is also seen in its adduct formation: $2SO_2 + O_2 \xrightarrow[400\text{–}500°C]{\text{Platinum}} 2SO_3$
Oxidizing property	When sulphur dioxide is introduced to burning potassium or magnesium metal, it oxidizes the metal to its oxide and sulphide: $2Mg + SO_2 \longrightarrow 2MgO + MgS$

Uses of Sulphur Dioxide

Sulphur dioxide, due to the above, mentioned properties, is useful in various fields. Sulphur dioxide is used:

1. In chemical industries for the preparation of sulphuric acid
2. In sugar industry to decolorize sugar cane juice
3. As a disinfectant due to its germicidal and insecticidal activity
4. As a bleaching agent
5. In refrigeration industry
6. As an antichlor to remove excess chlorine from articles

Sulphuric Acid

The level of industrialization of a country can be measured by the amount of sulphuric acid made by that country. It is also called **the king of the chemicals**, and **oil of vitriol** in certain cases.

In the free state, it is found in the hot water of sulphur springs and beds of mineral sulphides. In the combined state, it is found as mineral sulphates.

Manufacture of Sulphuric Acid

The large-scale manufacture of sulphuric acid is carried out by the contact process.

Contact Process

In this process, the basic raw material required is SO_2 which is produced by burning sulphur:

$$S + O_2 \longrightarrow SO_2$$

Manufacture of sulphuric acid from SO_2 takes place in two steps:

Step I: Sulphur dioxide and oxygen in a ratio of 2 : 1 by volume are passed over vanadium pentoxide, maintained at 450°C under high-pressure conditions. Under these conditions, the sulphur dioxide and oxygen react to form sulphur trioxide. Platinized asbestos can also be used in place of V_2O_5.

$$2SO_2 + O_2 \longrightarrow 2SO_3$$

Step II: Sulphur trioxide thus obtained is dissolved in sulphuric acid to form pyrosulphuric acid or oleum.

$$SO_3 + H_2SO_4 \longrightarrow \underset{\text{(Oleum)}}{H_2S_2O_7}$$

The pyrosulphuric acid on treatment with water gives sulphuric acid:

$$H_2S_2O_7 + H_2O \longrightarrow 2H_2SO_4$$

Info Bytes!

The sulphuric acid prepared by this method is pure and highly concentrated.

Physical Properties of Sulphuric Acid

Table 7.20 Physical properties of sulphuric acid

Parameters	Characteristics
Colour	Colourless
Odour	Odourless
Taste	Sour
State	Dense, oily liquid
Boiling point	338°C
Freezing point	−10.4°C
Solubility	Soluble in water
Physiological nature	Corrosive in nature

Chemical Properties of Sulphuric Acid

Table 7.21 Chemical properties of sulphuric acid

Properties	Reactions involved
Acidic nature	**(i) With metals** Metals which are more reactive than hydrogen, form metal sulphates with sulphuric acid, liberating hydrogen gas: $Zn + H_2SO_4 \longrightarrow ZnSO_4 + H_2 \uparrow$ $2Na + H_2SO_4 \longrightarrow Na_2SO_4 + H_2 \uparrow$ Copper and lead, however, react with sulphuric acid forming the corresponding sulphates, by liberating sulphur dioxide gas but not hydrogen gas: $Cu + 2H_2SO_4 \longrightarrow CuSO_4 + SO_2 + 2H_2O$
	(ii) With basic oxides Neutralization reaction takes place on reaction of sulphuric acid with basic oxides, giving metal sulphates and water: $K_2O + H_2SO_4 \longrightarrow K_2SO_4 + H_2O$ $CuO + H_2SO_4 \longrightarrow CuSO_4 + H_2O$
	(iii) With alkalis Sulphuric acid and alkalis undergo neutralization giving metal sulphates and water: $2NaOH + H_2SO_4 \longrightarrow Na_2SO_4 + H_2O$ $2KOH + H_2SO_4 \longrightarrow K_2SO_4 + H_2O$
	(iv) With chlorides and nitrates Sulphuric acid is a non-volatile acid. This on reaction with chlorides and nitrates gives hydrochloric acid and nitric acid: $Nacl + H_2SO_4 \longrightarrow NaHSO_4 + HCl \uparrow$ $KNO_3 + H_2SO_4 \longrightarrow KHSO_4 + HNO_3$
	(v) With carbonates and sulphites Reaction with carbonates and sulphites evolves carbon dioxide and sulphur dioxide gases, respectively, forming metal sulphates: $Na_2CO_3 + H_2SO_4 \longrightarrow Na_2SO_4 + H_2O + CO_2 \uparrow$ $Na_2SO_3 + H_2SO_4 \longrightarrow Na_2SO_4 + H_2O + SO_2 \uparrow$
Oxidizing property	Sulphuric acid on heating undergoes thermal decomposition giving nascent oxygen. Thus, sulphuric acid acts as an oxidizing agent. It can oxidize certain non-metals to its respective oxides $H_2SO_4 \longrightarrow H_2O \uparrow SO_2 \uparrow + [O]$ $S + 2H_2SO_4 \longrightarrow 2H_2O + 3SO_2 \uparrow$ $C + 2H_2SO_4 \longrightarrow 2H_2O + 2SO_2 \uparrow + CO_2 \uparrow$
Dehydrating property	Sulphuric acid is a very good dehydrating agent, i.e., it can remove hydrogen and oxygen in the form of water from a number of chemical compounds. Its dehydrating properties are clearly evident in removal of water from copper sulphate crystals, sugar and starch

(Continued)

Table 7.21 Continued

Properties	Reactions involved
	(i) Dehydration of hydrated salts Blue-coloured copper sulphate crystals ($CuSO_4.5H_2O$) which on treatment with sulphuric acid turns to a white powdery mass. This is because the water molecules associated with the crystal are being removed $\underset{\text{(Blue)}}{CuSO_4.5H_2O}+ \xrightarrow{H_2SO_4\text{(conc.)}} \underset{\text{(white powdery mass)}}{CuSO_4} + 5H_2O$
	(ii) Dehydration of sugars and starch Sugars and starch on treating with sulphuric acid turn to a black-coloured mass, i.e., carbon. All the hydrogen and oxygen atoms are removed as water, leaving behind carbon: $\underset{\text{(sugar)}}{C_{12}H_{22}O_{11}} \xrightarrow{\text{conc.} H_2SO_4} \underset{\text{(black mass)}}{12C} + 11H_2O$ $\underset{\text{(starch)}}{(C_5H_{10}O_5)_n} \xrightarrow{\text{conc.} H_2SO_4} 5nC + 5nH_2O$

Uses of Sulphuric Acid

Sulphuric acid being 'the king of the chemicals' has many uses in industry as well as regular life.

It is used:

1. In the manufacture of fertilizers
2. In making explosives, like, trinitrotoluene (TNT), trinitroglycerine (TNG), etc.
3. In storage batteries as an electrolyte
4. As a laboratory reagent
5. In extraction of metals
6. In pickling metals as sulphuric acid can remove metallic impurities

Hydrogen Sulphide

Hydrogen sulphide gas is well known for its rotten egg smell. In the free state, it is present in volcanic gases, water of springs and in the air near and around industrial areas.

Though the gas has bad smell and pollutes atmosphere, it is still prepared in the laboratory due to its certain unique properties and uses.

Laboratory Preparation of Hydrogen Sulphide

Ferrous sulphides react with hydrochloric acid to give ferrous chlorides, liberating hydrogen sulphide gas:

$$FeS + 2HCl \longrightarrow FeCl_2 + H_2S \uparrow$$

Physical Properties of Hydrogen Sulphide

Table 7.22 Physical properties of hydrogen sulphide

Parameters	Characteristics
Colour	Colourless
Odour	Smell of rotten eggs
Taste	Sour taste
Solubility	Fairly soluble in water
Vapour density	17 (1.2 times heavier than air)

Chemical Properties of Hydrogen Sulphide

Table 7.23 Chemical properties of hydrogen sulphide

Properties	Reactions involved
Acidic nature	Hydrogen sulphide is acidic in nature and can change blue litmus to red
Reducing nature	Hydrogen sulphide shows reducing properties by adding hydrogen atoms in some cases
	(i) With oxygen Hydrogen sulphide undergoes combustion during which it reduces oxygen to water: $2H_2S + O_2 \longrightarrow 2S + 2H_2O$ It, however, does not support combustion
	(ii) With chlorine Chlorine on reaction with hydrogen sulphide is reduced to hydrogen chloride: $H_2S + Cl_2 \longrightarrow 2HCl\uparrow + S$
	(iii) With potassium permanganate Decolourization of potassium permanganate is observed on its reaction with H_2S. This is because potassium permanganate is reduced to manganese sulphate by hydrogen sulphide, thus, decolourizing it: $2KMnO_4 + 3H_2SO_4 + 5H_2S \longrightarrow K_2SO_4 + 2MnSO_4 + 8H_2O + 5S$

Uses of Hydrogen Sulphide

The most important application of hydrogen sulphide gas is in analytical chemistry. Hydrogen sulphide on reaction with aqueous solutions of metal salts converts them to metal sulphides. These metal sulphides are in the form of precipitates. The colour of the precipitate depends upon the nature of metal ion. Therefore, hydrogen sulphide is mainly used for the detection of metal cations present in the metal salts.

$$Pb(NO_3)_2 + H_2S \longrightarrow \underset{\text{(Black precipitate)}}{PbS} + 2HNO_3$$

$$CuSO_4 + H_2S \longrightarrow \underset{\text{(Black precipitate)}}{CuS} + H_2SO_4$$

$$ZnSO_4 + H_2S \longrightarrow \underset{\text{(White precipitate)}}{ZnS} + H_2SO_4$$

$$MnSO_4 + H_2S \longrightarrow \underset{\text{(Flesh-coloured precipitate)}}{MnS} + H_2SO_4$$

Compounds of Chlorine

Chlorine is used in the manufacture of various industrially useful compounds. The compounds of chlorine find applications in various fields, such as, textiles, paper, dyestuffs, etc. Most of the applications of chlorine are basically due to its oxidizing and bleaching action.

Bleaching Powder

Bleaching powder is one of the most important compounds of chlorine which is widely used for the purification of drinking water owing to its germicidal and disinfectant action.

The chemical name of bleaching powder is calcium chlorohypochlorite or calcium oxychloride. The formula of bleaching powder is $CaOCl_2$.

Preparation of Bleaching Powder

Chlorine gas on passing through slaked lime at high temperature (400°C) gives bleaching powder:

$$Ca(OH)_2 + Cl_2 \longrightarrow CaOCl_2 + H_2O$$

Process: Manufacture of bleaching powder can be done in two types of plants, namely, Hasenclever plant and Bachmann plant.

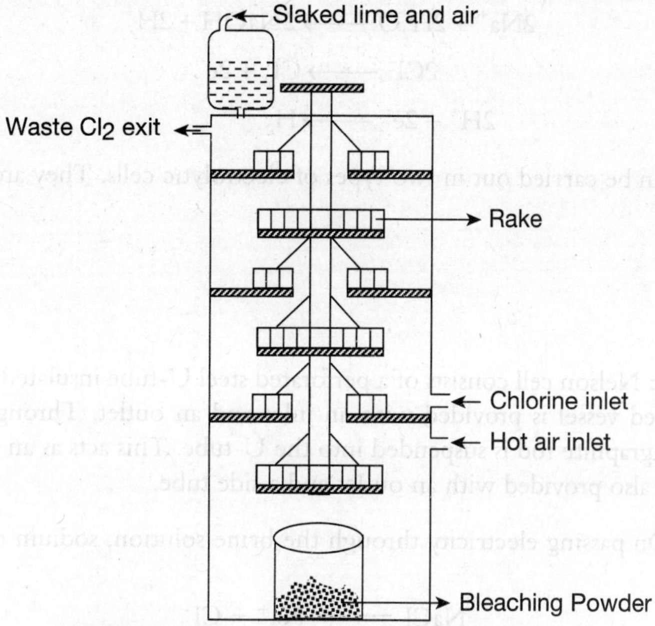

Figure 7.7 Preparation of bleaching powder

Bachmann Plant

The plant consists of a vertical tower made of cast iron. This is called **chlorinating tower**. Two inlets are provided at the base of the tower for the entry of chlorine gas and hot air into the tower. A hopper is provided at the top of the tower for the introduction of slaked lime into the tower. The entire tower is made up of horizontal shelves provided with rotating rakes.

Dry slaked lime is introduced into the chlorinating tower through hopper. Hot air and chlorine gas are sent into the tower through the inlets provided at the bottom of the plant. Due to the movement of rotating rakes, slaked lime moves downwards, whereas chlorine gas along with hot air moves upwards. This counter-current mechanism helps the thorough mixing up of chlorine gas with slaked lime which leads to completion of the reaction.

Uses of Bleaching Powder

1. The most important use of chlorine is the bleaching of cotton, linen and wood pulp. Due to this bleaching property, bleaching powder finds its use in textile industry and manufacture of paper.
2. Bleaching powder being a mild bleaching agent is best suited for bleaching of delicate articles, such as, silk, ivory, etc.
3. Another important application of bleaching powder is its use as a disinfectant and germicide.
4. Bleaching powder also finds its use in the manufacture of chloroform.

Industrial Application of Sodium Chloride

Common salt which is mainly used as a flavouring agent for foodstuffs has many industrial applications also. Sodium chloride is the most important raw material for the production of a number of compounds, such as, chlorine, hydrochloric acid, sodium hydroxide, etc.

Sodium Hydroxide

Manufacture of Sodium Hydroxide

An aqueous solution of sodium chloride is called **brine**. This brine solution on electrolysis produces sodium hydroxide as the principal product. Hydrogen and chlorine are obtained as by-products.

$$NaCl \longrightarrow Na^+ + Cl^-$$

$$2Na^+ + 2H_2O \longrightarrow 2NaOH + 2H^+$$

$$2Cl^- \longrightarrow Cl_2 + 2e^-$$

$$2H^+ + 2e^- \longrightarrow H_2$$

The process of electrolysis can be carried out in two types of electrolytic cells. They are:

1. Nelson cell
2. Castner–Kellner cell

Nelson Cell Method

Construction of Nelson cell: Nelson cell consists of a perforated steel U-tube insulated by asbestos lining. This U-tube acts as a cathode. The U-shaped vessel is provided with an inlet and an outlet. Through the inlet, a brine solution is introduced into the U-tube. A graphite rod is suspended into the U-tube. This acts as an anode. This cell is suspended in a rectangular steel tank. This is also provided with an outlet and a side tube.

Process of Electrolysis: On passing electricity through the brine solution, sodium chloride dissociates to give Na^+ and Cl^- ions.

$$NaCl \longrightarrow Na^+ + Cl^-$$

Chloride ions get discharged at anode liberating chlorine gas. This is collected through an outlet provided for the U-tube.

$$2Cl^- \longrightarrow Cl_2 + 2e^-$$

Steam is allowed to enter the rectangular steel tank. Sodium ions penetrate through asbestos and react with steam thereby forming sodium hydroxide:

$$Na^+ + H_2O \longrightarrow NaOH + H^+$$

H^+ ions get discharged at the cathode where they undergo reduction to liberate hydrogen gas which is collected through the outlet provided for in the rectangular steel tank:

$$2H^+ + 2e^- \longrightarrow H_2$$

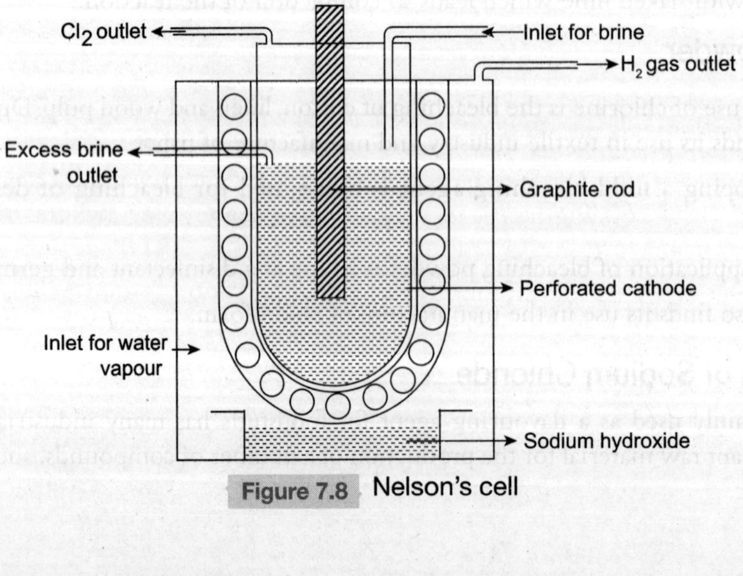

Figure 7.8 Nelson's cell

Castner–Kellner Cell

Construction of Electrolytic Cell: The cell consists of a rectangular iron tank which is made into three compartments by means of two non-porous slate partitions. These partitions should be suspended from the top in such a way that they do not touch the bottom of the cell. Mercury is taken at the bottom of the cell. This mercury can be made to circulate in the three compartments by means of the eccentric wheels arranged at the bottom of the cell. The mercury taken in the bottom part of the cell acts as an intermediate electrode. In the middle compartment it acts as an anode, whereas in the two outer compartments, it acts as a cathode. The two outer compartments are filled with the brine solution and the central compartment is filled with dilute sodium hydroxide solution. Graphite rods are inserted in the outer compartments which act as the anode. A bunch of iron rods suspended in the middle compartment functions as the cathode.

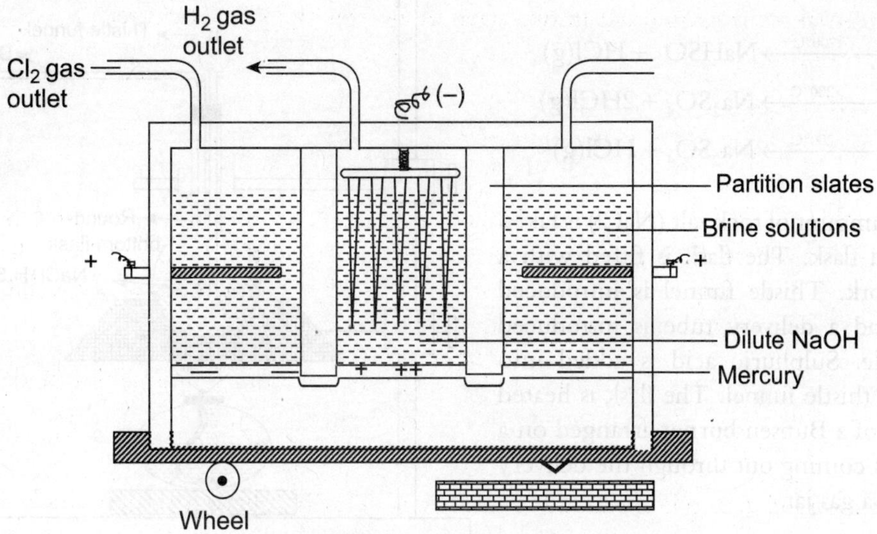

Figure 7.9 Castner–Kellner cell

Process of Electrolysis: On passing electricity through the electrolytic solution, sodium chloride dissociates as Na^+ and Cl^- ions:

$$2NaCl \longrightarrow 2Na^+ + 2Cl^-$$

Chloride ions get discharged at anode and chlorine gas is liberated at anode:

$$\textbf{Anode: } 2Cl^- \longrightarrow Cl_2 + 2e^-$$

Since mercury present in the outer compartments acts as cathode, Na^+ ions get discharged there and lose their charge. Sodium metal which is formed combines with mercury to form sodium amalgam:

$$\textbf{Hg cathode: } Hg + 2Na^+ + 2e^- \longrightarrow Na_2Hg$$

Sodium amalgam thus formed in the outer compartments is brought into the central compartment by the rotatory movement of the eccentric wheels. Sodium amalgam reacts with water forming sodium hydroxide solution which is removed and concentrated.

On evaporation and subsequent cooling of concentrated NaOH solution, solid pellets of sodium hydroxide are obtained:

$$\textbf{Hg anode: } Na_2Hg - 2e^- \longrightarrow 2Na^+ + Hg$$

$$\textbf{Cathode: } 2H_2O + 2e^- \longrightarrow H_2 + 2OH^-$$

$$2\,Na^+ + 2OH^- \longrightarrow 2NaOH$$

Hydrogen Chloride

The electrolysis of a brine solution gives sodium hydroxide as the major product and hydrogen and chlorine as the minor products. These by-products are used in the manufacture of industrially useful compounds, such as, hydrogen chloride.

Preparation of Hydrogen Chloride

Laboratory Method

Metallic chlorides on heating with concentrated sulphuric acid liberate hydrogen chloride gas. This gas on dissolution in water produces hydrochloric acid. Example: sodium chloride on treatment with H_2SO_4 liberates hydrogen chloride gas:

$$NaCl + H_2SO_4 \xrightarrow{<200°C} NaHSO_4 + HCl(g)$$

$$2NaCl + H_2SO_4 \xrightarrow{>200°C} Na_2SO_4 + 2HCl(g)$$

$$NaHSO_4 + NaCl \xrightarrow{>200°C} Na_2SO_4 + HCl(g)$$

Process: Specific amount of rock salt (NaCl) is taken in a round-bottomed flask. The flask is fitted with a two-holed rubber cork. Thistle funnel is introduced through one hole and a delivery tube is introduced through another hole. Sulphuric acid is added into the flask through the thistle funnel. The flask is heated gently with the help of a Bunsen burner arranged on a tripod stand. HCl gas coming out through the delivery tube is collected into a gas jar.

Collection of gas: Since HCl is heavier than air, it is collected by upward displacement of air.

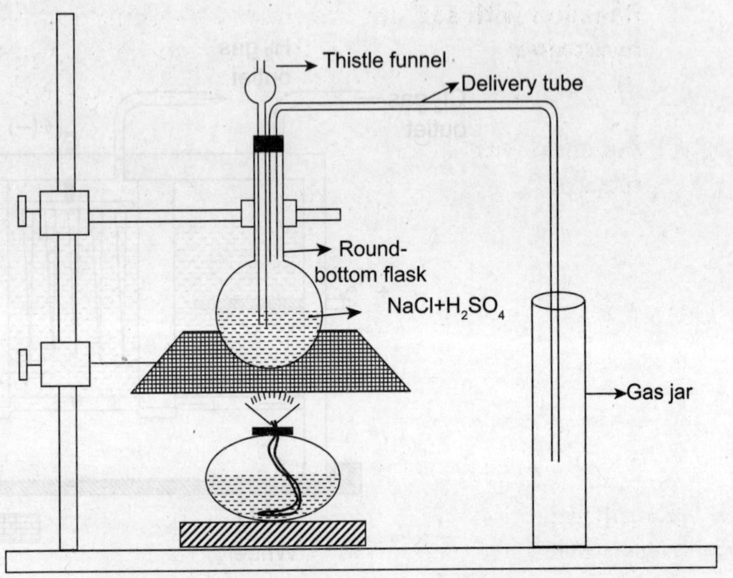

Figure 7.10 Preparation of hydrogen chloride

Industrial Method

Hydrogen and chlorine gas when taken in equal volumes and exposed to diffuse sunlight give hydrogen chloride. This is a photochemical reaction since it takes place in presence of light. Mild heating of hydrogen gas in the atmosphere of chlorine gas also gives hydrogen chloride:

$$H_2 + Cl_2 \xrightarrow{Sunlight} 2HCl$$

Physical Properties of Hydrogen Chloride

Table 7.24 Physical properties of hydrogen chloride

Parameters	Characteristics
Colour	Colourless
Odour	Pungent smell
Density	Heavier than air (VD = 18)
Solubility	Highly soluble in water forming hydrochloric acid. Also soluble in moist air. Dense white fumes appear due to the formation of tiny droplets of hydrochloric acid

Chemical Properties of Hydrogen Chloride

Table 7.25 Chemical properties of hydrogen chloride

Parameters	Characteristics
Reaction with ammonia	When a glass rod dipped in ammonia is introduced into a gas jar containing hydrogen chloride gas, dense white fumes of ammonium chloride are formed: $NH_3 + HCl \longrightarrow NH_4Cl$
Reaction with sodium hydroxide	Hydrogen chloride gas on reaction with sodium hydroxide forms sodium chloride and water. This is called **neutralization reaction**: $HCl + NaOH \longrightarrow NaCl + H_2O$
Reaction with silver nitrate	When a solution of HCl is added to silver nitrate solution, a white precipitate of silver chloride is formed: $HCl + AgNO_3 \longrightarrow AgCl\downarrow + HNO_3$

Uses of Hydrogen Chloride

1. As a laboratory reagent
2. In the preparation of chlorine
3. In the manufacture of silver chloride needed for making photographic films

Human civilization started with observation of nature. People observed nature and implemented their ideas to develop different articles, like, wheel, potteries, simple weapons by using some natural resources, like, clay, wood, sand, stone, etc., for minimizing their day-to-day struggle for existence. Then the discovery of certain metals and non-metals was a major breakthrough in the course of civilization. Slowly people started exploring more and more natural resources and converting them into different forms to achieve a comfortable and easy lifestyle, and this effort ultimately led to the industrial revolution. Invention of glass and ceramic was a big stride towards the modern civilization. Invention of chemical fertilizers has brought major changes in the cultivation of crops and yield of food products which lead to the green revolution.

Other than this, invention of many other chemical substances, like, polymers, plastics, synthetic fibres; like, nylon, rayon and soaps and detergents brought a paradigm change in the comfort zone of human life. In view of their significant role in the socio-economic development of society, appreciable industrial importance has been attributed to these substances which make their study inevitable.

EXAMPLE 7.4 What is the difference between the reaction of HCl with ammonia to that of HCl with silver nitrate?

SOLUTION

HCl reaction with ammonia:

When a glass rod dipped in ammonia is introduced into a gas jar containing hydrogen chloride gas, dense white fumes of ammonium chloride is formed:

$$NH_3 + HCl \rightarrow NH_4Cl$$

HCl reaction with silver nitrate:

When a solution of HCl is added to silver nitrate solution, a white precipitate of silver chloride is formed:

$$HCl + AgNO_3 \rightarrow AgCl\downarrow + HNO_3$$

Some Industrially Important Compounds

Glass

Glass is a homogeneous supercooled liquid. Its very high viscosity gives it an appearance of a solid. Major constituents of glass are sodium silicate, calcium silicate and silica. The arrangement of the constituent particles in the glass does not follow any regular pattern.

Manufacture of Glass

Raw Material: The raw materials used in the manufacture of glass are soda ash (Na_2CO_3), limestone ($CaCO_3$) and silica (SiO_2).

Process: Finely powdered silica, sodium carbonate and calcium carbonate are mixed with broken glass pieces called **cullet** and heated at about 1600 K–1700 K. Cullet increases the fusibility of the raw material. Sodium carbonate and calcium carbonate react with silica to form respective silicates with the evolution of CO_2. The most significant part of manufacture of glass is cooling of molten glass which should be carried out carefully at a moderate and uniform rate in order to achieve the required properties of glass.

Manufacture of Glassware

Different methods are adopted for the manufacture of different types of glass ware from molten glass.

Blowing

Hollow glass articles are manufactured by glass-blowing technology. There are two different methods of glass blowing:

1. **Free-blowing:** The process of free-blowing involves the blowing of air to inflate the molten glass which is gathered at one end of the blowpipe to give the desired shape. Here the perfection depends on the skill of the glass worker.
2. **Mould-blowing:** Mould-blowing is an alternate glass-blowing method that was developed after the technique of free-blowing. In this process, molten glass is inflated into a wooden or metal-carved mould with the help of the blow pipe which gives the molten glass the shape and design of the interior of the mould.

Pressing

In this process, a motorized plunger is used to press the molten glass taken inside the blank mould to make the glass containers and utensils.

Float Glass Method

Besides the above processes, the flat or sheet glass which is widely used as window panes, glass walls, glass doors, etc., is manufactured by floating molten glass on a bed of molten tin. This sheet of glass made by this process possesses uniform thickness and very flat surface.

Types of Glass

Since glass has a wide variety of applications, the characteristics of glass are required to be changed to achieve the specific properties suitable for the end products. This can be done by doping different compounds in glass.

Silica Glass

The raw material of silica glass is almost 100% pure form of quartz, and hence, it is very expensive. It undergoes very less thermal expansion and has high chemical resistance. Due to these characteristics, it is used for the manufacture of laboratory apparatus.

Borosilicate Glass

Borosilicate glass is composed of about 80% silica, 13% boron trioxide, small amount of oxides of sodium and aluminium. Its coefficient of thermal expansion is low, softening point is very high and it is resistant to a wide variety of chemicals. These properties make it suitable for the manufacture of laboratory ware.

Alkali Silicate Glass

The raw materials of alkali silicate glass are sand and soda. It is also known as water glass because it is soluble in water and used only as a solution. It is generally used for making gums and adhesives.

Lead Glass

In lead glass, lead oxide is added which increases the density of the glass thereby increasing its refractive index. This type of glass is used for the manufacture of ornamental glassware, decorative articles, etc.

Optical Glass

Optical glass is required to be absolutely flawless because it is used for the manufacture of optical instruments, like, binoculars, spectacles, lenses, prisms, telescopes, microscopes, etc. This type of glass is completely transparent and can be ground into the required shape. Optical glass generally contains phosphorus and lead silicate with little cerium oxide which absorbs the UV radiation. However, it has the widest range of composition with slight variation in the ingredients which gives rise to slight variation in optical properties and makes the glass suitable for the specific end product.

Coloured Glass

The colour of the glass can be obtained by the homogeneous distribution of different ions throughout the glass during the manufacture of glass. Presence of different oxides of iron gives green or brown colour, whereas the presence of oxides of copper gives rise to light blue or red colour. This type of glass is used for decorative, technical and scientific purposes.

Table 7.26 Compounds used in coloured glasses

Compounds	Colours
Iron oxides	Green, brown
Manganese oxides	Deep amber, amethyst, used as decolorizer
Cobalt oxide	Deep blue

Processed Glass

Properties of glass are not only attributed to the slight alteration of the ingredients but also to the processing of the glass. Some of the examples of processed glass and their applications are given below:

Table 7.27 Different types of processed glass and their uses

Processed glass	Applications
Laminated glass	Doors and windows of automobiles because it provides good strength to the glass
Fibre glass	Used for reinforcing purpose due to its high tensile strength
Foam glass	Light weight glass used for civil construction and insulation purposes
Opaque glass	Non-transparent glass filters the light entering into it and provides an aesthetic look

Ceramics

Ceramics are hard, brittle substances made up of oxides, nitrides, carbides, borides, etc., which have high resistance to heat, electricity and chemicals and can have high-mechanical strength and impact resistance. Ceramics find a wide variety of applications ranging from simple pottery, sanitary wave and floor tiles to nuclear fuel, superconductors and joint replacements in human body.

Pottery

Pottery is representation of the articles which are made up of clay. Clay is a mixture of fine particles of quartz, feldspar, mica, mineral carbonates, oxides and sulphides of iron in varying proportions. When mixed with the right proportion of water, it exhibits a unique property called **plasticity**. Due to this property, articles of different shapes can be made from the clay kneaded with definite proportion of water. After drying, the articles are strongly heated in a kiln. During heating at a suitably high temperature, different physical and chemical changes occur in those substances which convert clay to ceramic material.

Pottery can be classified into three categories depending on the raw materials used and the temperature at which the objects are fired:

1. **Earthenware:** In this type of potteries, clay is the major constituent and the objects are fired at a comparatively lower temperature. Colourful glazes can be used at this temperature to make the pottery impervious to liquid and give a glossy appearance. Earthenware includes utensils, crockery, decorative items, etc.
2. **Stoneware:** During the manufacture of this type of potteries, the clay articles are heated at a much higher temperature, and hence, it has a greater strength. Drain water pipes, sanitary ware, etc., are the examples of stoneware.
3. **Porcelain:** It is the purest and the most delicate type of pottery. The raw materials used are kaolin, a fine white clay, controlled amount of feldspar and flint. After firing at a higher temperature, these articles become impermeable. Porcelain ware are glazed and enamelled for further beautification. Different metallic oxides are used in the process of enamelling which impart a variety of colours to the articles. Bone china is a kind of porcelain which is made translucent to light by adding calcium phosphate to clay. Porcelain finds applications ranging from crockery, statues, decorative items to plumbing fixtures, electrical insulators as well as in aerospace industries.

Fertilizer

Like other living beings, plants require food for their growth. A wide variety of elements are required for many different purposes for the nourishment of plants. Among these carbon, oxygen and hydrogen are the principal nutrients. Nitrogen, phosphorus, potassium, magnesium, sulphur, calcium and iron play significant role for the growth and development of plants. These elements are called **major plant nutrients**. Some other elements, like, manganese, molybdenum, copper, boron, zinc, iron, chlorine, etc., are used by the field crops in very small quantities. These are called **minor plant nutrients**.

The sources of carbon, hydrogen and oxygen are air and water, whereas the other elements are required to be absorbed by the plants from the soil. Assimilation of these nutrients in the required proportions leads to the growth of healthy plants. But the soil may become deficient of nutrients. Manures and fertilizers are added to replenish the nutrients in the soil. Some of the common manures are cow dung, compost, bone meal, remains of fish, etc. But the ever, increasing demand for food crops which could not be met by the available natural manures necessitated the development and use of chemical fertilizers.

Konnect

Micronutrients are also added to the soil in the form of fertilizer. These are called **secondary fertilizers**. Before applying the fertilizer, the soil is analysed chemically. The selection of the fertilizer depends upon the condition of the soil and the crops to be grown in that soil.

Chemical fertilizers can be broadly classified into three types:

1. **Nitrogenous fertilizers:** Ammonium sulphate and urea
2. **Phosphatic fertilizers:** Superphosphate and ammonium phosphate
3. **Potash fertilizers:** Potassium chloride and potassium sulphate

Fibre

Biologically fibres are the continuous filaments which hold tissues together, and hence, the natural sources of fibre are plants and animals. Application of fibre in our daily life is diverse. A simple thread which is used for stitching clothes, household decorative items, like, carpet, gunny bags for storage of food items and variety of fabrics are originated from fibres. Depending on the source and process of manufacture, fibres can be classified into the following two broad categories.

Natural Fibre

Fibre obtained from natural sources is known as a **natural fibre**. Cotton, silk, wool, etc., are the examples of the natural fibres. Basic constituent of cotton is cellulose which is obtained from plants, whereas wool and silk are obtained from animals the basic constituents of these fibres being the protein molecules.

Synthetic Fibre

Fibres which are manufactured artificially through chemical processes are called **synthetic fibres**. Rayon is a fibre which is manufactured from the natural resources like cellulose present in wood pulp and it is called **regenerated fibre**. Rayon can be considered as an intermediate between the natural and synthetic fibres. Nylon, dacron, terylene, etc., are obtained from petroleum (crude oil). The yarns, i.e., the long threads of synthetic fibre are manufactured by passing the solution of the polymers produced from the crude oil through a sieve with very fine holes.

Synthetic fibres have many advantages over natural fibres. These fibres can be manufactured at large scale and the cost of production is lesser. They are more durable and less wettable when compared to cotton. However, with respect to comfort, natural fibres are ahead of synthetic fibres.

Plastic

Plastics are made up of long chains of polymers obtained by the interlinkage of certain specific molecules each of same chemical composition. Examples of such polymers are polyethylene, polystyrene, polyamide, etc. Like fibre, plastic also has diversified fields of application from domestic articles to a wide range of industrial equipment, namely, body of automobiles, furniture, construction materials of buildings, telecommunication equipment, etc., owing to its unique properties, like, light weight, mechanical strength and aesthetic appearance. Based on the thermal behaviour, plastics can be divided into two categories—Thermoplastics and thermosets.

Thermoplastics

This type of plastics can be processed repeatedly by melting and subsequent solidification without undergoing any chemical change. Hence, they can be reused. Examples of thermoplastics are polyethylene, polyvinyl chloride, etc.

Thermosets

Plastics of this variety cannot be softened by heating, and thus, they cannot be reused. Examples of thermosets are urea–formaldehyde resin, epoxy resin, etc.

Soaps and Detergents

Soaps and detergents are the two artificially synthesised substances which are indispensable in our daily activity. Based on chemical composition soaps are the sodium or potassium salts of fatty acids, whereas detergents are sodium or potassium salts of alkyl sulphonic acids. Both soaps and detergents are soluble in water and act as surfactants which reduce the surfaces tension of water to a great extent. This increases the water–fabric interaction as a consequence of which dirt particles, grease spots, etc., are washed away effectively. In other words, soaps and detergents enhance the cleansing action of water.

Detergents can be used with hard water containing soluble chloride and sulphate salts of calcium and magnesium effectively, while soaps being ineffective with hard water due to the formation of curdy precipitates with the above salts with poor lather formation.

EXAMPLE 7.5 Why is common salt sprinkled over pots during the heating process while making pots?

SOLUTION

At high temperature, common salt ionizes to Na^+ and Cl^-. These ions fill up the pores of the pot giving it a smooth and glassy finish.

EXAMPLE 7.6

(a) Why are plastic containers preferred for storing chemicals?

(b) Why are the materials made of plastic more in use rather than other substances?

(c) Why are handles of screw drivers used for electrical works made of plastics?

(d) Mention two examples of plastics in the medical field.

(e) Name the special plastic used for non-stick coating pans.

SOLUTION

(a) Plastics are chemically resistant. Hence, plastic containers are preferred for storing chemicals

(b) Plastics are cheap, durable and available in attractive shapes and colours. Hence, the materials made of plastic more in use rather than other substances

(c) As plastics are poor conductors of electricity handles of screw drivers used for electrical works made of plastics

(d) Plastics are used in packing tablets, doctor gloves, syringes, etc.

(e) Teflon is the special plastic used for non-stick coating pans.

POINTS TO REMEMBER

- ✔ Some non-metals in the form of their compounds occupy the most pivotal position in the industrial sector and they are rightly called industrial chemicals.
- ✔ The mixture of calcium cyanamide and graphite is known as nitrolim.
- ✔ The process of conversion of the atmospheric nitrogen into the usable form either by natural or artificial means is called nitrogen fixation.
- ✔ The entire process of nitrogen fixation and the reconversion of this fixed nitrogen into free nitrogen is called nitrogen cycle.
- ✔ The phenomenon of existence of an element in more than one form is called allotropy, and those different forms of an element are called allotropes.
- ✔ The liquid sulphur obtained after distillation is collected in the form of solid rolls, and hence, called roll sulphur.
- ✔ 95.6°C is called transition temperature of the two allotropes of sulphur.
- ✔ The level of industrialization of a country can be measured by the amount of sulphuric acid made by that country. It is also called the king of the chemicals, and oil of vitriol in certain cases.
- ✔ Bachmann Plant consists of a vertical tower made of cast iron. This is called chlorinating tower.
- ✔ Nitrogen, phosphorus, potassium, magnesium, sulphur, calcium and iron play significant role for the growth and development of plants. These elements are called major plant nutrients.
- ✔ Some other elements, like, manganese, molybdenum, copper, boron, zinc, iron, chlorine, etc., are used by the field crops in very small quantities. These are called minor plant nutrients.
- ✔ Micronutrients are also added to the soil in the form of fertilizer. These are called secondary fertilizers.
- ✔ Fibre obtained from natural sources is known as a natural fibre.
- ✔ Fibres which are manufactured artificially through chemical processes are called synthetic fibres.
- ✔ Rayon is a fibre which is manufactured from the natural resources like cellulose present in wood pulp and it is called regenerated fibre.
- ✔ Plastics are made up of long chains of polymers obtained by the interlinkage of certain specific molecules each of same chemical composition.

PRACTICE QUESTIONS CLASSROOM WING

Very Short Answer Type Questions

Direction for questions from 1 to 5: **Fill in the blanks.**

1. Sugar, on treating with sulphuric acid, turns to a black coloured mass. The property of sulphuric acid exploited in this process is ________.
2. Hydrogen sulphide, on combustion, gives sulphur and water. This reaction indicates the ________ of hydrogen sulphide.
3. Formula of fluorapatite is ________.
4. ________ process is used to extract sulphur from deposits near the earth's crust.
5. Equal volumes of nitrogen and oxygen react to give ________.

Direction for questions from 6 to 26: **Answer the following questions.**

6. Aqueous solution of 'X' on treatment with copper sulphate solution gives a pale blue precipitate of 'Y'. What could be X and Y?
7. Identify 'X' and 'Y' in the following flowchart.

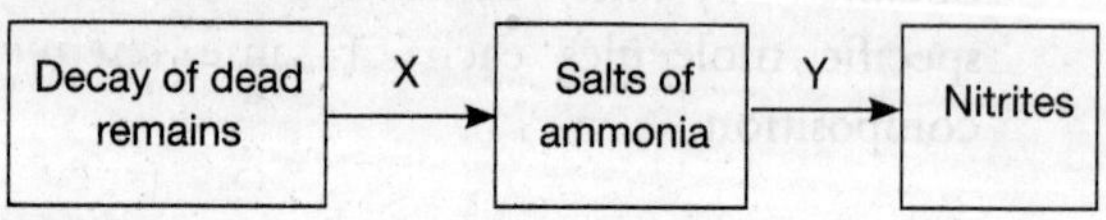

8. In the olden days, white phosphorus was used in safety matches. Now, it has been replaced by red phosphorus. What is the reason for the replacement?
9. Copper sulphate on treatment with excess aqueous solution of 'X' gives a dark blue solution of 'Y'. Identify X and Y.
10. What happens when chlorine reacts with phosphorus?
11. Explain the acidic nature of sulphur dioxide based on its reactivity with water.
12. Give a brief description of the structure of white phosphorous.
13. Explain the chemical reaction of chlorine with hydrogen sulphide.
14. Why soap is ineffective with hard water?
15. What is the valency of nitrogen in ammonia? What is CAN? How is it useful?
16. Define glass blowing. What are the different methods employed for glass blowing?
17. What are the advantages of synthetic fibres over natural fibres?
18. How does nitrogen occur in the combined state?
19. Mention the chemical formulae of the following:
    (i) phosgene
    (ii) tear gas
    (iii) chloroform
20. What is the composition of ceramics?
21. What are the major and minor plant nutrients? Give three examples for each.
22. Write the balanced chemical reaction of the burning of ammonia in oxygen
23. What is nitrolim? How is it obtained?
24. Discuss the physical properties of chlorine.
25. How is principle of countercurrents is useful in Bachmann plant?
26. Why are dense white fumes formed when hydrogen chloride is dissolved in moist air?

Short Answer Type Questions

27. Write the equation for the following:
    (i) addition of concentrated HNO_3 to copper
    (ii) addition of dilute HNO_3 to zinc
28. Write a note on safety matches.
29. Describe how sulphur is extracted using the Sicilian process.
30. (A) Differentiate between rhombic and monoclinic sulphur.
    (B) The most significant part of manufacture of glass is cooling of molten glass. Mention the desirable conditions for cooling and give reasons.
31. How is H_2S used as an analytical reagent?

32. Mention the uses of chlorine.

33. Explain the reaction of chlorine gas with turpentine.

34. Name the products formed in the following reactions:

(i) reaction of sodium nitrate with ammonium sulphate

(ii) reaction of potassium iodide with nitric acid

(iii) addition of HNO_3 to sulphur

35. Explain the cleansing action of a soap.

36. Write two uses of ammonia.

37. Discuss briefly the chemical properties of H_2S.

38. Explain various types of chemical fertilizers with examples.

39. Why does sulphur dioxide act as a bleaching agent?

40. What is plastic? Write a short note on different categories of plastic.

41. Explain with equations the electrical process for the extraction of phosphorous.

Essay Answer Type Questions

42. Write in detail about the compounds formed by phosphorous and their uses.

43. Explain in detail how sulphuric acid is prepared by the contact process.

44. Explain the construction and working of a Nelson cell.

45. Discuss the method of preparation of bleaching powder.

46. Explain the basic working of the Castner–Kellner cell, used for producing NaOH (sodium hydroxide).

47.

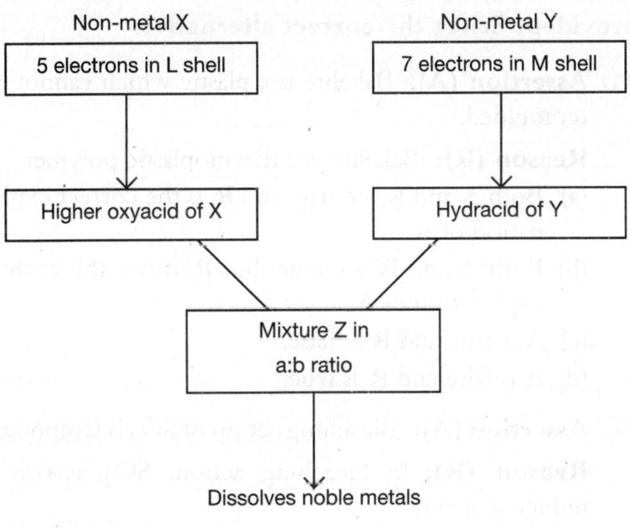

(i) Identify X and Y.

(ii) What are the values of a and b?

(iii) What is Z called?

(iv) A Hungarian chemist named Georgy de Hensey dissolved two noble prizes made u gold in the mixture Z in order to protect them from Nazis. How was it possible and he revive the gold?

PRACTICE QUESTIONS COMPETITION WING

Level 1: Apply Your Concepts

Directions for questions from 1 to 12 :
State whether the following statements are true or false.

1. Both rhombic sulphur and monoclinic sulphur are crystalline and soluble in CS_2.
2. The chemical formula of nitre is $NaNO_3$.
3. Ammonia on reaction with excess chlorine gives white dense fumes.
4. Sodium is deposited at the cathode during the electrolysis of brine solution.
5. Zinc sulphate solution on passage of H_2S gives a flesh-coloured precipitate.
6. Generally laboratory apparatus are made with borosilicate glass.
7. Urea is a nitrogenous fertilizer.
8. Carbon dioxide and dust particles are removed before air for liquefaction.
9. Nitrogen is used in rat poison.
10. Atomicity of chlorine is 3.
11. The basic component of cotton is cellulose.
12. Chlorine does not react with magnesium.

Directions for questions from 13 to 19 :
Fill in the blanks.

13. Liquid ________ is used for preserving biological specimen.
14. Density of white phosphorus is ________ than red phosphorus.
15. In Castner–Kellner cell, sodium ions react with mercury to form ________.
16. In Nelson cell, H_2 is liberated at ________.
17. Oxygen required for the combustion of safety matches can be produced from ________.
18. ________ bacteria convert atmospheric nitrogen into nitrogenous compounds.
19. Ammonia on reaction with potassium gives ________.

Directions for question 20:
Match the entries in column A with the appropriate ones in Column B.

20. Match the statements of Column A with those of Column B.

Column A	Column B
(i) Nitrogen	(a) Gunpowder
(ii) Phosphorus	(b) Storage batteries
(iii) Sulphur	(c) Rat poison
(iv) Hydrogen sulphide	(d) Refrigerant
(v) Sulphuric acid	(e) Analytical reagent

Directions for questions from 21 to 42:
For each of the questions, four choices have been provided. Select the correct alternative.

21. **Assertion (A):** Bakelite is a plastic which cannot be remoulded.

Reason (R): Bakelite is a thermoplastic polymer.

(a) Both A and R are true and R is the correct explanation of A.
(b) Both A and R are true, but R is not the correct explanation of A.
(c) A is true and R is false.
(d) A is false and R is true.

22. **Assertion (A):** Bleaching action of SO_2 is temporary.

Reason (R): In bleaching action, SO_2 acts as a reducing agent.

(a) Both A and R are true and R is the correct explanation of A.
(b) Both A and R are true, but R is not the correct explanation of A.
(c) A is true and R is false.
(d) A is false and R is true.

23. **Assertion (A):** Nitric acid is used in the purification of gold.

Reason (R): HNO_3 is a strong reducing agent.

(a) Both A and R are true and R is the correct explanation of A.

(b) Both A and R are true, but R is not the correct explanation of A.

(c) A is true and R is false.

(d) A is false and R is true.

24. **Assertion (A):** Thermosetting plastics are used for making handles of kitchenware.

Reason (R): Thermosetting plastics are made up of cross-linked polymeric chains.

(a) Both A and R are true and R is the correct explanation of A.

(b) Both A and R are true, but R is not the correct explanation of A.

(c) A is true and R is false.

(d) A is false and R is true.

25. Identify the incorrect statements regarding alpha sulphur (X), beta sulphur (Y), and gamma sulphur (Z).

(a) X → Rhombic sulphur; Y → Prismatic sulphur; Z → Plastic sulphur

(b) Both X and Y are more stable at normal temperatures.

(c) X possesses an octahedral shape and Y has a needle shape.

(d) Z does not have a sharp melting point.

26. Which of the following is false regarding epoxy resin?

(a) It is a thermosetting polymer.

(b) It is less brittle in nature.

(c) It has relatively weak bonds.

(d) It has cross-linking among polymeric chains.

27. When Mg is burnt in the atmosphere of an element X, a white powder is obtained. When this is dissolved in water, it gives a compound Y with a pungent smell. What are X and Y?

(a) C, CH_4 (b) N_2, NH_3

(c) P, PH_3 (d) S, H_2S

28. The reducing property of SO_2 is shown in which of the following reactions?

(a) $SO_2 + H_2O + Cl_2 \longrightarrow 2HCl + H_2SO_4$

(b) $2H_2S + SO_2 \longrightarrow 2H_2O + 3S$

(c) $KOH + SO_2 \longrightarrow K_2SO_3 + H_2O$

(d) none of the above

29. The transparency of glass is attributed to which of the following properties of glass?

(a) high viscosity

(b) regular pattern of arrangement of silicate units

(c) irregular pattern of arrangement of silicate units

(d) high coefficient of thermal expansion

30. A soil is supplied with ammonium phosphate fertilizer. Which of the following types of bacteria is not involved in the process of the absorption of this fertilizer by plants?

(a) ammonifying bacteria (b) nitrosifying bacteria

(c) nitrifying bacteria (d) none of these

31. The gas liberated when concentrated sulphuric acid is treated with copper is

(a) H_2 (b) SO_3

(c) H_2S (d) SO_2

32. A soil is highly deficient in nitrogen. The crop requires nitrogen for immediate requirement as well as long-term requirement. Which among the following is the most suitable fertilizer for the soil?

(a) urea

(b) ammonium sulphate

(c) ammonium nitrate

(d) calcium ammonium nitrate

33. The process of glazing of ceramic article does not

(a) make it impervious

(b) impart glossy appearance

(c) make it impact resistant

(d) all of these

34. Sulphur, on heating, follows which of the following sequence?

(a) solid ⟶ thick viscous liquid ⟶ thin liquid ⟶ gas

(b) solid ⟶ semisolid ⟶ liquid ⟶ gas

(c) solid ⟶ thin liquid ⟶ thick viscous ⟶ thin liquid ⟶ gas

(d) solid ⟶ powdery solid ⟶ thick viscous liquid ⟶ gas

35. Which among the following is true with regard to thermoplastics and thermosetting?

(a) Thermosettings are permanent setting resins but thermoplastics are not since they can be softened on cooling.

(b) Thermoplastics are less brittle when compared to thermosettings due to the absence of long chain polymers.

(c) Thermosettings are more brittle when compared to thermoplastics due to the presence of strong bonds.

(d) The chemical nature of thermoplastics can be altered by repeated heating and cooling.

36. Steps involved in the Frasch process are given below. Arrange them in the correct sequence.

(1) This melts the sulphur below melting point.
(2) The sulphur foam formed rises in the middle pipe and is collected.
(3) Superheated steam under pressure is sent through the outermost pipe.
(4) Hot compressed air is sent through the innermost pipe, which froths up the molten sulphur below.
(5) Three concentric pipes are drilled through the ground to the sulphur deposits.

(a) 5 3 1 4 2 (b) 5 1 4 3 2
(c) 5 1 4 2 3 (d) 5 4 1 3 2

37. Different steps involved in the manufacture of sulphuric acid in the contact process are given below. Arrange them in the correct sequence.

(1) formation of oleum (2) oxidation of SO_2
(3) hydrolysis of oleum (4) combustion of sulphur

(a) 4 1 3 2 (b) 1 4 2 3
(c) 4 2 1 3 (d) 1 4 3 2

38. Arrange the different forms of sulphur formed during heating followed by cooling:

(1) μ sulphur
(2) flower of sulphur
(3) rhombic sulphur
(4) sulphur vapour
(5) lambda sulphur
(6) monoclinic sulphur

(a) 5 3 6 1 4 2 (b) 3 6 5 1 4 2
(c) 3 6 1 5 4 2 (d) 3 6 5 1 2 4

39. Slaked lime on reaction with ammonium chloride gives

(a) calcium hydroxide and ammonia
(b) calcium hydroxide and nitrogen
(c) calcium chloride and nitrogen dioxide
(d) calcium chloride and ammonia

40. Different steps involved in the mechanism of preparation of sodium hydroxide by Castner process are given below. Arrange them in correct sequence.

(1) $2Cl^- \rightarrow Cl_2 + 2e^-$
(2) $Na_2Hg - 2e^- \rightarrow 2Na^+ + Hg$
(3) $2H_2O + 2e^- \rightarrow H_2 + 2OH$
(4) $Hg + 2Na^+ + 2e^- \rightarrow Na_2Hg$
(5) $2NaCl \rightarrow 2Na^+ + 2Cl^-$
(6) $2Na^+ + 2OH^- \rightarrow 2NaOH$

(a) 5 4 3 2 1 6 (b) 5 2 3 1 4 6
(c) 4 2 1 5 3 6 (d) 5 1 4 2 3 6

41. The steps involved in the manufacture of glass are given below. Arrange them in the correct sequence.

(1) moderate cooling
(2) addition of cullet
(3) formation of respective silicates
(4) preparation of fine powder of raw materials
(5) heating of cullet at about 1600 K to 1700 K

(a) 4 2 5 3 1 (b) 4 5 2 1 3
(c) 4 5 3 2 1 (d) 4 2 3 5 1

42. Different processes involved in the manufacture of pottery or ceramic materials are given below. Arrange them in a proper sequence.

(1) change in the physical and chemical properties of the substances
(2) heating to a suitable high temperature
(3) drying of the mixture
(4) preparation of mixture by adding water to raw materials

(a) 2 1 4 3 (b) 4 3 2 1
(c) 4 3 1 2 (d) 3 4 2 1

Level 2: Review Your Concepts

43. In the reaction shown below does H_2SO_4 show oxidizing property?

$C + 2H_2SO_4 \rightarrow 2H_2O + 2SO_2 + CO_2$

44. 'X' and 'Y' are two allotropic forms of phosphorus and Y is used preferably in match industry. What can you say regarding the two samples X and Y?

45. When a burning paraffin candle is introduced into two jars containing oxygen and chlorine gases separately, what observations can be made? Explain with appropriate reasons.

46. When chlorine reacts with hot and concentrated caustic alkali XOH, one of the products, Y is formed by this reaction is used as an oxidizer in the match industry. Identify the compound Y and the element X.

47. Two samples of sulphur are heated separately starting at 60°C. One sample is found to melt at 114°C and the other one melts at 119°C. How do you account for this?

48. Bone ash contains both micro- and macronutrients in it. However, it is not used as a fertilizer. It is converted to superphosphate of lime which is an important fertilizer. Justify.

49. An iron rod is dipped in conc. HNO_3. Then it is made to react with copper sulphate solution. What observations are made in this process? Give reasons in support of your answer.

50. 'Noble metals, like, gold and platinum are insoluble both in HCl and in HNO_3. But they are soluble in aquaregia.' Justify.

51. Farmers are advised to grow beans or pea plants in crop rotation. Give reasons in support of your answer.

52. When copper metal is subjected to treatment with nitric acid, different oxides of nitrogen are liberated with different concentrations of nitric acid. Explain the reason.

53. Ammonium chloride on reaction with quick lime gives a gas X which turns red litmus blue. Excess of X and greenish yellow gas are taken in container A and excess of greenish yellow gas and X are taken in container B which on reaction gives different sets of products. When moist litmus paper is introduced into the jars, it turned to red in jar B. Identify the reactions involved and give equations.

54. Hydrogen chloride gas can be subjected to drying only with conc. H_2SO_4 but not with quick lime or phosphorus pentoxide. Explain.

55. Why are soaps ineffective during usage with hard water which contains soluble salts of calcium and magnesium?

56. When a binary salt of iron reacts with hydrochloric acid, it gives out a gas which can be used for identification of many metal ions. Identify the salt, the gas and explain how it is useful in detecting metal ions.

57. Nitric acid is colourless when freshly prepared. But, on long standing, it turns to yellow. How do you account for this?

58. Two research scholars Rony and Jony, needed red phosphorus and white phosphorus, respectively, for a research programme. Both of them went to a chemical store to purchase red phosphorus and white phosphorus. The storekeeper gave a normal glass bottle containing red phosphorus and a glass bottle containing white phosphorus which was kept in water. Justify the above observations.

59. A solid non-metal A on exposure to air forms a compound B which on dissolution in water forms the highest oxyacid C. Identify different type of salts which can be formed when C reacts with caustic potash.

60. (A) Though P_2O_5 is a very good desiccant, its utility for drying is limited. Give reasons.

(B)

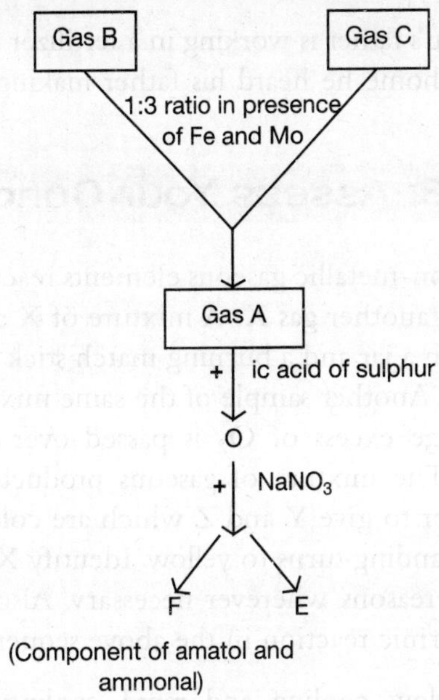

(i) Identify A, B, C, D, E and F.

(ii) Write the reactions associated with the above process and identify the types of reactions involved.

61. In an industry, H_2S gas is mixed with chlorine gas before releasing it into the atmosphere. Give the appropriate reason.

62. A solid non-metal X on burning gives a compound Y which under high temperature and pressure conditions in presence of catalyst gets oxidized to Z. Z can give the 'ic' acid of the non-metal on dissolution in water. However, it is not a preferred reaction for the preparation of the acid. Give reason and explain the method employed for the preparation of the ic-acid from Z and mention the precautions required during dilution of the acid.

63. Concentrated HNO_3 and concentrated H_2SO_4 can't be used for the preparation of H_2S. Give a reason.

64. Rekha and Lekha took two fresh red roses and kept them in two containers A and B into which anhydride of sulphurous acid and a greenish yellow-coloured gas are passed, respectively. After a few minutes these two roses lose their colour but on being exposed to the atmosphere, it was observed that Rekha's rose regained its colour but Lekha's rose did not. How do you account for the above changes?

65. During the summer vacation, a chemistry laboratory assistant stored the chemicals in their respective bottles. After a few months it was observed that the lids of the bottles in which sodium hydroxide was stored was struck tight. He went to a lecturer for finding the solution for this problem. What solution could be suggested by the lecturer?

66. Ranchu's father is working in a fertilizer industry. One day at home he heard his father making a suggestion to his colleague that 'between nitrate salts and ammonium salts, nitrate salts are preferable for use as a fertilizer.' The next day Ranchu asked his brother the reason for their father's suggestion. What answer did his brother give?

67. Thermoplastics can be moulded again and again, whereas thermosettings cannot be moulded. Give a reason.

Level 3: Assess Your Concepts

68. Two non-metallic gaseous elements react in 1 : 3 ratio to give another gas X. A mixture of X and oxygen is taken in a jar and a burning match stick is introduced into it. Another sample of the same mixture containing large excess of O_2 is passed over heated platinum. The mixture of gaseous products is dissolved in water to give Y and Z which are colourless. Z on long standing turns to yellow. Identify X, Y and Z by giving reasons wherever necessary. Also identify the exothermic reaction in the above sequence.

69. Both slow cooling and rapid cooling of glass are avoided. How do you account for this?

70. Phosphorite rock when treated with phosphoric acid gives a fertilizer which is preferred to a fertilizer obtained from the same mineral on treatment with conc. sulphuric acid. Justify

71. Why is the compound AgCl used in photogrey lenses?

72. Bleaching powder in cold water is an excellent bleaching agent. But it cannot act as a good bleaching agent when dissolved in hot water. Why?

73. (A) Hydrofluoric acid cannot be stored in glass bottles like all other acids. Give a reason.

(B)

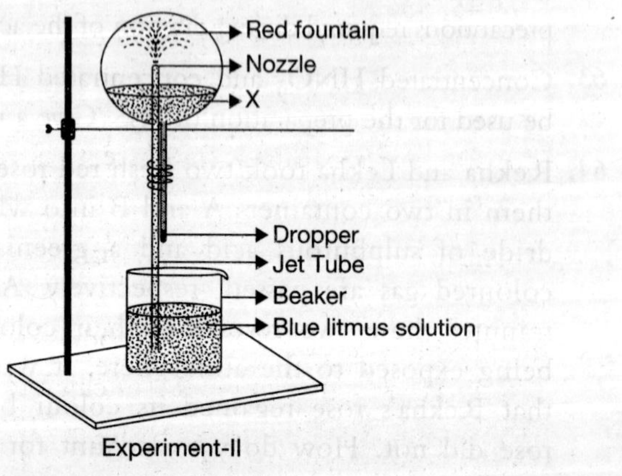

Experiment-II

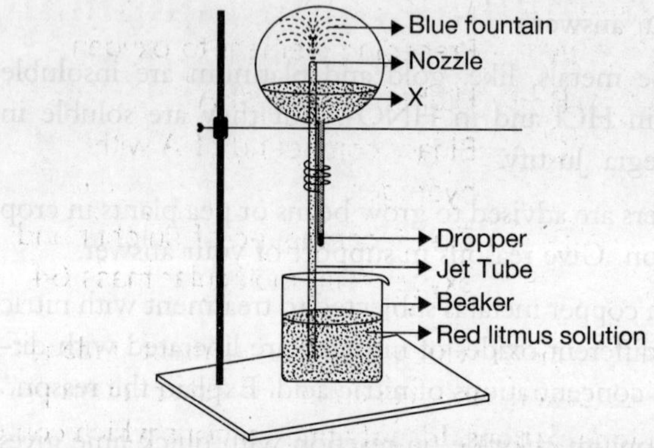

Experiment-I

(a) Comment on the nature of X and Y.

(b) Name the property of X and Y exploited to carry out the above experiments.

(c) Identify X and Y. X is the compound of nitrogen and Y is oxide of sulphur.

(d) Y on oxidation gives a gas which on treatment with sulphuric acid forms Z. Z on hydrolysis forms an acid 'A'. Explain the method of dilution of A.

(e) Name the properties of A exploited in the following reactions.

(i) $CuO + A \longrightarrow CuSO_4 + H_2O$

(ii) $C\,(\text{Carbon}) + A \longrightarrow H_2O + SO_2 + CO_2$

(iii) $(C_6H_{10}O_6)_n + A \longrightarrow C + H_2O$

74. Certain phosphates are helpful in making hard water soft. Which phosphates are used and how do they help in making water soft?

75. Both H_2SO_4 and HNO_3 cause damage to skin when the skin comes in contact with them. Compare and contrast the reasons.

76. Nitric acid attacks all the metals except noble metals but the nature of products of same metal along with corresponding nitrates depends upon the concentration of HNO_3. Explain.

PRACTICE QUESTIONS JEE-NEET SPECIAL WING

Multiple-Answer Type Questions

Directions for questions from 1 to 5:
Select one or more correct alternative(s) from the given choices.

1. Identify the substances which have tendency to act as oxidising agents and reducing agents.

	Element	Description
(a)	A	Preceding element to oxygen
(b)	B	Higher oxyacid of A
(c)	C	Binary compound of A with hydrogen
(d)	D	Binary compound of sulphur and oxygen with molecular mass 64

2. The reactions in which the same element undergoes both oxidation and reduction are called disproportionation reactions. Identify the reactions which come under that category.
(a) Reaction of copper with concentrated nitric acid
(b) Reaction of chlorine with sodium hydroxide
(c) Reaction of zinc with sodium hydroxide
(d) Reaction of phosphorus with sodium hydroxide

3. Sulphur undergoes transformation to various forms when it is subjected to heating. Identify the correctly matched sets with respect to temperature range and the structural changes sulphur undergoes.
(a) 160°C–Breaking of puckered rings to form a thick viscous fluid
(b) 118°C–Separation of puckered rings to form a pale yellow mobile liquid
(c) 960°C–Rearrangement of puckered rings for transformation from one allotrope to another
(d) 445°C–Breaking of puckered rings to form amorphous form of sulphur

4. Identify the correct sets of reactants and products among the following.

	Element	Reagent Added	Product
(a)	2, 8, 13, 2	Dilute nitric acid	NO
(b)	2, 8, 15, 2	Concentrated HNO_3	N_2O
(c)	2, 8, 18, 2	Dilute nitric acid	N_2O
(d)	2, 8, 18, 2	Concentrated HNO_3	NO_2

5. Identify the gases which are collected by upward displacement of air.
(a) Hydrogen chloride
(b) Ammonia
(c) Chlorine
(d) Hydrogen sulphide

Comprehension-Based Questions

Directions for questions from 6 to 10:
Read the content given in the following passage and answer the questions given below.

The invention of matchsticks has been an amazing milestone in the history of human civilisation. The process of making matchsticks involves the following steps. Certain types of wood are taken and chopped into square splints. These splints are inserted into the holes of aluminium plates. These splints are first dipped into ammonium phosphate and allowed to dry. One end of the splits are coated molten paraffin wax. These are then dipped into glue containing a mixture of potassium chlorate and antimony trisulphide. These matches once dried are packed into boxes containing the striking surface. The striking surface is made by coating it with a mixture of powdered glass and red phosphorus mixed with glue.

6. Which of the following is likely to happen if red phosphorus is replaced by white phosphorus?
(a) The stick may burn when struck against any surface
(b) The stick may not be ignited easily
(c) The sticks get ignited easily and hence might lead to explosion
(d) On ignition it may produce toxic chemicals as residue.

7. Identify the first step of the mechanism of burning of match stick.
(a) Burning of phosphorus to produce heat
(b) Decomposition of potassium chlorate
(c) Burning of antimony sulphide to produce flame
(d) Conversion of red phosphorus to white phosphorus

8. Which among the following substances prevents the burning of the entire wooden splint?
(a) Ammonium phosphate (b) Glue
(c) Antimony sulphide (d) Paraffin wax

9. Which step of the process is hindered if powdered glass is missing in the composition?
(a) Burning of antimony sulphide
(b) Conversion of red phosphorus to white phosphorus
(c) Ignition of red phosphorus
(d) Decomposition of potassium chlorate

10. Assertion (A): Lucifer matches provide better safety when compared to the matches in use

Reason (R): Lucifer matches contain a compound of phosphorus in place of elemental phosphorus.
(a) Both A and R are correct and R is the correct explanation of A
(b) Both A and R are correct and R is not the correct explanation of A
(c) A is correct and R is wrong
(d) R is correct and A is wrong

Directions for questions from 11 to 18:
Observe this schematic diagram representing nitrogen cycle and answer the following questions.

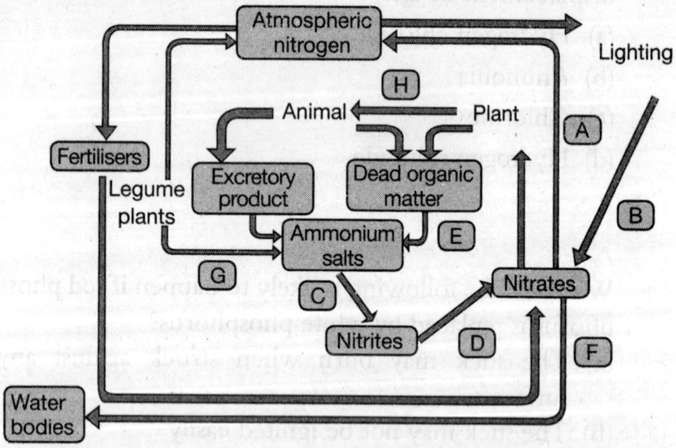

The table given below lists the various bacteria involved in nitrogen cycle.

Process	Names of Bacteria
Ammonification	Streptomyces
NH_4^+ to NO_2^-	Nitrosomonas
NO_2^- to NO_3^-	Nitrobactor
Denitrification	Pseudomonas
Nitrogen fixation	Rhizobium

11. Which of the processes represented in the above nitrogen cycle is responsible for introducing bean plants in the crop rotation system which is a well-known agricultural practice?
(a) F (b) G
(c) C (d) E

12. Give the name of the process represented by 'F'.
(a) Nitrogen fixation
(b) Biological oxygen demand
(c) Eutrophication
(d) Biomagnification

13. Assertion (A): Plants generally take up nitrogen in the form of nitrate salts.

Reason (R): Nitrate salts are highly soluble in water.
(a) Both A and R are correct, and R is the correct explanation of A
(b) Both A and R are correct, and R is not the correct explanation of A
(c) A is correct and R is wrong
(d) R is correct and A is wrong

14. Name the substance formed in the first step of the process 'B'.
(a) Nitric acid (b) Ammonium nitrate
(c) Nitrogen dioxide (d) Nitric oxide

15. The nitrogen isolated from the atmospheric air is utilised for the manufacture of nitrate fertilisers. This is also part of nitrogen cycle as it comes under the artificial nitrogen fixation. Predict the name of the process employed for this.
(a) Contact process (b) Haber process
(c) Ostwald's process (d) Both b and c

16. Identify the bacteria which replenish the soil fertility by being in symbiotic association.
(a) Pseudomonas (b) Nitrosomonas
(c) Nitrobacter (d) Rhizobium

17. Which bacteria help to convert the complex proteins and amino acids in the living organisms into simple inorganic form?
(a) Nitrobacter (b) Rhizobium
(c) Clostridium (d) Pseudomonas

18. Match the entries in Column I with those in Column II.

Column I		Column II	
(a)	E	(i)	Nitrification
(b)	B	(ii)	Ammonification
(c)	A	(iii)	Assimilation
(d)	H	(iv)	Nitrogen fixation
(e)	D	(v)	Denitrification

ANSWER KEYS

Crossword

Across

4. Red phosphorus
6. Aquaregia
11. Plastic sulphur
12. Phosphor bronze
14. Bleaching powder
16. Hydrogen sulphide
17. Sulphuric acid
18. Habers process
19. Sulphur
20. Contact proces

Down

1. Caustic potash
2. Sodium hydroxide
3. Sulphuryl chloride
5. Hypo
7. Nitrolim
8. Chlorine
9. Sulphur dioxide
10. Nitric acid
13. Nesslers reagent
15. Phosphorus

Classroom Wing

Very Short Answer Type Questions

1. dehydrating property
2. Acidic nature
3. $3Ca_3(PO_4)CaF_2$
4. Sicilian
5. nitric oxide (NO)

Competition Wing

Level 1: Apply Your Concepts

1. True
2. False
3. False
4. False
5. False
6. True
7. True
8. True
9. False
10. False
11. True
12. False
13. nitrogen
14. less
15. sodium amalgam
16. cathode
17. $KClO_3$
18. nitrogen-fixing bacteria (or) symbiotic
19. KNH_2
20. (i) → (D), (ii) → (C), (iii) → (E), (v) → (B)
21. (c)
22. (a)
23. (c)
24. (a)
25. (b)
26. (d)
27. (b)
28. (a)
29. (c)
30. (a)
31. (d)
32. (d)
33. (c)
34. (c)
35. (c)
36. (a)
37. (c)
38. (b)
39. (d)
40. (d)
41. (a)
42. (b)

JEE-NEET Special Wing

Multiple-Answer Type Questions

1. (a, d)
2. (b, d)
3. (a, b, c)
4. (c, d)
5. (a, c, d)

Comprehension-Based Questions

6. (c)
7. (c)
8. (a)
9. (b)
10. (d)
11. (b)
12. (c)
13. (a)
14. (d)
15. (d)
16. (d)
17. (c)
18. (a)-(ii); (b)-(iv); (c)-(v); (d)-(iii); (e)-(i)

Hints and Explanations

CLASSROOM WING

Very Short Answer Type Questions

1. Sugar, on treating with conc. H_2SO_4, turns into a black-coloured mass due to the removal of hydrogen and oxygen present in sugar as water.
   Hence, the property of sulphuric acid exploited in this process is the dehydrating property.
2. Hence, Hydrogen sulphide, on combustion, gives sulphur and water. This reaction indicates the acidic nature of hydrogen sulphide.
3. $3Ca_3(PO_4)CaF_2$
4. Sicilian
5. nitric oxide (NO)
6. X is NH_3; Y $\rightarrow$ $Cu(OH)_2$
   Aqueous solution of NH_3 on treatment with $CuSO_4$ solution gives a pale blue precipitate of $Cu(OH)_2$.
7. 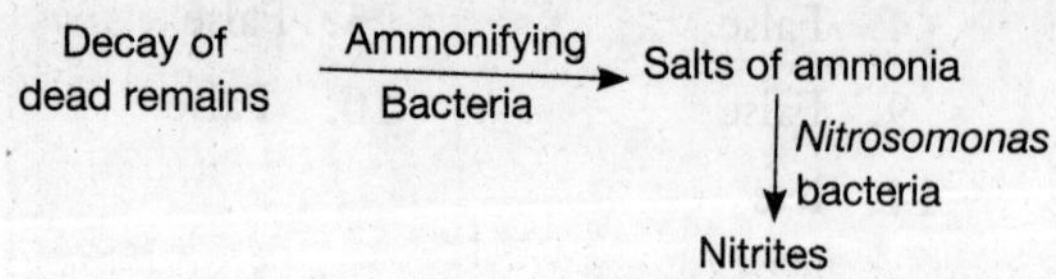

   Hence, X is ammonifying bacteria. Y is *Nitrosomonas* bacteria.
8. Red phosphorous is used in safety matches rather than white phosphorous because white phosphorous has a lower ignition temperature.
9. X $\rightarrow$ NH_3; Y $\rightarrow$ $[Cu(NH_3)_2]SO_4$
   Copper sulphate, on treatment with excess aqueous solution of NH_3, gives a dark blue solution of $[Cu(NH_3)_2]SO_4$.
10. $2P + 3Cl_2 \longrightarrow 2PCl_3$;
    $5P + 5Cl_2 \longrightarrow 2PCl_5$
11. $H_2O + SO_2 \longrightarrow H_2SO_3$
12. Isolated tetrahedral; P_4 units
13. $H_2S + Cl_2 \longrightarrow 2HCl\uparrow + S$
14. formation of precipitates
15. 3, calcium ammonium nitrate, fertilizer
16. Manufacture of different glass articles; free blowing, mould blowing
17. large-scale production, cost, durability
18. in the form of minerals, organic matter
19. (i) $COCl_2$
    (ii) CCl_3NO_2
    (iii) $CHCl_3$
20. oxides, nitrides, carbides and borides
21. the nutrients which are required in large and small quantities, respectively. Nitrogen, phosphorus and potassium are major nutrients. Copper, boron and zinc are minor nutrients.
22. $4NH_3 + 3O_2 \longrightarrow 2N_2 + 6H_2O$
23. Nitrolim is mixture of calcium cyanamid and graphite. Obtained by the reaction of nitrogen and calcium carbide.
24. greenish yellow, pungent smell, sparingly soluble in water, heavier than air, vapour density is 35.5 and atomicity is 2
25. Mixing up of chlorine gas with slaked lime.
26. due to formation of hydrochloric acid

Short Answer Type Questions

27. $Cu + conc.4HNO_3 \rightarrow Cu(NO_3)_2 + 2NO_2 + H_2O$
    $4Zn + 10HNO_3 + \rightarrow 4Zn(NO_3)_2 + N_2O + 5H_2O$
28. These burn only when they are made to strike on a particular surface. The chemical on the stick is composed of potassium chlorate and antimony sulphide mixed with glue. When this is rubbed on a surface made of red phosphorous, antimony sulphide and fine glass powder, a small part of phosphorous detaches and catches fire. This spark initiates the ignition of antimony sulphide which further helps in the decomposition of potassium chlorate which provides oxygen for combustion.
29. This process is used to extract sulphur which is near to the earth's crust (deposits in Sicily). This process is carried out in brick kilns built on sloping hill sides.

Process: Large amounts of clay and stone are mixed with crude sulphur and is stacked inside the brick kiln leaving small spaces in between. This is covered with a layer of powdered sulphur which is then subjected to burning. The heat evolved during the burning of this sulphur leads to melting of the remaining sulphur that lies in the bottom layers. The molten sulphur is allowed to flow down and is collected in wooden moulds.

Purification: The sulphur obtained in the above process contains about 5% of earthly impurities.

30. (A) (i) other names
(ii) preparation
(iii) colour
(iv) shape/structure
(v) density
(vi) solubility
(vii) melting point
(viii) conductivity
(ix) boiling point

(B) The most significant part of manufacture of glass is cooling of molten glass which should be carried out carefully at a moderate and uniform rate in order to achieve the required properties of glass.

31. Hydrogen sulphide on reaction with aqueous solutions of metal salts converts them to metal sulphides. These metal sulphides are in the form of precipitates. The colour of the precipitate depends upon the nature of metal ion. Therefore, hydrogen sulphide is mainly used for the detection of metal cations present in the metal salts.

32. (i) bleaching action
(ii) In the preparation of hydrochloric acid.
(iii) extraction of metals
(iv) industries

33. Chlorine gas is passed over a filter paper dipped in hot turpentine. It burns with a black sooty flame with the formation of black soot of carbon.

34. (i) Nitrogen, sodium sulphate and water.
(ii) Potassium diiodoiodate(I), nitrogen dioxide, potassium nitrate and water.
(iii) Sulphuric acid, water and nitrogen dioxide

35. (i) the negative and positive ends of soap
(ii) interaction of polar end of soap with water
(iii) decrease in surface tension of water

36. (i) solvent
(ii) refrigerant

37. (i) acidic nature
(ii) reducing nature
(iii) reaction with potassium permanganate
(iv) HCl formation

38. (i) definition of chemical fertilizers
(ii) nitrogenous fertilizers
(iii) Phosphatic fertilizers
(iv) potash fertilizers

39. (i) reducing agent
(ii) production of nascent hydrogen with water

40. (i) definition of plastic
(ii) thermoplastics
(iii) thermosets

41. (i) raw materials
(ii) electric furnace set up
(iii) reactions involved
(iv) purification

Essay Answer Type Questions

42. (i) phosphorous oxides
(ii) phosphorous acids
(iii) salts of acids
(iv) metal phosphates, metal phosphate, superphosphates
(v) dehydrating agent, pharmaceuticals, petroleum field

43. Sulphur dioxide and oxygen in a ratio of 2 : 1 by volume is passed over vanadium pentoxide, maintained at 450°C under high pressure conditions. Under these conditions, the sulphur dioxide and oxygen react to form sulphur trioxide. Platinised asbestos can also be used in place of V_2O_5. Sulphur trioxide thus obtained is dissolved in sulphuric acid to form pyrosulphuric acid or oleum. The pyrosulphuric acid on treatment with water gives sulphuric acid.

44. Construction: Nelson cell consists of a perforated steel U tube insulated by asbestos lining. This U tube acts as a cathode. The U-shaped vessel is provided with an inlet and an outlet. Through the inlet, a brine solution is introduced into the U-tube. A graphite rod is suspended into the U-tube. This acts as an anode.

This cell is suspended in a rectangular steel tank. This is also provided with an outlet and a side tube.

(i) electrolytic dissociation of NaCl

(ii) liberation of chlorine gas

(iii) liberation of hydrogen gas

(iv) formation of NaOH

45. (i) chlorine gas, slaked lime

(ii) chlorinating tower

(iii) counter-current mechanism

46. (i) mercury

(ii) intermediate electrode

(iii) anode, cathode

(iv) brine solution

(v) electrolytic dissociation of NaCl

(vi) liberation of chlorine gas

(vii) formation of sodium amalgam

(viii) formation of sodium hydroxide

47. (i) X = N ; Y = Cl

(ii) a = 1 ; b = 3

(iii) Z = Aqua regia

(iv) $HCl + HNO_3 \longrightarrow NOCl + H_2O + [Cl]$

$$Au + [Cl] \longrightarrow AuCl_3$$

$$AuCl_3 + HCl \longrightarrow \underset{\text{Tetrachloroauric acid}}{HAuCl_4}$$

$$HAuCl_4 + SO_2 \longrightarrow Au + HCl + H_2SO_4$$

Competition Wing

Level 1: Apply Your Concepts

1. True. Both rhombic sulphur and monoclinic sulphur are crystalline and soluble in CS_2.

20. Liquid nitrogen is used as a refrigerant. Zinc phosphide is used as rat poison. Sulphur is used in the manufacture of gunpowder.

Hydrogen sulphide is a good analytical reagent. H_2SO_4 is used in storage batteries.

21. Assertion (A) is true. Bakelite cannot be remoulded once it has been set.

Reason (R) is false. Bakelite is not a thermoplastic polymer. It is a thermosetting polymer. Thermoplastics can be remoulded upon heating, while thermosetting plastics, like Bakelite, cannot be remoulded once they are set.

Hence, the correct option is (c).

22. SO_2, on treatment with excess water in the presence of oxygen, gives nascent hydrogen. Hence, SO_2 acts as a reducing agent. The nascent hydrogen produced on being exposed to moisture acts as a bleach mg agent. It reduces the coloured matter to colourless. This process is reversible. The colourless product, on exposure to atmospheric oxygen, can get oxidized and thus regain its colour.

Hence, the correct option is (a).

23. Since HNO_3 is a good oxidising agent, it oxidises the impurities present on the surface of gold but does not react with gold.

Hence, the correct option is (c).

25. X is rhombic sulphur, Y is monoclinic sulphur, and Z is plastic sulphur. X possesses an octahedral shape and Y is needle shaped. Since Z is amorphous, it does not have a sharp melting point.

24. Thermosetting plastics are made up of cross-linked polymeric chains and hence are highly heat resistant and poor thermal conductors. Due to these characteristics, they are used for making handles of kitchenware.

Hence, the correct option is (a).

36. (i) three concentric pipes are drilled through the ground to the sulphur deposits

(ii) superheated steam under pressure is sent through the outermost pipe

(iii) this melts the sulphur below its melting point

(iv) hot compressed air is sent through the innermost pipe, which froths up the molten sulphur below

(v) the sulphur foam formed rises in the middle pipe and is collected

Hence, correct option is (a).

37. (i) combustion of sulphur

(ii) oxidation of SO_2

(iii) formation of oleum

(iv) hydrolysis of oleum

Hence, correct option is (c).

38. (i) rhombic sulphur

(ii) monoclinic sulphur

(iii) lambda sulphur

(iv) μ sulphur

(v) sulphur vapour

(vi) flower of sulphur

Hence, correct option is (b).

39. $Ca(OH)_2 + 2NH_4Cl \rightarrow CaCl_2 + 2NH_3 + 2H_2O$

Hence, correct option is (d).

40. (i) $2NaCl \rightarrow 2Na^+ + 2Cl^-$

(ii) $2Cl \rightarrow Cl_2 + 2e^-$

(iii) $Hg + 2Na^+ + 2e \rightarrow Na_2Hg$

(iv) $Na_2Hg - 2e^- \rightarrow 2Na^+ + Hg$

(v) $2H_2O + 2e^- \rightarrow H_2 + 2OH^-$

(vi) $2Na^+ + 2OH^- \rightarrow 2NaOH$

Hence, correct option is (d).

41. (i) preparation of fine powder of raw materials

(ii) preparation of cullet

(iii) heating of cullet at about 1600 K to 1700 K

(iv) formation of respective silicates

(v) moderate cooling

Hence, correct option is (a).

42. (i) preparation of mixture by adding water to raw materials

(ii) drying of the mixture

(iii) heating to a suitable high temperature

(iv) change in the physical and chemical properties of the substances

Hence, correct option is (b).

Level 2: Review Your Concepts

43. Sulphuric acid, on thermal decomposition, gives nascent oxygen and hence, H_2SO_4 acts as an oxidizing agent. It can oxidize carbon to CO_2.

44. As Y is used in the match industry, it is red phosphorus and X is white phosphorus. In Y, each P_4 unit is linked by P-P bonds.

45. (i) composition of paraffin candle and comparison of reactivity of the constituents present in candle with O_2 and Cl_2
(ii) affinity of the constituents of paraffin candle towards chlorine
(iii) products obtained when these constituents react with chlorine
(iv) physical states of the products
(v) products obtained due to the reaction between constituents of paraffin candle and oxygen

46. (i) oxidizer in match industry
(ii) identification of a substance used in match stick which supplies O_2
(iii) balanced chemical equation
(iv) identification of X from the balanced chemical equation

47. (i) allotropes of sulphur
(ii) stability of allotropes at different temperatures
(iii) comparison of melting points of different allotropes
(iv) pattern of heating to be employed
(v) effect of pattern of heating on the allotropic transformation

48. (i) requisite of a good fertilizer
(ii) constituent of bone ash which contains macronutrients required for plants
(iii) soluble nature of the above constituent
(iv) manufacture of superphosphate of lime from this constituent
(v) solubility of superphosphate of lime

49. (i) reactivity of iron with HNO_3
(ii) reactivity of iron with HNO_3
(iii) product obtained
(iv) reactivity of the product obtained

50. (i) product obtained from the mixture HCl and HNO_3
(ii) composition of aquaregia
(iii) reactivity of gold with aquaregia
(iv) product formed

51. (i) microorganism present in roots of bean or pea plants
(ii) the role of the microorganisms present in beans and pea plants in trapping the aerial nitrogen
(iii) role of nitrogen in the growth of plants

52. (i) property of HNO_3
(ii) nature of HNO_3
(iii) effect of concentration on oxidizing capacity of HNO_3

53. (i) identification of product formed in the reaction of NH_4Cl and CaO
(ii) reaction between X and the greenish yellow gas in container A
(iii) reaction between X and the greenish yellow gas in container B
(iv) comparison of nature of the products formed in the two containers, A and B
(v) effect of nature of products on litmus paper

54. (i) reaction of P_2O_5 and CaO with HCl
(ii) reactivity of HCl with H_2SO_4, CaO, P_2O_5
(iii) reactions which are feasible
(iv) products obtained
(v) requisite for a drying agent

55. (i) composition of soap
(ii) reason for hardness of water
(iii) reaction between components of soap and salts imparting hardness to water
(iv) the nature of the products formed
(v) effect of the products on lather formation

56. (i) gas used for detection of ions
(ii) identification of the gas
(iii) balanced chemical equation
(iv) identification of binary salt from the balanced chemical equation
(v) reactivity of metal ions with the gas
(vi) products obtained
(vii) colour of the products formed

57. (i) decomposition of nitric acid
(ii) effect of light on HNO_3
(iii) effect of product formed on cold HNO_3

58. The ignition temperature of white phosphorus is very low as compared to red phosphorus. Hence, it catches fire in the presence of air. So, white phosphorous is preserved under water as its density is high. Therefore, the phosphorus settles down. As a result, it is not exposed to air. In contrats, red phosphorus has a high ignition temperature and does not catch fire on exposure to air. So, it is stored in normal glass bottles.

59. $4P + 5O_2 \rightarrow 2P_2O_5$

A B

$P_2O_5 + 3H_2O \rightarrow 2H_3PO_4$

B C

$H_3PO_4 + KOH \rightarrow KH_2PO_4 + H_2O$

$H_3PO_4 + 2KOH \rightarrow K_2HPO_4 + 2H_2O$

$H_3PO_4 + 3KOH \rightarrow K_3PO_4 + 3H_2O$

60. (A) P_2O_5 is a very good dehydrating agent, but is not used popularly as a dehydrating agent, because the water absorbed by this forms a protective viscous coating that inhibits further dehydration. However, granular form of P_4O_{10} can be used as a good dehydrating agent.

(B)

(i) $A \rightarrow NH_3$ $D \rightarrow (NH_4)_2SO_4$

$B \rightarrow N_2$ $E \rightarrow Na_2SO_4$

$C \rightarrow H_2$ $F \rightarrow NH_4NO_3$

(ii) Haber process $\longrightarrow$ Ammonia

$N_2 + 3H_2 \xrightarrow[\text{Ho}]{\text{Fe}} 2NH_3 \longrightarrow$ combination

(synthesis)

B C A

$NH_3 + H_2SO_4 \longrightarrow (NH_4)_2SO_4 \longrightarrow$

combination

Comp - Comp

$(NH_4)_2SO_4 + NaNO_3 \xrightarrow{D} NH_4NO_3 + Na_2SO_4$

Double displacement F E

Amatol $\longrightarrow$ TNT + NH_4NO_3

Ammonal $\longrightarrow$ TNT + NH_4NO_3 + Al powder

explosives

61. H_2S gas is poisonous and the antidote for this gas is chlorine. Chlorine has the property to destroy the effect of H_2S by oxidizing it to sulphur:

$H_2S + Cl_2 \rightarrow HCl + S$

62. $S + O_2 \rightarrow SO_2$

X Y

$2SO_2 + O_2 \xrightarrow[V_2O_5]{\text{High pressure and temp}} 2SO_3$

Y Z

$SO_3 + H_2O \rightarrow H_2SO_4$

However, in the preparation of H_2SO_4, the above reaction is not preferred since it is highly exothermic and leads to explosion. Instead, SO_3 is dissolved in H_2SO_4 to give oleum which on dilution with water gives H_2SO_4:

$SO_3 + H_2SO_4 \rightarrow H_2S_2O_7$

oleum

$H_2S_2O_7 + H_2O \rightarrow 2H_2SO_4$

Dilution of H_2SO_4 is also a highly exothermic reaction. Therefore, H_2SO_4 should not be diluted by adding water to the acid. Instead, water is taken and H_2SO_4 is added slowly by stirring. This leads to dissipation of released heat during dilution process.

63. Both concentrated HNO_3 and concentrated H_2SO_4 are strong oxidizing agents. As a result, they react with H_2S formed and oxidizes it to sulphur. Here the acids are reduced to SO_2 and NO_2, respectively:

$H_2S + H_2SO_4 \rightarrow S + SO_2 + H_2O$

$H_2S + 2HNO_3 \rightarrow S + 2NO_2 + 2H_2O$

64. Anhydride of sulphurous acid is SO_2.

Greenish yellow coloured gas is Cl_2.

When the two fresh red roses are exposed to SO_2 and Cl_2, the roses fade away as both SO_2 and Cl_2 act as bleaching agents. Once these two roses are exposed again to air, one of the roses which is bleached by SO_2 in jar A regains its colour. This is due to the reason that SO_2 bleaches by reduction and once the rose is exposed to air oxidation takes place. However, Cl_2 bleaches by oxidation.

65. Sodium hydroxide on being exposed to air reacts with the CO_2 present in the air to form sodium carbonate. This solidifies and the lid gets stuck due to this. The lids can be removed by using dilute acid with the help of cotton.

66. Both nitrate salts and ammonium salts are highly soluble in water and provide nitrogen to the soils. However, plants can take in and use nitrogen only in the form of nitrates. Nitrate salts when added to soils can be immediately made available for the plants. Ammonium salts cannot be directly taken in by the plants. Ammonium ions have to be first converted to nitrate ions and only then they are made available to the plants. Therefore, ammonium salts supply nitrogen after a long time, whereas nitrate salts serve the immediate requirement of the plants.

67. Thermoplastic plastics consist of long chains which can be moulded again and again, whereas in case of thermosetting plastics, they consist of long chain and are cross-linked with each other. Linkage prevents the displacement of individual chains on being heated, and thus, thermosetting polymers do not change once they have set.

Level 3: Assess Your Concepts

68. (i) identification of the acid which turns to yellow on long standing
(ii) identification of X
(iii) products obtained in the two jars
(iv) comparison of reactivity of products in the respective jars with water
(v) products obtained
(vi) identification of Y and Z

69. (i) thermal conductivity of glass
(ii) importance of process of cooling of softened glass to obtain good quality of glass
(iii) changes that takes place in the quality of glass on rapid cooling
(iv) changes that takes place in the quality of glass on slow cooling
(v) relation between the process of cooling of glass and its physical properties

70. (i) composition of superphosphate of lime and triple phosphate
(ii) composition of phosphorite rock
(iii) products formed when phosphorite rock is treated with H_3PO_4 and H_2SO_4 separately
(iv) comparison of percentage of phosphorus in the products
(v) comparison of soluble nature of the products

71. (i) change in AgCl in the presence of sunlight
(ii) effect of UV light on AgCl
(iii) products obtained
(iv) changes observed
(v) effect of the product on the colour of lenses

72. Bleaching powder reacts with cold water to produce chloride and hypochlorite ions. Hypochlorite ions dissociate producing nascent oxygen which is responsible for bleaching:

$$CaOCl_2 + H_2O \rightleftharpoons Ca^{+2} + Cl^- + ClO^- + H^+ + OH^-$$

Bleaching powder reacts with hot water and produces chloride and chlorate ions:

$$3ClO^- \rightarrow 2Cl^- + ClO_3^-$$

73. (A) As glass is a silicate and HF reacts with the silicates to form SiF_4 and fluoride of metal:

$$Na_2SiO_3 + 6\ HF \rightarrow 2\ NaF + SiF_4 + 3H_2O$$

$$3SiF_4 + 3H_2O \rightarrow H_2SiO_3 + 2H_2SiF_6$$

(B)
(a) X is basic in nature and Y is acidic in nature
(b) Change in the color of litmus in the presence ofan acid or a base
(c) X = Ammonia (NH_3) ; Y = Sulphur dioxide (SO_2)
(d) $SO_2 + [O] \longrightarrow SO_3$

$$SO_3 + H_2SO_4 \longrightarrow \underset{\substack{\text{oleum}\\ Z}}{H_2S_2O_7}$$

$$H_2S_2O_7 + H_2O \longrightarrow \underset{A}{2H_2\ SO_4}$$

For dilution, acid A is added into the water slowly.

(e) (i) Acidic Nature
(ii) Oxidising agent
(iii) Dehydrating agent

74. Soluble phosphates when added to hard water form calcium and magnesium phosphates, which are insoluble precipitates. Thus, as the calcium and magnesium ions are precipitated, the water becomes soft and can give lather with soap.

75. H_2SO_4 being a dehydrating agent removes hydrogen and oxygen from the skin in the form of water thereby damaging the skin. HNO_3 reacts with skin proteins forming xanthoproteins, and hence, imparts yellow colour to skin and forms painful blisters.

76. In conc. HNO_3, more number of NO_3^- ions is present per unit volume, and these NO_3^- ions acts as an oxidizing agent. It gets reduced to NO_2 due to more production of oxygen. In case of dilute HNO_3, less number of NO_3^- ions is present. So, it gets reduced to nitric oxide.

$$Cu + \underset{\text{(conc.)}}{4\ HNO_3} \rightarrow Cu\ (NO_3)_2 + 2NO_2 + 2H_2O$$

$$3Cu + \underset{\text{(dil.)}}{8\ HNO_3} \rightarrow 3Cu\ (NO_3)_2 + 2NO + 4H_2O$$

JEE Special Wing

Multiple-Answer Type Questions

1. The preceding element to oxygen is nitrogen. It can get oxidised as well as reduced. 'D' is sulphur dioxide. It can be oxidised to sulphur trioxide and can be reduced to sulphur. Therefore, these two substances show the tendency of oxidising and reducing agents. The higher oxyacid of nitrogen is nitric acid which is a strong oxidising agent. The binary compound with hydrogen is ammonia which is a strong reducing agent.

2. $4P + 3NaOH + 3H_2O \rightarrow PH_3 + 3NaH_2PO$

   $Cl_2 + 2NaOH \rightarrow 5NaCl + NaOCl + 3H_2O$

   These two reactions are considered as disproportionation reactions. Phosphorus and chlorine get reduced as well as oxidised in both the reactions.

3. At 96°C, the puckered rings get separated and get rearranged to change rhombic sulphur to monoclinic sulphur. At 118°C, the puckered rings completely get separated to form pale yellow mobile fluid. At 160°C, the puckered rings break to form small chains which entangle with each other resulting in thick viscous fluid. At 445°C, sulphur gets vapourised to give sulphur vapour.

4.

Element	Element	Reagent Added	Product
(a) 2, 8, 13, 2	Mn	Dil. HNO_3	NO
(b) 2, 8, 15, 2	Co	Conc. HNO_3	N_2O
(c) 2, 8, 18, 2	Zn	Dil. HNO_3	N_2O
(d) 2, 8, 18, 2	Cu	Conc. HNO_3	NO_2

5. Hydrogen chloride, chlorine and hydrogen sulphide are either highly or fairly soluble in water and they are heavier than air. Hence, they can be collected by upward displacement of air.

Comprehension-Based Questions

6. The sticks get ignited easily and hence might lead to explosion.

7. Conversion of red phosphorus to white phosphorus is the first step of the process of burning of match stick. When the match stick is struck against the side of the matchbox, the friction produces little amount of heat and helps in the conversion of little amount of red phosphorus to white phosphorus. This then undergoes burning resulting in release of heat which causes the decomposition of potassium chlorate.

8. The wooden splints are first coated with ammonium phosphate which acts as a fire retardant. This prevents the burning of the wooden splinter.

9. The purpose of addition of powdered glass to the mixture is to provide rough surface required for causing friction. The heat produced due to friction helps in the transformation of red phosphorus into white phosphorus.

10. Lucifer matches provide lesser safety when compared to the matches in use. This is because in lucifer matches, phosphorus is present on the tip of the matchstick instead of safety matches which are in use. This results in the burning of matchstick when struck against any rough surface and hence are not safe.

11. The process 'G' represents biological nitrogen fixation in which the bacteria in the root nodules of bean plants convert the atmospheric nitrogen into the usable form of soil nitrogen. Hence, growing of these plants is supposed to replenish the soil nutrition. Thus, these plants are included in the crop rotation system.

12. 'F' represents eutrophication which is the phenomenon of growth of algae in the water bodies with excess nutrients caused due to the leaching away of nitrogen salts through the agricultural run off.

13. Plants generally take up nitrogen in the form of nitrate salts due to the reason that nitrate salts are highly soluble in water.

14. Process 'B' indicates lightning which involves the combination of atmospheric nitrogen and oxygen under certain conditions to form nitric oxide which further gets oxidised to nitrogen dioxide which in turn dissolves in rain water to form the oxy acids.

15. Haber process involves the manufacture of ammonia while Ostwald's process is employed for the manufacture of nitric acid. These two compounds are the major raw materials for the manufacture of most of the nitrogenous fertilisers.

16. Rhizobium bacteria are present in the root nodules of leguminous plants and live in symbiotic association with the plants. They absorb the atmospheric nitrogen and enrich the soil fertility.

17. The process of conversion of proteins and amino acids present in the dead and decaying or excretory matter of living beings into simpler inorganic form of ammonium salts is known as ammonification. This is carried out by ammonifying bacteria such as *Clostridium*.

18.

	Column I		Column II
(a)	E	(ii)	Ammonification
(b)	B	(iv)	Nitrogen fixation
(c)	A	(v)	Denitrification
(d)	H	(iii)	Assimilation
(e)	D	(i)	Nitrification

Photo Credits

CHAPTER 1

Page 1.8—Designua. Shutterstock; **Page 1.9**—Pearson Education Ltd; **Page 1.24**—chemistrygod/ Shutterstock

CHAPTER 2

Page 2.5—Honourr/Shutterstock; **Page 2.5**—Gritsalak Karalak. 123rf.com; **Page 2.6**—ivandivandelen/Shutterstock; **Page 2.6**—Netfalls Remy Musser/Shutterstock; **Page 2.7**—KPG_ Payless/Shutterstock; **Page 2.20**—Pearson Education Ltd; **Page 2.20**—Oxford Designers & Illustrators Ltd. Pearson Education Ltd; **Page 2.33**—Sansanorth/Shutterstock; **Page 2.34**—Pearson Education Ltd

CHAPTER 4

Page 4.5—Inna Bigun. Shutterstock

CHAPTER 5

Page 5.3—Oxford Designers & Illustrators Ltd. Pearson Education Ltd

CHAPTER 6

Page 6.4—Oxford Designers & Illustrators Ltd. Pearson Education Ltd

CHAPTER 7

Page 7.7—photoiconix. Shutterstock